PRENTICE HALL

Teacher's SCIENCE EXPLORER **Edition**

Animals

PRENTICE HALL
Needham, Massachusetts
Upper Saddle River, New Jersey

ISBN 0-13-434560-6
2 3 4 5 6 7 8 9 10   05 04 03 02 01 00 99

PRENTICE HALL

SCIENCE EXPLORER

GET READY FOR A CONTENT-RICH, HANDS-ON EXPLORATION!

15 Books In All

PRENTICE HALL
SCIENCE EXPLORER
Earth's Waters

PRENTICE HALL
SCIENCE EXPLORER
Motion, Forces and Energy

PRENTICE HALL
SCIENCE EXPLORER
Animals

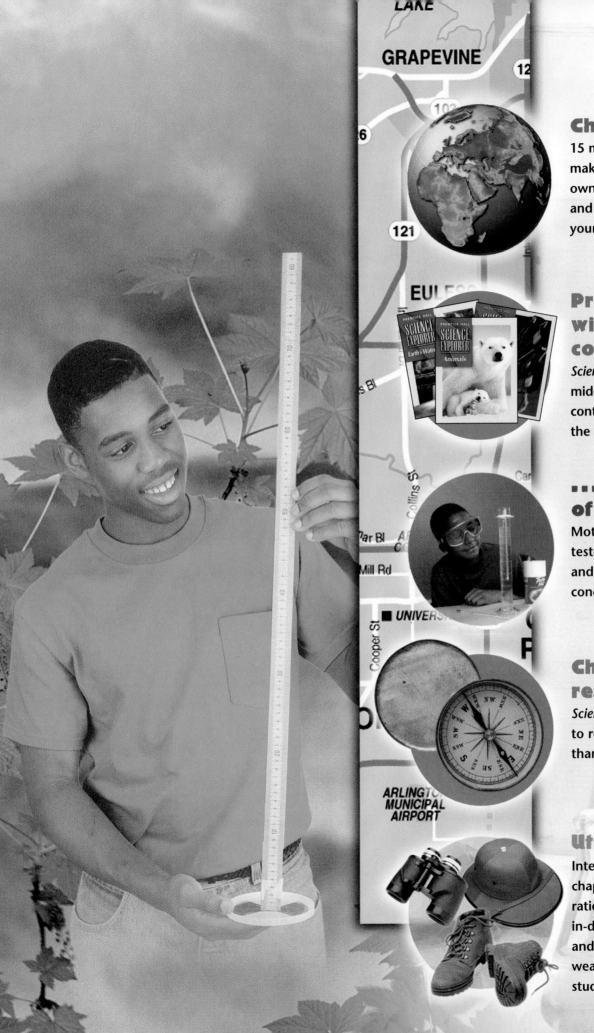

Chart your own course.

15 motivational hardcover books make it easy for you to create your own curriculum; meet local, state, and national guidelines; and teach your favorite topics in depth.

Prepare your students with rich, motivating content...

Science Explorer is crafted for today's middle grades student, with accessible content and in-depth coverage of all the important concepts.

...and a wide variety of inquiry activities.

Motivational student- and teacher-tested activities reinforce key concepts and allow students to explore science concepts for themselves.

Check your compass regularly.

Science Explorer gives you more ways to regularly check student performance than any other program available.

Utilize a variety of tools.

Integrated science sections in every chapter and Interdisciplinary Explorations in every book allow you to make in-depth connections to other sciences and disciplines. Plus, you will find a wealth of additional tools to set your students on a successful course.

Chart the course you want with 15 motivating books that easily match your curriculum.

Each book in the series contains:

- Integrated Science sections in every chapter
- Interdisciplinary Explorations for team teaching at the end of each book
- Comprehensive skills practice and application—assuring that you meet the National Science Education Standards and your local and state standards

For custom binding options, see your local sales representative.

EXPLORATION TOOLS: BASIC PROCESS SKILLS

Observing

Measuring

Calculating

Classifying

Predicting

Inferring

Graphing

Creating data tables

Communicating

LIFE SCIENCE TITLES

From Bacteria to Plants
1 Living Things
2 Viruses and Bacteria
3 Protists and Fungi
4 Introduction to Plants
5 Seed Plants

Animals
1 Sponges, Cnidarians, and Worms
2 Mollusks, Arthropods, and Echinoderms
3 Fishes, Amphibians, and Reptiles
4 Birds and Mammals
5 Animal Behavior

Cells and Heredity
1 Cell Structure and Function
2 Cell Processes and Energy
3 Genetics: The Science of Heredity
4 Modern Genetics
5 Changes Over Time

Human Biology and Health
1 Healthy Body Systems
2 Bones, Muscles, and Skin
3 Food and Digestion
4 Circulation
5 Respiration and Excretion
6 Fighting Disease
7 The Nervous System
8 The Endocrine System and Reproduction

Environmental Science
1 Populations and Communities
2 Ecosystems and Biomes
3 Living Resources
4 Land and Soil Resources
5 Air and Water Resources
6 Energy Resources

 Integrated Science sections in every chapter

Posing questions

Forming operational definitions

Developing hypotheses

Controlling variables

Interpreting data

Interpreting graphs

Making models

Drawing conclusions

Designing experiments

EARTH SCIENCE TITLES

Inside Earth
1 Plate Tectonics
2 Earthquakes
3 Volcanoes
4 Minerals
5 Rocks

Earth's Changing Surface
1 Mapping Earth's Surface
2 Weathering and Soil Formation
3 Erosion and Deposition
4 A Trip Through Geologic Time

Earth's Waters
1 Earth: The Water Planet
2 Fresh Water
3 Freshwater Resources
4 Ocean Motions
5 Ocean Zones

Weather and Climate
1 The Atmosphere
2 Weather Factors
3 Weather Patterns
4 Climate and Climate Change

Astronomy
1 Earth, Moon, and Sun
2 The Solar System
3 Stars, Galaxies, and the Universe

PHYSICAL SCIENCE TITLES

Chemical Building Blocks
1 An Introduction to Matter
2 Changes in Matter
3 Elements and the Periodic Table
4 Carbon Chemistry

Chemical Interactions
1 Chemical Reactions
2 Atoms and Bonding
3 Acids, Bases, and Solutions
4 Exploring Materials

Motion, Forces, and Energy
1 Motion
2 Forces
3 Forces in Fluids
4 Work and Machines
5 Energy and Power
6 Thermal Energy and Heat

Electricity and Magnetism
1 Magnetism and Electromagnetism
2 Electric Charges and Current
3 Electricity and Magnetism at Work
4 Electronics

Sound and Light
1 Characteristics of Waves
2 Sound
3 The Electromagnetic Spectrum
4 Light

 Integrated Science sections in every chapter

T5

Place your students in the role of science explorer through a variety of inquiry activities.

Motivational student- and teacher-tested activities reinforce key concepts and allow students to explore science concepts for themselves. More than 350 activities are provided for each book in the Student Edition, Teacher's Edition, Teaching Resources, Integrated Science Lab Manual, Inquiry Skills Activity Book, Interactive Student Tutorial CD-ROM, and *Science Explorer* Web Site.

STUDENT EDITION ACTIVITIES

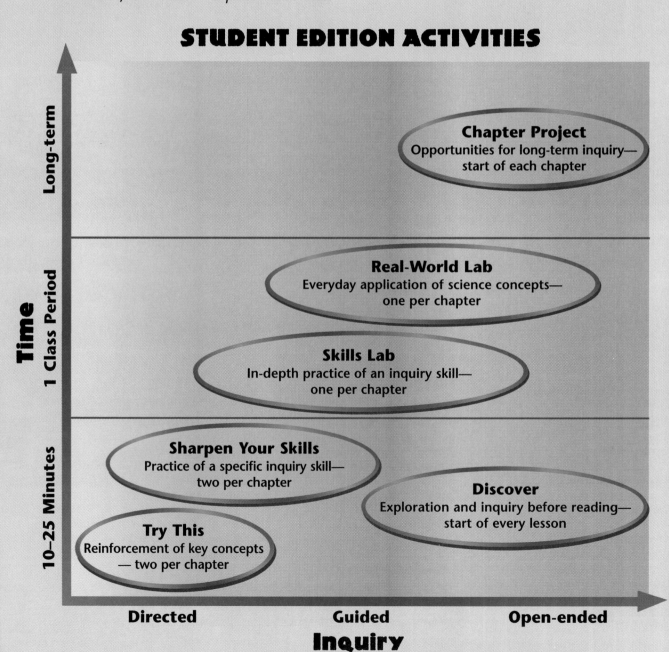

Time

Long-term

1 Class Period

10–25 Minutes

Chapter Project
Opportunities for long-term inquiry—
start of each chapter

Real-World Lab
Everyday application of science concepts—
one per chapter

Skills Lab
In-depth practice of an inquiry skill—
one per chapter

Sharpen Your Skills
Practice of a specific inquiry skill—
two per chapter

Discover
Exploration and inquiry before reading—
start of every lesson

Try This
Reinforcement of key concepts
— two per chapter

Directed   **Guided**   **Open-ended**

Inquiry

Check your compass regularly with integrated assessment tools.

Prepare for state exams with traditional and performance-based assessment.

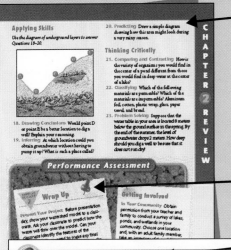

- **Comprehensive Chapter Reviews** include a wide range of question types that students will encounter on standardized tests. Types include multiple choice, enhanced true/false, concept mastery, visual thinking, skill application, and critical thinking. Also includes Chapter Project "Wrap Up."

- **Chapter Projects** contain rubrics that allow you to easily assess student progress.

- **Section Reviews** provide "Check your Progress" opportunities for the Chapter Project, as well as review questions for the section.

Additional *Science Explorer* assessment resources:

- **Assessment Resources with CD-ROM**
- **Resource Pro® with Planning Express® CD-ROM**
- **Standardized Test Practice Book**
- **On-line review activities** at www.phschool.com
  See page T9 for complete product descriptions.

Self-assessment opportunities help students keep themselves on course.

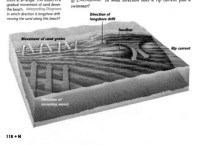

- **Caption Questions** throughout the text assess critical thinking skills.

- **Checkpoint Questions** give students an immediate content check as new concepts are presented.

- **Interactive Student Tutorial CD-ROM** provides students with electronic self-tests, review activities, and Exploration activities.

- **Got It! Video Quizzes** motivate and challenge students with engaging animations and interactive questions.

- **www.science-explorer.phschool.com** provides additional support and on-line test prep.

Utilize a wide variety of tools.

Easy-to-manage, book-specific teaching resources

15 Teaching Resource Packages, each containing a Student Edition, Teacher's Edition, Teaching Resources with Color Transparencies, Guided Reading Audiotape, Materials Kit Order form, and Correlation to the National Science Education Standards.

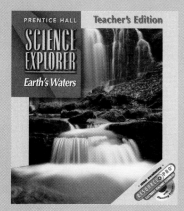

15 Teacher's Editions with a three-step lesson plan—*Engage/Explore, Facilitate,* and *Assess*— that is ideal for reaching all students. Chapter planning charts make it easy to find resources, as well as to plan for block scheduling and team teaching.

15 Teaching Resource Books with Color Transparencies offer complete support organized by chapter to make it easy for you to find what you need—when you need it.

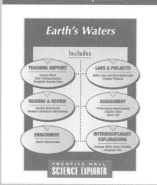

15 Guided Reading Audiotapes (English and Spanish) provide section summaries for students who need additional support.

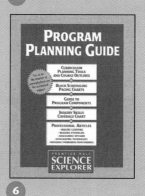

15 Explorer Videotapes allow students to explore concepts through spectacular short videos containing computer animations. Available in Spanish.

Program-wide print resources

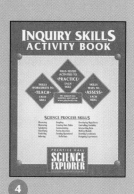

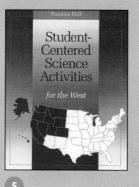

1. **Materials Kits**—Prentice Hall and Science Kit, Inc. have collaborated to develop a Consumable Kit and Nonconsumable Kit for each book. Ordering software makes it easy to customize!

2&3. **Integrated Science Laboratory Manual with Teacher's Edition**—74 in-depth labs covering the entire curriculum, with complete teaching support.

4. **Inquiry Skills Activity Book**—additional activities to teach, practice, and assess a wide range of inquiry skills.

5. **Student-Centered Science Activities**—five activity books for the Northeast, Southeast, Midwest, Southwest, and West.

6. **Program Planning Guide**—course outlines, block scheduling pacing charts, correlations, and more.

7. **Product Testing Activities by** *Consumer Reports*—19 student-oriented testing activities turn students into real-world explorers.

Additional print resources...

8. **Reading in the Content Area**—with Literature Connections

9. **Standardized Test Practice**—review and self-tests to prepare for statewide exams.

10. **15 Prentice Hall Interdisciplinary Explorations**

11. **How to Assess Student Work**

12. **How to Manage Instruction in the Block**

13. *Cobblestone, Odyssey, Calliope,* **and** *Faces* **Magazines**

Program-wide technology resources

1. **Resource Pro® CD-ROM**—the ultimate management tool with easy access to blackline masters and lab activities for all 15 books. Planning Express® software lets you customize lesson plans by day, week, month, and year. Also includes Computer Test Bank software.

2. **Assessment Resources with CD-ROM**—*Computer Test Bank* software with Dial-A-Test® provides you with unparalleled flexibility in creating tests.

3. *Science Explorer* **Web Site**—activities and teaching resources for every chapter at www.science-explorer.phschool.com

4. **Interactive Student Tutorial CD-ROMs**—provide students with self-tests, helpful hints, and Explorations. Tests are scored instantly and provide complete explanations to all answers.

5. **An Odyssey of Discovery CD-ROMs**—interactive labs encourage students to hypothesize and experiment. (Life and Earth Science).

6. **Interactive Earth CD-ROM**—explore global trends, search the media library, and zoom in on a 3-D globe.

7. **Mindscape CD-ROMs**—*The Animals!™, Oceans Below,* and *How Your Body Works* bring science alive with compelling videoclips, 3-D animations, and interactive databases.

8. **A.D.A.M. The Inside Story**—take an entertaining tour of each body system, designed for middle grades students.

9. **Interactive Physics**—explore physics concepts with computer simulations that encourage what-if questions.

10. **Explorer Videotapes and Videodiscs**—explore and visualize concepts through spectacular short documentaries containing computer animations (Spanish audio track).

11. **Got It! Video Quizzes**—make in-class review fun and prepare students for book tests and state assessments.

12. **Event-Based Science**—series of NSF-funded modules that engage students with inquiry-based projects. Includes video.

Options for Pacing *Animals*

The Pacing Chart below suggests one way to schedule your instructional time. The *Science Explorer* program offers many other aids to help you plan your instructional time, whether regular class periods or **block scheduling.** Refer to the Chapter Planning Guide before each chapter to view all program resources with suggested times for Student Edition activities.

Pacing Chart

	Days	Blocks		Days	Blocks
Nature of Science: An Amazon Discovery	1	1/2	**5** Integrating Earth Science: Vertebrate History in Rocks	2	1
Chapter 1 Sponges, Cnidarians, and Worms			Chapter 3 Review and Assessment	1	1/2
Chapter 1 Project Alive and Well	Ongoing	Ongoing	**Chapter 4 Birds and Mammals**		
1 What is an Animal?	4	2	Chapter 4 Project Bird Watch	Ongoing	Ongoing
2 Integrating Mathematics: Symmetry	3	1–2	**1** Birds	5	2–3
3 Sponges and Cnidarians	4	2	**2** Integrating Physics: The Physics of Bird Flight	2	1
4 Worms	4	2	**3** What Is a Mammal?	4	2
Chapter 1 Review and Assessment	1	1/2	**4** Diversity of Mammals	3	1 1/2
Chapter 2 Mollusks, Arthropods, and Echinoderms			Chapter 4 Review and Assessment	1	1/2
Chapter 2 Project Going Through Changes	Ongoing	Ongoing	**Chapter 5 Animal Behavior**		
1 Mollusks	3	1–2	Chapter 5 Project Learning New Tricks	Ongoing	Ongoing
2 Arthropods	4	2	**1** Why Do Animals Behave as They Do?	8	4
3 Insects	4	2	**2** Patterns of Behavior	5	3
4 Integrating Physics: The Sounds of Insects	2	1	**3** Integrating Chemistry: The Chemistry of Communication	1 1/2	1
5 Echinoderms	2–3	1–2	Chapter 5 Review and Assessment	1	1/2
Chapter 2 Review and Assessment	1	1/2	Interdisciplinary Exploration: The Secret of Silk	2–3	1–2
Chapter 3 Fishes, Amphibians, and Reptiles					
Chapter 3 Project Adaptations	Ongoing	Ongoing			
1 What Is a Vertebrate?	3	1 1/2			
2 Fishes	4	2			
3 Amphibians	3	1–2			
4 Reptiles	5	2–3			

RESOURCE PRO

The Resource Pro CD-ROM® is the ultimate scheduling and lesson planning tool. Resource Pro® allows you to preview all the resources in the Science Explorer program, organize your chosen materials, and print out any teaching resource. You can follow the suggested lessons or create your own, using resources from anywhere in the program.

Thematic Overview of *Animals*

The chart below lists the major themes of *Animals*. For each theme, the chart supplies a big idea, or concept statement, describing how a particular theme is taught in a chapter.

	Chapter 1	Chapter 2	Chapter 3	Chapter 4	Chapter 5
Patterns of Change	Adaptations of animals are the result of change over time.	Students learn about metamorphosis as a developmental pattern in arthropods.	The fossil record shows how animals moved out of the water and populated dry land.		Behavior patterns change in response to new stimuli and can be altered through a learning process.
Scale and Structure	While some animals are asymmetrical, most have radial or bilateral symmetry.	Mollusks, arthropods, and echinoderms are grouped according to anatomical characteristics.	Specialization in the skeletal, respiratory, and circulatory systems has enabled some animals to adapt to dry land.	Birds and mammals possess many specialized systems, each serving a specific function.	
Unity and Diversity	There are many types of animals, but they all share basic characteristics.	All arthropod groups share certain characteristics, such as an exoskeleton.	Fish, reptiles, and amphibians are all vertebrates, because they all possess a backbone.	Birds and mammals have distinctive characteristics, but both have a four-chambered heart.	While different animals behave in different ways, most animal behaviors help an animal survive and reproduce.
Systems and Interactions	Animals interact with other living things in feeding relationships, such as predator and prey.	Insects damage plants by eating them. However, insects also pollinate plants and prey on harmful insects.	Organisms interact as part of the environment. Artificial environments must supply all of an animal's needs.	The interaction of the respiratory and circulatory systems in both birds and mammals provides these organisms with energy.	Animals interact through behaviors such as competition, establishing a territory, and mating.
Evolution	A diagram of an evolution tree shows how the major animal phyla are related.	The natural history of mollusks is recorded by fossils. Arthropods arose in the oceans.	An evolution-tree diagram shows relationships among major vertebrate groups.	Birds and mammals both evolved from reptiles. The fossil record shows vertebrate evolution.	The behaviors of animals are adaptations that have evolved over time.
Energy	Food provides animals with energy for their bodies' activities.	Feeding strategies of mollusks, arthropods, and echinoderms are explained.		Birds eat an enormous amount of food to provide energy for flight.	
Modeling			Students construct models of reptiles, amphibians, and fishes in order to understand how adaptations aid survival.	Students create models demonstrating the ability of wool to provide insulation.	

Inquiry Skills Chart

The Prentice Hall *Science Explorer* program provides comprehensive teaching, practice, and assessment of science skills, with an emphasis on the process skills necessary for inquiry. The chart lists the skills covered in the program and cites the page numbers where each skill is covered.

Basic Process SKILLS				
	Student Text: Projects and Labs	**Student Text: Activities**	**Student Text: Caption and Review Questions**	**Teacher's Edition: Extensions**
Observing	14–15, 26–27, 42, 46–47, 53, 68–69, 118–119, 124–125, 150–151, 168–169	16, 20, 28, 32, 35, 40, 48, 50, 58, 62, 70–71, 82, 87–88, 95, 98, 103, 111, 121, 127, 130, 133, 135, 141, 152, 161, 170	19, 24, 52, 66, 76, 110, 122	17, 29–30, 36, 38, 49, 51–52, 55, 58–59, 71, 90, 92, 104, 126, 136, 143
Inferring	26–27, 42, 68–69, 106–107, 125–126, 168–169	20, 40, 48, 54, 62, 70, 73, 82, 87, 95, 101, 103, 109, 121, 133, 135, 141, 157, 161, 170	38, 67, 76, 85, 114, 136, 146, 161, 175	38, 49, 57, 67, 72, 85, 96, 102–103, 134, 142, 162, 171–172
Predicting	106–107	70–71, 73, 82, 130, 152, 154	45, 52, 93, 149, 158, 163, 171–172, 175	36–37, 136, 161
Classifying	68–69, 118–119, 124–125, 168–169	23, 32, 48, 50, 137	17, 33, 49, 79, 89, 143, 175	20–21, 127, 144
Making Models	80–81, 94	18, 73, 84, 98, 101, 131		32, 56, 60, 74, 91, 96
Communicating	14–15, 80–81, 150–151	15, 30, 34, 44, 47, 66, 78, 81, 88, 97, 112, 116, 119, 121, 140, 148, 151, 161, 174, 178, 181, 183		59–60, 84, 121, 155
Measuring	53, 124–125, 139		45	112
Calculating	53, 159	58, 163		
Creating Data Tables	46–47, 53, 106–107, 118–119, 139, 168–169	58, 194	79	
Graphing	53, 106–107, 119, 139	64, 194–196	79, 149	
Advanced Process SKILLS				
Posing Questions	14–15, 94, 168–169			155
Developing Hypotheses	42, 124–125, 159	189		155
Designing Experiments	42, 46–47, 53, 124–125, 139, 159, 168–169	189		136, 155
Controlling Variables	46–47, 139, 159	189	45, 47, 117	122, 155

Advanced Process SKILLS (continued)

	Student Text: Projects and Labs	Student Text: Activities	Student Text: Caption and Review Questions	Teacher's Edition: Extensions
Forming Operational Definitions		16, 161		165
Interpreting Data	42, 46–47, 53, 106–107, 118–119, 125–126, 139, 159	58, 109, 189	56, 79, 117, 149	191
Drawing Conclusions	46–47, 53, 124–125, 150–151	109, 189	45, 79, 117, 149	38, 122, 136

Critical Thinking SKILLS

	Student Text: Projects and Labs	Student Text: Activities	Student Text: Caption and Review Questions	Teacher's Edition: Extensions
Comparing and Contrasting	47, 80–81, 94, 119, 139, 159	18, 28, 35, 62, 131, 133, 190	22, 31, 32, 45, 61, 79, 83, 90, 108, 117, 126, 129, 134, 149	55–56, 63, 65, 134, 137, 166
Applying Concepts	26, 42, 68, 94, 139, 168–169	82, 98, 131, 190	23, 25, 56, 61, 72, 79, 97, 117, 153, 157, 167, 175	19, 24, 40, 83, 89, 156, 163
Interpreting Diagrams, Graphs Photographs, and Maps	106, 124	11, 166, 178, 190	21, 40, 86, 88, 96, 114, 175	51, 63, 75
Relating Cause and Effect	15, 47, 81, 151	119, 191	41, 45, 79, 100, 102, 131–132	84, 99
Making Generalizations	119	163, 191	55, 86, 92, 105, 110, 138, 149	60
Making Judgments		34, 140, 191	79	
Problem Solving	15, 68–69, 151	191	175	19, 155

Information Organizing SKILLS

	Student Text: Projects and Labs	Student Text: Activities	Student Text: Caption and Review Questions	Teacher's Edition: Extensions
Concept Maps		192	78, 174	
Compare/ Contrast Tables		192	116, 148	
Venn Diagrams		193		56, 63
Flowcharts		193	44	
Cycle Diagrams		193		

The *Science Explorer* program provides additional teaching, reinforcement, and assessment of skills in the Inquiry Skills Activities Book and the Integrated Science Laboratory Manual.

Throughout the *Science Explorer* program, every effort has been made to keep the materials and equipment *affordable, reusable,* and *easily accessible.*

The *Science Explorer* program offers an abundance of activity options so you can pick and choose those activities that suit your needs. To help you order supplies at the beginning of the year, the Master Materials List cross-references the materials by activity. If you prefer to create your list electronically, use the electronic order forms at:
www.science–explorer.phschool.com

There are two kits available for each book of the *Science Explorer* program, a Consumable Kit and a Nonconsumable Kit. These kits are produced by **Science Kit and Boreal Laboratories,** the leader in providing science kits to schools. Prentice Hall and Science Kit collaborated throughout the development of *Science Explorer* to ensure that the equipment and supplies in the kits precisely match the requirements of the program activities.

The kits provide an economical and convenient way to get all of the materials needed to teach each book. For each book, Science Kit also offers the opportunity to buy equipment and safety items individually. For a current listing of kit offerings or additional information about materials to accompany *Science Explorer*, please, contact Science Kit at:
1-800-828-7777
or at their Internet site at:
www.sciencekit.com

Master Materials List

Consumable Materials

*	Description	Quantity per class	Textbook Section(s)	*	Description	Quantity per class	Textbook Section(s)
SS	Aluminum foil, roll 12" x 25'	1	2-2 (TT) 5-3 (DIS)	C	Hydra, brown, live	1	1-3 (TT)
C	Ants, live (100)	1	5-2 (Lab)	SS	Insect collection	5	2-3 (DIS)
C	Bags, polyethylene 8" x 12", pkg. 10, heavy duty	1	3-3 (TT)	C	Lid, for 9 oz. cup	15	4-3 (Lab)
C	Battery, size D	10	1-4 (Lab)	C	Owl pellets, pkg. of 6	1	4-1 (Lab)
SS	Bottle, 2-L, plastic	5	2-3 (Lab) 5-2 (Lab)	SS	Paper towels, roll (120 sheets)	1	1-4 (Lab) 2-2 (TT)
SS	Box, shoe, with lid	5	2-2 (TT)	SS	Paper, construction, assorted pkg. of 50	1	1-1 (TT) 3-4 (TT) 5-2 (TT)
SS	Bread crumbs	5	5-2 (Lab)	SS	Paper, construction, black, pkg. of 15	1	5-2 (Lab)
SS	Can, aluminum	5	1-1 (TT)	SS	Paper, construction, green, pkg. of 50	1	3-3 (DIS)
SS	Cardboard, corrugated 32 x 32 cm	5	1-4 (Lab)	SS	Paper, single sheet	30	1-2 (DIS) 3-4 (Lab) 3-5 (DIS) 4-2 (DIS) 4-2 (TT) 5-1 (Lab)
SS	Cardboard, white 11" x 12"	5	2-2 (DIS)				
SS	Chameleons, American, live set of 3 (Anolis carolinesis)	2	3-4 (TT)	SS	Pencil	5	2-4 (TT) 3-4 (Lab) 5-1 (Lab)
C	Cheesecloth, 2-m piece	1	2-3 (Lab)				
C	Clay, modeling (red, blue, green, yellow), 1 lb.	3	1-1 (TT) 3-5 (DIS)	C	Pencil, marking, black wax	5	5-2 (Lab)
SS	Cracker	5	4-3 (DIS)	C	Perch, preserved - under 7", pkg. of 5	1	3-2 (SYS)
SS	Cup, paper 360 mL	5	3-3 (DIS)	C	Pill bugs, live (24)	2	2-2 (TT)
C	Cup, clear plastic, 9 oz.	15	4-3 (Lab)	C	Pipe cleaners, white, 12", pkg. of 100	1	1-1 (TT)
C	Earthworms, live (12)	1	1-4 (SYS) 1-4 (Lab)	C	Planaria, live	1	1-4 (DIS)
SS	Egg, uncooked	5	4-1 (TT)	SS	Plants, water, live	5	3-2 (Lab)
C	Extract, banana, 60 mL	1	5-3 (DIS)	C	Rubber band, #31, pkg. of 52	1	3-3 (TT) 3-4 (DIS)
C	Extract, mint, 60 mL	1	5-3 (DIS)	C	Rubber bands, #33, pkg. of 50	1	2-3 (Lab) 2-4 (DIS) 5-2 (Lab) 4-2 (TT)
C	Extract, vanilla, 8 oz.	1	5-3 (DIS)				
C	Fish food, Tetramin, 28 g	1	3-2 (Lab)				
C	Gloves, laboratory latex, medium, pkg. of 100	1	4-3 (TT)				
SS	Glue, white, 4 oz.	5	4-2 (TT)	C	Seeds, green split pea, 1 lb.	1	3-3 (DIS)
SS	Goldfish, live (12)	1	3-2 (DIS)	C	Seeds, Yellow Split Pea 1 lb.	1	3-3 (DIS)
SS	Grapefruit	5	3-4 (DIS)	SS	Shortening, solid	1	4-3 (TT)
SS	Graph paper	10	2-1 (Lab) 4-3 (Lab)				
SS	Guppies, live (12)	1	3-2 (Lab)				

KEY: **DIS**: Discover; **SYS**: Sharpen Your Skills; **TT**: Try This; **Lab**: Lab
* Items designated **C** are in the Consumable Kit, **NC** are in the Nonconsumable Kit, and **SS** are School Supplied.

Quantities based on 5 lab groups per class.

Master Materials List

Consumable Materials (cont.)

*	Description	Quantity per class	Textbook Section(s)	*	Description	Quantity per class	Textbook Section(s)
C	Snail, Black Ramshorn, live (15)	1	2-1 (Lab) 3-2 (Lab)	SS	Tape, masking 3/4" x 60 yd.	1	2-2 (DIS) 2-2 (TT) 4-4 (DIS) 5-2 (TT) 5-2 (Lab)
SS	Soil & leaf litter, fresh	5	2-3 (Lab)				
C	Soil, potting, 4 lb.	1	1-4 (SYS)				
C	Soil, sandy, 2.5 kg	2	5-2 (Lab)	SS	Tape, transparent, roll, 27 ft.	5	4-2 (TT)
SS	Stapler	5	4-2 (TT)	C	Toothpicks, flat pkg. of 750	1	1-3 (TT) 1-4 (DIS)
C	Steel wool pads, pkg. of 6	1	2-3 (Lab)				
C	String, cotton, 200 ft.	1	3-1 (TT) 4-2 (TT)	SS	Vertebrate, small, live	5	5-1 (DIS)
				SS	Water, spring, 1 gal.	1	1-4 (DIS) 2-1 (Lab)
SS	Sugar, granulated 454 g	1	5-2 (Lab)				

Nonconsumable Materials

*	Description	Quantity per class	Textbook Section(s)	*	Description	Quantity per class	Textbook Section(s)
NC	Beads, plastic w/hole, pkg. of 125	1	3-1 (TT)	NC	Jar, plastic, 16 oz.	5	2-3 (Lab)
				NC	Jar, plastic, 60 mL, wide-mouth	5	2-3 (Lab)
SS	Beaker, Pyrex, 1000 mL	5	4-3 (Lab)	SS	Lamp	5	2-3 (Lab)
SS	Book	5	4-2 (DIS)	NC	Magnifying glass, 3x-6x	5	1-3 (DIS) 1-3 (TT) 1-4 (DIS) 2-3 (DIS) 2-3 (Lab) 3-2 (SYS) 4-1 (DIS) 4-1 (Lab) 4-1 (TT) 5-2 (Lab)
SS	Bowl	5	4-1 (TT)				
NC	Brush, paint 7"	5	1-4 (DIS)				
NC	Container, plastic, 250 mL	6	5-3 (DIS)				
SS	Container, storage	5	1-4 (SYS) 1-4 (Lab)				
NC	Dip net, aquarium, 3"	1	3-2 (Lab)				
NC	Dropper, plastic	5	1-3 (TT) 1-4 (DIS) 1-4 (Lab) 2-5 (DIS)	NC	Mirror, plastic	5	4-3 (DIS)
				SS	Objects to make imprints	5	3-5 (DIS)
				NC	Pan, aluminum foil	5	1-4 (Lab) 5-2 (Lab)
NC	Feather, white	5	4-1 (DIS)				
NC	Flashlight, plastic	5	1-4 (Lab)	NC	Paper clips, pkg. of 100	1	4-2 (TT)
SS	Glass	5	1-2 (DIS) 2-4 (TT)	NC	Petri dish, plastic, 100 mm	5	1-3 (TT) 1-4 (DIS) 2-1 (Lab)
SS	Gravel, aquarium, 10 lbs.	1	3-2 (Lab)				

KEY: **DIS**: Discover; **SYS**: Sharpen Your Skills; **TT**: Try This; **Lab**: Lab
* Items designated **C** are in the Consumable Kit, **NC** are in the Nonconsumable Kit, and **SS** are School Supplied.

Nonconsumable Materials (cont.)

*	Description	Quantity per class	Textbook Section(s)
SS	Ruler, plastic	5	2-1 (Lab) 3-2 (Lab) 4-1 (Lab) 4-2 (DIS)
SS	Scissors	5	1-2 (DIS) 1-3 (DIS) 2-3 (Lab) 4-2 (DIS) 4-3 (Lab) 5-2 (TT)
NC	Screen, fiberglass 12" x 26"	2	5-2 (Lab)
NC	Shells, assorted, pkg. of 30	1	1-1 (DIS) 2-1 (DIS)
SS	Socks, cotton, pair	3	3-4 (DIS)
SS	Socks, wool, pair	5	4-3 (Lab)
NC	Sponge, synthetic	5	1-3 (DIS) 5-2 (Lab)
NC	Sponge, natural, pkg. of 6	1	1-1 (DIS) 1-3 (DIS)
NC	Starfish shell	5	1-1 (DIS)
SS	Stopwatch	5	1-4 (Lab) 2-1 (Lab) 3-3 (DIS) 4-3 (Lab)
NC	Straight teasing needle, 145 mm	5	4-1 (Lab)
NC	Student forceps, straight, 115 mm	5	4-1 (Lab) 5-2 (Lab)

*	Description	Quantity per class	Textbook Section(s)
NC	Thermometer, high temp., −40°C to 110°C	15	2-1 (Lab) 3-2 (Lab) 4-3 (Lab)
SS	Trowel	5	2-3 (Lab)
NC	Tuning fork, 256 Hz	5	2-4 (TT)
SS	Umbrella	5	3-1 (DIS)

Equipment

*	Description	Quantity per class	Textbook Section(s)
SS	Aquarium heater	1	3-2 (Lab)
SS	Aquarium filter kit	1	3-2 (Lab)
SS	Aquarium, glass	1	3-2 (DIS) 3-2 (Lab) 3-4 (TT) 5-1 (DIS)
SS	Goggles, chemical splash, class set	1	2-1 (Lab) 2-3 (Lab) 3-2 (SYS) 4-3 (Lab) 5-2 (Lab)

KEY: **DIS**: Discover; **SYS**: Sharpen Your Skills; **TT**: Try This; **Lab**: Lab
* Items designated **C** are in the Consumable Kit, **NC** are in the Nonconsumable Kit, and **SS** are School Supplied.

PRENTICE HALL
SCIENCE EXPLORER

Animals

Program Resources
Student Edition
Annotated Teacher's Edition
Teaching Resources Book with Color Transparencies
Animals Materials Kits

Program Components
Integrated Science Laboratory Manual
Integrated Science Laboratory Manual, Teacher's Edition
Inquiry Skills Activity Book
Student-Centered Science Activity Books
Program Planning Guide
Guided Reading English Audiotapes
Guided Reading Spanish Audiotapes and Summaries
Product Testing Activities by Consumer Reports™
Event-Based Science Series (NSF funded)
Prentice Hall Interdisciplinary Explorations
Cobblestone, Odyssey, Calliope, and *Faces* Magazines

Media/Technology
Science Explorer Interactive Student Tutorial CD-ROMs
Odyssey of Discovery CD-ROMs
Resource Pro® (Teaching Resources on CD-ROM)
Assessment Resources CD-ROM with Dial-A-Test®
Internet site at www.science-explorer.phschool.com
Life, Earth, and Physical Science Videodiscs
Life, Earth, and Physical Science Videotapes
Got It! Video Quizzes

Science Explorer Student Editions

From Bacteria to Plants

Animals

Cells and Heredity

Human Biology and Health

Environmental Science

Inside Earth

Earth's Changing Surface

Earth's Waters

Weather and Climate

Astronomy

Chemical Building Blocks

Chemical Interactions

Motion, Forces, and Energy

Electricity and Magnetism

Sound and Light

Staff Credits

The people who made up the *Science Explorer* team—representing editorial, editorial services, design services, field marketing, market research, marketing services, on-line services/multimedia development, product marketing, production services, and publishing processes—are listed below. Bold type denotes core team members.

Kristen E. Ball, **Barbara A. Bertell,** Peter W. Brooks, **Christopher R. Brown, Greg Cantone,** Jonathan Cheney, **Patrick Finbarr Connolly,** Loree Franz, Donald P. Gagnon, Jr., **Paul J. Gagnon, Joel Gendler,** Elizabeth Good, Kerri Hoar, **Linda D. Johnson,** Katherine M. Kotik, Russ Lappa, Marilyn Leitao, David Lippman, **Eve Melnechuk, Natania Mlawer,** Paul W. Murphy, **Cindy A. Noftle,** Julia F. Osborne, Caroline M. Power, Suzanne J. Schineller, **Susan W. Tafler,** Kira Thaler-Marbit, Robin L. Santel, Ronald Schachter, **Mark Tricca,** Diane Walsh, Pearl B. Weinstein, Beth Norman Winickoff

Acknowledgment for pages 180–181: Excerpt from *Dragons and Dynasties: An Introduction to Chinese Mythology,* by Yuan Ke, translated by Kim Echlin & Nie Zhixiong. Copyright © Foreign Languages Press, 1991, 1992, 1993. Used by permission of Foreign Languages Press, Beijing.

ISBN 0-13-434477-4
2 3 4 5 6 7 8 9 10   05 04 03 02 01 00 99

Cover: A polar bear cub rests comfortably on its mother.

Teacher's Edition ISBN 0-13-434560-6

Program Authors

Michael J. Padilla, Ph.D.
Professor
Department of Science Education
University of Georgia
Athens, Georgia

Michael Padilla is a leader in middle school science education. He has served as an editor and elected officer for the National Science Teachers Association. He has been principal investigator of several National Science Foundation and Eisenhower grants and served as a writer of the National Science Education Standards.

As lead author of *Science Explorer,* Mike has inspired the team in developing a program that meets the needs of middle grades students, promotes science inquiry, and is aligned with the National Science Education Standards.

Ioannis Miaoulis, Ph.D.
Dean of Engineering
College of Engineering
Tufts University
Medford, Massachusetts

Martha Cyr, Ph.D.
Director, Engineering
   Educational Outreach
College of Engineering
Tufts University
Medford, Massachusetts

Science Explorer was created in collaboration with the College of Engineering at Tufts University. Tufts has an extensive engineering outreach program that uses engineering design and construction to excite and motivate students and teachers in science and technology education.

Faculty from Tufts University participated in the development of *Science Explorer* chapter projects, reviewed the student books for content accuracy, and helped coordinate field testing.

Book Author

Jan Jenner, Ph.D.
Science Writer
Talladega, Alabama

Contributing Writers

Fred Holtzclaw
Science Instructor
Oak Ridge High School
Oak Ridge, Tennessee

Theresa K. Holtzclaw
Former Science Instructor
Clinton, Tennessee

Evan P. Silberstein
Science Instructor
Spring Valley High School
Spring Valley, New York

Reading Consultant

Bonnie B. Armbruster, Ph.D.
Department of Curriculum
   and Instruction
University of Illinois
Champaign, Illinois

Interdisciplinary Consultant

Heidi Hayes Jacobs, Ed.D.
Teacher's College
Columbia University
New York, New York

Safety Consultants

W. H. Breazeale, Ph.D.
Department of Chemistry
College of Charleston
Charleston, South Carolina

Ruth Hathaway, Ph.D.
Hathaway Consulting
Cape Girardeau, Missouri

Tufts University Program Reviewers

Behrouz Abedian, Ph.D.
Department of Mechanical
Engineering

Wayne Chudyk, Ph.D.
Department of Civil and
Environmental Engineering

Eliana De Bernardez-Clark, Ph.D.
Department of Chemical Engineering

Anne Marie Desmarais, Ph.D.
Department of Civil and
Environmental Engineering

David L. Kaplan, Ph.D.
Department of Chemical Engineering

Paul Kelley, Ph.D.
Department of Electro-Optics

George S. Mumford, Ph.D.
Professor of Astronomy, Emeritus

Jan A. Pechenik, Ph.D.
Department of Biology

Livia Racz, Ph.D.
Department of Mechanical Engineering

Robert Rifkin, M.D.
School of Medicine

Jack Ridge, Ph.D.
Department of Geology

Chris Swan, Ph.D.
Department of Civil and
Environmental Engineering

Peter Y. Wong, Ph.D.
Department of Mechanical Engineering

Content Reviewers

Jack W. Beal, Ph.D.
Department of Physics
Fairfield University
Fairfield, Connecticut

W. Russell Blake, Ph.D.
Planetarium Director
Plymouth Community
Intermediate School
Plymouth, Massachusetts

Howard E. Buhse, Jr., Ph.D.
Department of Biological Sciences
University of Illinois
Chicago, Illinois

Dawn Smith Burgess, Ph.D.
Department of Geophysics
Stanford University
Stanford, California

A. Malcolm Campbell, Ph.D.
Assistant Professor
Davidson College
Davidson, North Carolina

Elizabeth A. De Stasio, Ph.D.
Associate Professor of Biology
Lawrence University
Appleton, Wisconsin

John M. Fowler, Ph.D.
Former Director of Special Projects
National Science Teacher's Association
Arlington, Virginia

Jonathan Gitlin, M.D.
School of Medicine
Washington University
St. Louis, Missouri

Dawn Graff-Haight, Ph.D., CHES
Department of Health, Human
Performance, and Athletics
Linfield College
McMinnville, Oregon

Deborah L. Gumucio, Ph.D.
Associate Professor
Department of Anatomy and Cell Biology
University of Michigan
Ann Arbor, Michigan

William S. Harwood, Ph.D.
Dean of University Division and Associate
Professor of Education
Indiana University
Bloomington, Indiana

Cyndy Henzel, Ph.D.
Department of Geography
and Regional Development
University of Arizona
Tucson, Arizona

Greg Hutton
Science and Health
Curriculum Coordinator
School Board of Sarasota County
Sarasota, Florida

Susan K. Jacobson, Ph.D.
Department of Wildlife Ecology
and Conservation
University of Florida
Gainesville, Florida

Judy Jernstedt, Ph.D.
Department of Agronomy and Range Science
University of California, Davis
Davis, California

John L. Kermond, Ph.D.
Office of Global Programs
National Oceanographic and
Atmospheric Administration
Silver Spring, Maryland

David E. LaHart, Ph.D.
Institute of Science and Public Affairs
Florida State University
Tallahassee, Florida

Joe Leverich, Ph.D.
Department of Biology
St. Louis University
St. Louis, Missouri

Dennis K. Lieu, Ph.D.
Department of Mechanical Engineering
University of California
Berkeley, California

Cynthia J. Moore, Ph.D.
Science Outreach Coordinator
Washington University
St. Louis, Missouri

Joseph M. Moran, Ph.D.
Department of Earth Science
University of Wisconsin–Green Bay
Green Bay, Wisconsin

Joseph Stukey, Ph.D.
Department of Biology
Hope College
Holland, Michigan

Seetha Subramanian
Lexington Community College
University of Kentucky
Lexington, Kentucky

Carl L. Thurman, Ph.D.
Department of Biology
University of Northern Iowa
Cedar Falls, Iowa

Edward D. Walton, Ph.D.
Department of Chemistry
California State Polytechnic University
Pomona, California

Robert S. Young, Ph.D.
Department of Geosciences and
Natural Resource Management
Western Carolina University
Cullowhee, North Carolina

Edward J. Zalisko, Ph.D.
Department of Biology
Blackburn College
Carlinville, Illinois

Teacher Reviewers

Stephanie Anderson
Sierra Vista Junior
    High School
Canyon Country, California

John W. Anson
Mesa Intermediate School
Palmdale, California

Pamela Arline
Lake Taylor Middle School
Norfolk, Virginia

Lynn Beason
College Station Jr. High School
College Station, Texas

Richard Bothmer
Hollis School District
Hollis, New Hampshire

Jeffrey C. Callister
Newburgh Free Academy
Newburgh, New York

Judy D'Albert
Harvard Day School
Corona Del Mar, California

Betty Scott Dean
Guilford County Schools
McLeansville, North Carolina

Sarah C. Duff
Baltimore City Public Schools
Baltimore, Maryland

Melody Law Ewey
Holmes Junior High School
Davis, California

Sherry L. Fisher
Lake Zurich Middle
    School North
Lake Zurich, Illinois

Melissa Gibbons
Fort Worth ISD
Fort Worth, Texas

Debra J. Goodding
Kraemer Middle School
Placentia, California

Jack Grande
Weber Middle School
Port Washington, New York

Steve Hills
Riverside Middle School
Grand Rapids, Michigan

Carol Ann Lionello
Kraemer Middle School
Placentia, California

Jaime A. Morales
Henry T. Gage Middle School
Huntington Park, California

Patsy Partin
Cameron Middle School
Nashville, Tennessee

Deedra H. Robinson
Newport News Public Schools
Newport News, Virginia

Bonnie Scott
Clack Middle School
Abilene, Texas

Charles M. Sears
Belzer Middle School
Indianapolis, Indiana

Barbara M. Strange
Ferndale Middle School
High Point, North Carolina

Jackie Louise Ulfig
Ford Middle School
Allen, Texas

Kathy Usina
Belzer Middle School
Indianapolis, Indiana

Heidi M. von Oetinger
L'Anse Creuse Public School
Harrison Township, Michigan

Pam Watson
Hill Country Middle School
Austin, Texas

Activity Field Testers

Nicki Bibbo
Russell Street School
Littleton, Massachusetts

Connie Boone
Fletcher Middle School
Jacksonville Beach, Florida

Rose-Marie Botting
Broward County
    School District
Fort Lauderdale, Florida

Colleen Campos
Laredo Middle School
Aurora, Colorado

Elizabeth Chait
W. L. Chenery Middle School
Belmont, Massachusetts

Holly Estes
Hale Middle School
Stow, Massachusetts

Laura Hapgood
Plymouth Community
    Intermediate School
Plymouth, Massachusetts

Sandra M. Harris
Winman Junior High School
Warwick, Rhode Island

Jason Ho
Walter Reed Middle School
Los Angeles, California

Joanne Jackson
Winman Junior High School
Warwick, Rhode Island

Mary F. Lavin
Plymouth Community
    Intermediate School
Plymouth, Massachusetts

James MacNeil, Ph.D.
Concord Public Schools
Concord, Massachusetts

Lauren Magruder
St. Michael's Country
    Day School
Newport, Rhode Island

Jeanne Maurand
Glen Urquhart School
Beverly Farms, Massachusetts

Warren Phillips
Plymouth Community
    Intermediate School
Plymouth, Massachusetts

Carol Pirtle
Hale Middle School
Stow, Massachusetts

Kathleen M. Poe
Kirby-Smith Middle School
Jacksonville, Florida

Cynthia B. Pope
Ruffner Middle School
Norfolk, Virginia

Anne Scammell
Geneva Middle School
Geneva, New York

Karen Riley Sievers
Callanan Middle School
Des Moines, Iowa

David M. Smith
Howard A. Eyer Middle School
Macungie, Pennsylvania

Derek Strohschneider
Plymouth Community
    Intermediate School
Plymouth, Massachusetts

Sallie Teames
Rosemont Middle School
Fort Worth, Texas

Gene Vitale
Parkland Middle School
McHenry, Illinois

Zenovia Young
Meyer Levin Junior
    High School (IS 285)
Brooklyn, New York

PRENTICE HALL
SCIENCE EXPLORER

Contents

Animals

Prepare your students with rich, motivating content

Science Explorer is crafted for today's middle grades student, with accessible content and in-depth coverage. **Integrated Science Sections** support every chapter and the **Interdisciplinary Exploration** provides an engaging final unit.

Check your compass— regularly assess student progress.

Self-assessment tools are built right into the student text and **on-going assessment** is woven throughout the Teacher's Edition. You'll find a wealth of **assessment technology** in the Resource Pro®, Interactive Student Tutorial, and Assessment Resources CD-ROMs.

Activities

Inquiry Activities

CHAPTER PROJECT
Opportunities for long-term inquiry

DISCOVER
Exploration and inquiry before reading

Sharpen your Skills
Practice of specific science inquiry skills

TRY THIS
Reinforcement of key concepts

Draw upon the world around you.

Interdisciplinary Activities connect to every discipline and give science a meaningful, real-world context.

Interdisciplinary Activities

Skills Lab

In-depth practice of inquiry skills

Real-World Lab

Everyday application of science concepts

EXPLORING

Visual exploration of concepts

An Amazon Discovery

Focus on Zoology

This four-page feature introduces the process of scientific inquiry by involving students in a high-interest, magazine-like article about a working scientist, biologist Russell A. Mittermeier. Using Dr. Mittermeier's investigation of dwarf marmosets in the Amazon rain forest, the article focuses on observing and problem solving as key elements of scientific inquiry.

Mammals are presented in Chapter 4, Sections 4-3 and 4-4, of this book. However, students need not have any previous knowledge of that chapter's content to understand and appreciate this article.

Scientific Inquiry

◆ Before students read the article, let them read the title, examine the pictures, and read the captions on their own. Then ask: **What questions came into your mind as you looked at these pictures?** *(Students might suggest questions such as "How did Dr. Mittermeier discover the marmoset?" "How did the scientists in the rain forest know where to look for the marmoset?" "How do scientists know what monkeys eat?" and "How do monkeys get sap from a tree?")* Point out to students that just as they had questions about what they were seeing, scientists too have questions about what they observe.

AN AMAZON DISCOVERY

Dr. Russell A. Mittermeier is President of Conservation International and a leader in the effort to understand and preserve biodiversity around the world. Since 1977, he has served as chairman of the Primate Specialist group of the World Conservation Union Species Survival Commission. He has described several previously unknown species of monkeys.

I f you think scientists spend their days in clean, white laboratories and their nights hunched over computers and notebooks, you haven't met Dr. Russell Mittermeier. An adventurer and well-known authority on primates (monkeys, apes, and similar animals), Dr. Mittermeier tells captivating tales of his treks.

He recalls a major expedition he made into the Amazon rainforest in 1973. Dr. Mittermeier was traveling on the powerful Amazon River, carrying his photographic equipment, binoculars, notebooks, and other gear in a motorized canoe. In the choppy waves, his boat took on water and sank beneath him into the river. To reach shore safely, he had to swim past hungry crocodile-like black caimans. He made it, but lost all his gear except a plastic cup he carried for his toothbrush! Fortunately, the event didn't discourage him. Mittermeier accepts such setbacks when studying animals in the wild.

The dwarf marmoset is the second smallest monkey ever discovered. Its scientific name is *Callithrix humilis*. It measures about 10 centimeters and weighs around 158 grams.

Background

Zoology is the study of animals. Zoologists in the past spent their time classifying animals and studying their anatomy. Modern zoologists study subjects such as genetics, ecology, and biochemistry. They usually specialize in one of many sub disciplines, such as entomology (insects), ichthyology (fish), herpetology (amphibians and reptiles), and ornithology (birds).

Within each sub discipline, a zoologist can specialize in areas such as morphology (the structure of the animal's body), animal behavior, ecology (how animals interact with their natural environment), or zoogeography (how animals are distributed over Earth). In any branch of zoology, field work is very important. There are many areas of the world, including the tropical rain forests, where field work can still produce new and important discoveries.

An Early Interest in Wildlife

Dr. Mittermeier traces his interest in animals and adventure to his childhood in New York. "When I was young, my mother read books to me about Africa and South America. She dragged me every week to the Museum of Natural History and to the Bronx Zoo. So from a very early age, I grew up interested in wildlife. In first grade, when teachers asked what we wanted to be when we grew up, my answer was a jungle explorer. In today's language that would probably be a field biologist."

Though Dr. Mittermeier's driving interest is in science, he admits that the spirit of adventure still moves him. "At the age of thirteen, I discovered Edgar Rice Burroughs' Tarzan books. I've been very, very much a Tarzan fan ever since."

In 1997 Dr. Mittermeier set out on an extraordinary expedition to Brazil's Amazon jungle to search for the world's second smallest monkey. The adventure really began in 1996, when Dr. Mittermeier visited his long-time colleague Marc Van Roosmalen in the Brazilian city of Manaus. A local man had brought an orphaned baby monkey to Van Roosmalen's primate clinic. The man said he'd found the monkey about 500 kilometers away.

Van Roosmalen "showed me this tiny, little, baby monkey. It was about the size of my fist. We looked at each other and realized it was a new species, and a really distinctive one," Dr. Mittermeier relates. Finding a new kind of monkey is a rare scientific accomplishment.

The tiny monkey looked similar to the pygmy marmoset, the world's smallest monkey, which also lives in

The triangle of land between the Rio Madeira and the Rio Aripuanã is a small part of the huge Amazon rain forest. It was in this isolated area that scientists found the tiny monkeys.

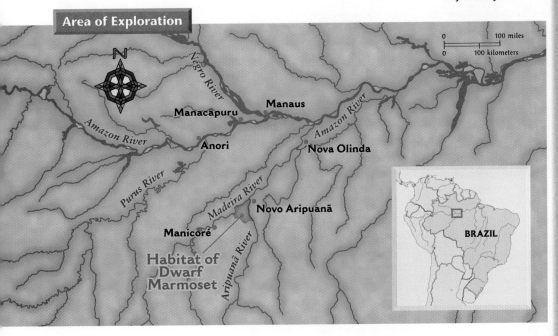

Area of Exploration

N

Negro River

Amazon River

Manacapuru

Manaus

Anori

Amazon River

Nova Olinda

Purus River

Madeira River

Novo Aripuanã

Manicoré

Aripuanã River

Habitat of Dwarf Marmoset

0   100 miles
0   100 kilometers

BRAZIL

◆ Explain that scientists who study animals are called zoologists. Encourage students to tell what they already know about zoology—the kinds of animals that people study, what scientists want to learn about animals, some discoveries that scientists have made about animals, and the variety of places where zoologists work.

◆ Ask students who have seen animals in zoos or who have watched nature documentaries on television to share with the class an interesting fact they learned about an animal.

◆ Have a volunteer read aloud the caption next to the marmoset's photo on page 10. Help students pronounce the scientific name. Ask: **Is this marmoset the smallest monkey known?** *(No; the caption says it is the second smallest monkey ever discovered.)* Challenge interested students to find out the name and the size of the smallest monkey known.

◆ If students seem particularly interested in marmosets, share the information in Background below. Also suggest that they consult library books to learn more about marmosets or about Dr. Mittermeier's other adventures.

Background

Marmosets are monkeys that live in the trees of tropical rain forests in South America. They have long tails, curved claws instead of nails, nonopposable thumbs, and soft fur. Marmosets are small, quick, tree-dwellers that eat fruits and insects. They have often been kept as pets, but require special care to maintain good health.

Marmosets are divided into five groups and include tamarins. The most common marmoset is 18 to 30 cm long and has long black and white fur. This animal has thick white tufts of fur on its ears and a black and white tail that is almost twice as long as its body.

Most marmosets are endangered because their habitats are being destroyed.

◆ Ask: **What animal would you most like to study? What questions do you have about this monkey? What unique challenges do you think you would face studying this animal?** *(Use students' responses to these questions to draw parallels between their own interests and Dr. Mittermeier's interest in animals.)*

◆ If any students have read one of Burroughs' Tarzan books, ask them to describe the book to the class.

◆ Ask: **How did the scientists first learn about the new monkey species?** *(A local man had brought an orphaned monkey to the scientists' primate clinic.)* **What do you think the functions of a primate clinic are?** *(Students' answers will vary; samples: study primates, heal sick primates)* Have a volunteer look up the definition of primate in a dictionary and share the definition with the class.

◆ Ask students to use an atlas or world map to compare the size of Australia to the size of the Amazon rain forest. *(Australia without Tasmania is about the same size as Amazonia.)* Lead students to appreciate how difficult it would be to find one species of tiny monkey in a region of this size. Invite students to imagine they are in charge of finding this monkey species in this region. Have students brainstorm for ideas on how they would find the monkey. Record students' ideas on the board. After students have contributed 10 or 12 good suggestions, lead them to make generalizations about the kinds of skills that zoologists need to be successful.

◆ Ask students: **Why did Dr. Mittermeier think that finding this monkey would be expensive?** *(Students' answers will vary; sample: They could search for a long time and never find any monkeys. They would need money for food and supplies and wages for a long time. They might need to hire many local people to help them find the monkeys. The rain forest is difficult to reach so special equipment would be needed.)*

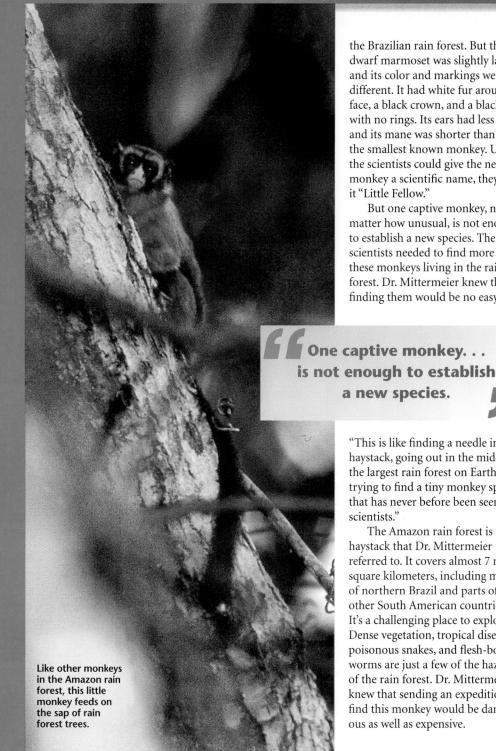

Like other monkeys in the Amazon rain forest, this little monkey feeds on the sap of rain forest trees.

the Brazilian rain forest. But this dwarf marmoset was slightly larger and its color and markings were different. It had white fur around its face, a black crown, and a black tail with no rings. Its ears had less hair and its mane was shorter than that of the smallest known monkey. Until the scientists could give the new monkey a scientific name, they called it "Little Fellow."

But one captive monkey, no matter how unusual, is not enough to establish a new species. The scientists needed to find more of these monkeys living in the rain forest. Dr. Mittermeier knew that finding them would be no easy task.

> **" One captive monkey. . . is not enough to establish a new species. "**

"This is like finding a needle in a haystack, going out in the middle of the largest rain forest on Earth and trying to find a tiny monkey species that has never before been seen by scientists."

The Amazon rain forest is the haystack that Dr. Mittermeier referred to. It covers almost 7 million square kilometers, including much of northern Brazil and parts of eight other South American countries. It's a challenging place to explore. Dense vegetation, tropical diseases, poisonous snakes, and flesh-boring worms are just a few of the hazards of the rain forest. Dr. Mittermeier knew that sending an expedition to find this monkey would be danger-ous as well as expensive.

Background

PBS produced a documentary on marmosets with the help of Marc Van Roosmalen. The documentary, "Gremlins: Faces in the Forest" was made while Van Roosmalen was searching for other new species of marmosets. Marmosets and tamarins are nicknamed gremlins because of their appearance and their mischievous behavior.

Van Roosmalen and the filmmakers asked local people to help them find marmosets.

When the Satare Maues Indians led them to one area, Van Roosmalen and the film-makers discovered a rare golden white tassel ear marmoset with hairless ears. The Satare Maues also helped Van Roosmalen find an entirely new marmoset species.

Further information on marmosets and details on how to order the PBS video can be found online at **www.wnet.org/nature.**

◄ The orphaned dwarf marmoset at 2 months (left) and at 7 months (right) at the primate clinic.

♦ Challenge interested students to find out more about what marmosets eat. Invite students to share their findings with the class.

In Your Journal To help students appreciate Dr. Mittermeier's work, suggest that they compare and contrast his everyday life with that of an office worker. Ask: **What challenges does Dr. Mittermeier face that an office worker does not? What aspects of Dr. Mittermeier's daily life in the rain forest would you most enjoy? What aspects would you most dislike?** Extend the discussion by asking: **What skills does Dr. Mittermeier need in the field that an office worker does not need?** Lead students to appreciate the skills a field scientist needs to live and work for long periods in remote regions like the rain forest.

Introducing Animals

Remind students that monkeys are mammals and have them look through the book to find the parts that relate most closely to this article. *(Chapter 4, Birds and Mammals, particularly sections 4-3, What Is a Mammal? and 4-4, Diversity of Mammals, and the Discover feature, How Is a Thumb Useful? on page 141)* Ask: **Besides mammals, what else is this book about?** *(many other kinds of animals)* **What kinds of things do you think you will be learning about?** *(Accept all responses without comments.)*

To obtain money, Dr. Mittermeier returned to the United States. He is president of an international organization that works to protect the rich variety of plants and animals living on Earth. He splits his time between that Washington-based conservation group and the rain forests of the world. Back in the United States, Dr. Mittermeier was able to obtain money for Van Roosmalen's expeditions.

After several unsuccessful attempts, Van Roosmalen finally located monkeys like "Little Fellow." They were in an area isolated from the rest of the rain forest by two rivers. This dwarf marmoset was given the scientific name *Callithrix humilis*. Finally, in 1997 Dr. Mittermeier joined the group of scientists in the Brazilian rain forest who were photographing and observing these monkeys in the wild. They found that the behavior and eating habits of the monkeys were similar to those of other Amazon monkeys. They feed on the sap of rain forest trees.

"Nonhuman primates" says Dr. Mittermeier, "are our closest living relatives, and you would think they would be very well known. In fact, since 1990 we've managed to find seven new ones just in the country of Brazil. That doesn't count the new ones we've found in Madagascar and a few other places."

It's not that surprising when someone finds a new tropical forest canopy beetle or a soil microorganism in the floor of the rain forest. But the discovery of a new primate species indicates that there may still be many creatures in the world that people don't even know exist.

In Your Journal

In a paragraph, write what interests you about Russell Mittermeier as a scientist. What do you think motivates him? What surprises you about how he works? What skills does a scientist like Mittermeier need?

Sponges, Cnidarians, and Worms

Sections	Time	Student Edition Activities ACTIVITY	Other Activities
CHAPTER PROJECT 2 **Alive and Well** p. 15	Ongoing (3 weeks)	Check Your Progress, pp. 15, 22, 33, 41 Wrap Up, p. 45	
1 **What is an Animal?** pp. 16–22 ◆ List and describe four major characteristics that all animals share. ◆ Explain how biologists classify animals into groups. ◆ Describe animals' adaptations for getting food and escaping predators.	4 periods/ 2 blocks	**Discover** Is It an Animal? p. 16 **Try This** Get Moving, p. 18 **Sharpen Your Skills** Inferring, p. 20	TE Including All Students, p. 17 TE Building Inquiry Skills: Problem Solving, p. 19 TE Building Inquiry Skills: Classifying, p. 20 TE Inquiry Challenge, p. 21
2 *INTEGRATING MATHEMATICS* **Symmetry** pp. 23–27 ◆ Recognize bilateral and radial symmetry in animals.	3 periods/ 1–2 blocks	**Discover** How Many Ways Can You Fold It? p. 23 **Science at Home** p. 25 **Real-World Lab: You Solve the Mystery** A Tale Told by Tracks, pp. 26–27	TE Building Inquiry Skills: Applying Concepts, p. 24 TE Using the Visuals: Figures 8 and 9, p. 24
3 **Sponges and Cnidarians** pp. 28–34 ◆ Describe the organization of a sponge's body. ◆ Identify the main characteristics of cnidarians. ◆ Describe life on a coral reef.	4 periods/ 2 blocks	**Discover** How Do Natural and Synthetic Sponges Compare? p. 28 **Try This** Hydra Doing? p. 32 **Science and Society** Coral Reefs in Danger, p. 34	TE Integrating Chemistry , p. 30 TE Demonstration, p. 31 TE Language Arts Connection, p. 30 TE Including All Students, p. 31 IES "Where River Meets Sea," pp. 33–34
4 **Worms** pp. 35–42 ◆ Identify the three main groups of worms. ◆ List and identify the characteristics of the three groups of worms.	4 periods/ 2 blocks	**Discover** What Can You Learn About a Flatworm by Looking at It? p. 35 **Sharpen Your Skills** Observing, p. 40 **Skills Lab: Developing Hypotheses** Earthworm Responses, p. 42	TE Real-Life Learning, p. 37 TE Inquiry Challenge, p. 38 TE Including All Students, p. 39 TE Integrating Earth Science, p. 40 ISLM Lab B-1, "Observing Flatworms and Roundworms"
Study Guide/Chapter Review pp. 43–45	1 period/ $\frac{1}{2}$ block		ISAB Provides teaching and review of all inquiry skills.

For Standard or Block Schedule The Resource Pro® CD-ROM gives you maximum flexibility for planning your instruction for any type of schedule. Resource Pro® contains Planning Express®, an advanced scheduling program, as well as the entire contents of the Teaching Resources and the Computer Test Bank.

CHAPTER PLANNING GUIDE

Program Resources	Assessment Strategies	Media and Technology
TR Chapter 1 Project Teacher Notes, pp. 10–11 **TR** Chapter 1 Project Student Materials, pp. 12–15 **TR** Chapter 1 Project Rubric, p. 16	**SE** Performance Assessment: Chapter 1 Project Wrap Up, p. 45 **TE** Check Your Progress, pp. 15, 22, 33, 41 **TR** Chapter 1 Project Scoring Rubric, p. 16	Science Explorer Internet Site
TR 1-1 Lesson Plan, p. 17 **TR** 1-1 Section Summary, p. 18 **TR** 1-1 Review and Reinforce, p. 19 **TR** 1-1 Enrich, p. 20	**SE** Section 1 Review, p. 22 **TE** Ongoing Assessment, pp. 17, 19, 21 **TE** Performance Assessment, p. 22 **TR** 1-1 Review and Reinforce, p. 19	Exploring Life Science Videodisc, Unit 3 Side 2, "Through Their Eyes" Exploring Life Science Videodisc, Unit 3 Side 2, "How Does Everything Fit?" Audiotapes: English-Spanish Summary 1-1 Transparency 1, "Animal Classification Tree" Interactive Student Tutorial CD-ROM, B-1
TR 1-2 Lesson Plan, p. 21 **TR** 1-2 Section Summary, p. 22 **TR** 1-2 Review and Reinforce, p. 23 **TR** 1-2 Enrich, p. 24 **TR** Real-World Lab blackline masters, pp. 33–34	**SE** Section 2 Review, p. 25 **SE** Analyze and Conclude, p. 27 **TE** Performance Assessment, p. 25 **TR** 1-2 Review and Reinforce, p. 23	Audiotapes: English-Spanish Summary 1-2 Interactive Student Tutorial CD-ROM, B-1
TR 1-3 Lesson Plan, p. 25 **TR** 1-3 Section Summary, p. 26 **TR** 1-3 Review and Reinforce, p. 27 **TR** 1-3 Enrich, p. 28 **SES** Book K, *Chemical Building Blocks,* Chapter 2	**SE** Section 3 Review, p. 33 **TE** Ongoing Assessment, pp. 29, 31 **TE** Performance Assessment, p. 33 **TR** 1-3 Review and Reinforce, p. 27	Exploring Life Science Videodisc, Unit 3 Side 2, "Spineless" Audiotapes: English-Spanish Summary 1-3 Transparency 2, "Exploring a Sponge" Interactive Student Tutorial CD-ROM, B-1
TR 1-4 Lesson Plan, p. 29 **TR** 1-4 Section Summary, p. 30 **TR** 1-4 Review and Reinforce, p. 31 **TR** 1-4 Enrich, p. 32 **TR** Skills Lab blackline masters, pp. 36–37	**SE** Section 4 Review, p. 41 **SE** Analyze and Conclude, p. 42 **TE** Ongoing Assessment, pp. 37, 39 **TE** Performance Assessment, p. 41 **TR** 1-4 Review and Reinforce, p. 31	Exploring Life Science Videodisc, Unit 3 Side 2, "Spineless" Audiotapes: English-Spanish Summary 1-4 Transparency 3, "Exploring the Life Cycle of a Dog Tapeworm" Transparency 4, "Earthworm Anatomy" Interactive Student Tutorial CD-ROM, B-1
TR Chapter 1 Performance Assessment, pp. 166–168 **TR** Chapter 1 Test, pp. 169–172	**SE** Chapter Review, pp. 43–45 **TR** Chapter 1 Performance Assessment, pp. 166–168 **TR** Chapter 1 Test, pp. 169–172 **CTB** Chapter 1 Test	Interactive Student Tutorial CD-ROM, B-1 Computer Test Bank, Test B-1 Got It! Video Quizzes

Key: **SE** Student Edition   **TE** Teacher's Edition   **TR** Teaching Resources
     CTB Computer Test Bank   **SES** Science Explorer Series Text   **ISLM** Integrated Science Laboratory Manual
     ISAB Inquiry Skills Activity Book   **PTA** Product Testing Activities by *Consumer Reports*   **IES** Interdisciplinary Explorations Series

Meeting the National Science Education Standards and AAAS Benchmarks

National Science Education Standards	Benchmarks for Science Literacy	Unifying Themes
Science as Inquiry (Content Standard A) ◆ **Ask questions that can be answered by scientific investigations** What can be learned about animals by studying their tracks? *(Real-World Lab)* Do earthworms prefer dry or moist conditions? Do they prefer light or dark conditions? *(Skills Lab)* ◆ **Design and conduct a scientific investigation** Students design a plan to investigate whether earthworms prefer smooth or rough surfaces. *(Skills Lab)* **Life Science** (Content Standard C) ◆ **Diversity and adaptations of organisms** Students learn the main characteristics of animals and some of the adaptations animals use to get food and escape predators. *(Section 1)* Students learn the characteristics and adaptations of sponges and cnidarians. *(Section 3)* Students learn the characteristics and adaptations of the three main groups of worms. *(Section 4)* Students research the adaptations of a particular animal. *(Chapter Project)* ◆ **Populations and ecosystems** Students learn about the effects humans can have on coral reefs. *(Section 3)* ◆ **Structure and function of living systems** The bodies of complex animals all have either radial or bilateral symmetry. *(Section 2)*	**1B Scientific Inquiry** Students infer animal activities by the indirect evidence of animal tracks. They test hypotheses by conducting an experiment on earthworm responses to light. *(Real-World Lab; Skills Lab)* **5A Diversity of Life** Students learn the general characteristics of animals. Then they learn the specific characteristics of sponges, cnidarians, and worms. *(Sections 1, 3, 4)* **5D Interdependence of Life** Environmental interactions and dependence are presented. Parasite and host relationships are explained. *(Section 3, 4; Chapter Project; Science and Society)* **11C Constancy and Change** Bilateral and radial symmetry in animals is explored in detail. *(Sections 2, 3, 4)*	◆ **Patterns of Change** Adaptations of animals are the result of change over time. *(Section 1)* ◆ **Scale and Structure** While some animals are asymmetrical, most have radial or bilateral symmetry. Sponges, cnidarians, and worms all have specific body structures. *(Sections 2, 3, 4)* ◆ **Unity and Diversity** There are many types of animals, but they all share basic characteristics. *(Sections 1, 3, 4)* ◆ **Systems and Interactions** Students investigate the interactions of three animals by examining their tracks in the snow. *(Real-World Lab)* ◆ **Evolution** The wide variety of animals are classified into phyla that are related to each other in an evolutionary tree.

Media and Technology

Exploring Life Science Videodisc
◆ **Section 1** "Through Their Eyes" allows viewers to define and identify both vertebrates and invertebrates, and to look at life through the eyes of these animals. "How Does Everything Fit?" demonstrates the important interactions among all types of animals and the humans on Earth.

◆ **Section 3** "Spineless" provides information for viewers to compare the digestion, circulation, and respiration of a variety of invertebrates.

Interactive Student Tutorial CD-ROM
◆ **Chapter Review** Interactive questions help students assess their mastery of key chapter concepts.

Student Edition Connection Strategies

◆ **Section 2** Integrating Mathematics, p. 23–25

◆ **Section 3** Integrating Chemistry, p. 30
Language Arts Connection, p. 30
Science and Society, p. 34

◆ **Section 4** Integrating Earth Science, p. 41

USING THE INTERNET **ACTIVITY**

www.science-explorer.phschool.com

Visit the Science Explorer internet site to find an up-to-date activity for Chapter 1 of *Animals.*

Activity	Time (minutes)	Materials *Quantities for one work group*	Skills
Section 1			
Discover, p. 16	15	**Consumable** organisms that students can safely observe, such as earthworms, minnows, pill bugs, crickets, potted plants, ferns, and sponges	**Forming Operational Definitions, Observing, Classifying**
Try This, p. 18	30	**Consumable** paper, drawing materials, sculpting materials such as modeling clay, wire pipe cleaners, aluminum cans	**Making Models, Predicting, Inferring**
Sharpen Your Skills, p. 20	15	**Consumable** No special materials are required.	**Inferring**
Section 2			
Discover, p. 23	10	**Consumable** tracing paper **Nonconsumable** scissors, pen or pencil, circular object	**Classifying, Observing, Drawing Conclusions, Forming Operational Definitions**
Real-World Lab, pp. 26–27	30	**Consumable** No special materials are required.	**Observing, Inferring**
Section 3			
Discover, p. 28	20	**Consumable** natural sponges, synthetic kitchen sponges **Nonconsumable** scissors, hand lens or microscope	**Observing, Classifying**
Try This, p. 32	25	**Consumable** live hydra, toothpick **Nonconsumable** small glass bowl or petri dish, hand lens or microscope	**Classifying, Observing**
Section 4			
Discover, p. 35	15	**Consumable** live planarian, bottled water, toothpick **Nonconsumable** small paintbrush, small transparent container or petri dish, plastic dropper, hand lens	**Observing, Classifying**
Sharpen Your Skills, p. 40	15 minutes per day over several days	**Consumable** earthworm, construction paper, soil **Nonconsumable** transparent container, hand lens	**Observing**
Skills Lab, p. 42	15	**Consumable** water, paper towels **Nonconsumable** plastic dropper, cardboard, clock or watch, flashlight, 2 earthworms in a storage container, tray	**Developing Hypotheses**

A list of all materials required for the Student Edition activities can be found on pages T14–T16. You can order Materials Kits by calling 1-800-828-7777 or by accessing the Science Explorer internet site at **http://www.science-explorer.phschool.com.**

Alive and Well

Purpose By caring for an animal during this project, students will learn more about what animals need. They will also learn how to make careful observations.

Skills Focus Students will be able to
- pose questions about how to meet the needs of an animal;
- observe the behaviors and characteristics of their animal;
- communicate their findings about the animal to their classmates.

Project Time Line The project requires about five weeks. See Chapter 1 Project Teacher Notes on pages 10–11 in Teaching Resources for hints and detailed directions. Also give students the Chapter 1 Project Student materials and Scoring Rubic on pages 12–16 in Teaching Resources. During week one, students should choose their animals, design the habitats, and obtain approval for their plans. At the end of week one, students should have habitats ready for the animals to live in and can obtain the animal and place it in its new habitat.

During weeks two through four, students should place the animals in their habitats and observe their behaviors.

During week five, students should prepare their report. Have students present their findings to the class.

Suggested Shortcuts Simplify the project by placing students in groups. Have students complete Project Worksheets 1 and 2 with their groups.

You may also wish to choose the animal for the students. Alternatively, keep one animal for the entire class and have groups of students observe and take care of it on different days. To shorten the project time line, have students observe their animals for only one week.

Possible Materials Suitable project animals include slugs, snails, earthworms, pill bugs, spiders, millipedes, fruit flies, crickets, guppies, and anole lizards. Before students consider what animal to choose, explain any restrictions related to school policy on live animals in the classroom; limited classroom storage space, and local conditions such as nighttime and weekend temperatures. Food for the animals will vary depending on the chosen animal's requirements. Leaves, vegetable trimmings, and insects are some possibilities. All habitats must have an adequate supply of water.

The graceful tentacles of this yellow cup coral help it to lure and catch food.

WHAT'S AHEAD

Integrating Mathematics

SECTION 1 What Is an Animal?
Discover Is It an Animal?
Try This Get Moving
Sharpen Your Skills Inferring

SECTION 2 Symmetry
Discover How Many Ways Can You Fold It?
Real-World Lab A Tale Told by Tracks

SECTION 3 Sponges and Cnidarians
Discover How Do Natural and Synthetic Sponges Compare?
Try This Hydra Doing?

14 ◆ B

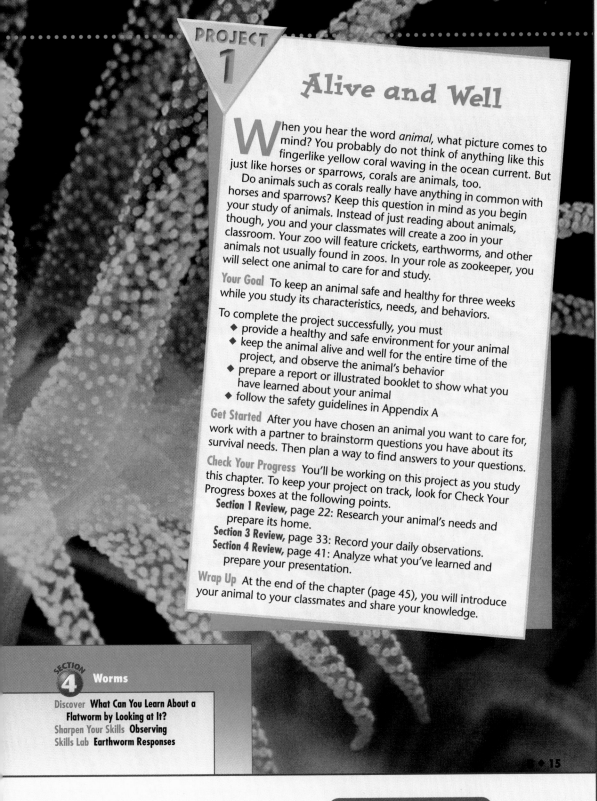

PROJECT 1

Alive and Well

When you hear the word *animal*, what picture comes to mind? You probably do not think of anything like this fingerlike yellow coral waving in the ocean current. But just like horses or sparrows, corals are animals, too.

Do animals such as corals really have anything in common with horses and sparrows? Keep this question in mind as you begin your study of animals. Instead of just reading about animals, though, you and your classmates will create a zoo in your classroom. Your zoo will feature crickets, earthworms, and other animals not usually found in zoos. In your role as zookeeper, you will select one animal to care for and study.

Your Goal To keep an animal safe and healthy for three weeks while you study its characteristics, needs, and behaviors.

To complete the project successfully, you must
- provide a healthy and safe environment for your animal
- keep the animal alive and well for the entire time of the project, and observe the animal's behavior
- prepare a report or illustrated booklet to show what you have learned about your animal
- follow the safety guidelines in Appendix A

Get Started After you have chosen an animal you want to care for, work with a partner to brainstorm questions you have about its survival needs. Then plan a way to find answers to your questions.

Check Your Progress You'll be working on this project as you study this chapter. To keep your project on track, look for Check Your Progress boxes at the following points.

Section 1 Review, page 22: Research your animal's needs and prepare its home.
Section 3 Review, page 33: Record your daily observations.
Section 4 Review, page 41: Analyze what you've learned and prepare your presentation.

Wrap Up At the end of the chapter (page 45), you will introduce your animal to your classmates and share your knowledge.

♦ 15

Students should construct a suitable habitat for their animals. A 2-liter soda bottle could serve as a nice terrarium for an insect. Students can carefully cut the top off the bottle, then fill it with soil, leaf litter, twigs, and plants for their animals. They can then cover the bottle with plastic wrap and cut tiny holes in the plastic wrap for ventilation.

Launching the Project When introducing the project, bring an animal into the classroom to show the students. Ask: **What kinds of things do you think this animal needs to live?** *(Food, water, a place to live)* Talk about where the animal lives, what it eats, and how to take care of it. Ask: **Where would you find this kind of information if you did not already know it?** *(In the library, on the Internet, or in a pet store)* **What kinds of things do you think you can find out by watching this animal's behavior?** *(Students may mention how and what the animal eats, how it moves, when it is quiet or active, where it stays in its habitat, and the characteristics of its body.)*

Allow students to read the description of the project in their text and in the Chapter 1 Project Overview on pages 12–13 in the Teaching Resources. Pass out copies of the Chapter 1 Project Worksheets on pages 14–15 for students to complete.

Performance Assessment

The Chapter 1 Project Scoring Rubric on page 16 of Teaching Resources will help you evaluate how well students complete the Chapter 1 Project. Students will be assessed on
- how well they plan for their animals' care;
- whether they observe and record their animals' behavior daily;
- the thoroughness and organization of their presentations, and
- how well they participate in group activities associated with the project.
By sharing the Chapter 1 Project Scoring Rubric with students at the beginning of the project, you will make it clear to them what they are expected to do.

Program Resources

- **Teaching Resources** Chapter 1 Project Teacher's Notes, pp. 10–11; Chapter 1 Project Student Materials, pp. 12–15; Chapter 1 Project Scoring Rubric, p. 16

Objectives

After completing the lesson, students will be able to

◆ list and describe four major characteristics that all animals share;

◆ explain how biologists classify animals;

◆ describe animals' adaptations for getting food and escaping predators.

Key Terms species, heterotroph, autotroph, sexual reproduction, fertilization, asexual reproduction, adaptation, herbivore, carnivore, predator, prey, omnivore, phylum, invertebrate, vertebrate

1 Engage/Explore

Activating Prior Knowledge

Ask: **What does an animal look like? How is it different from a flower or a tree?** Have students brainstorm ideas. Have students sketch an animal on a piece of paper and list three things that make it an animal. *(Sample answer: An animal must eat other living things.)* Lead students to realize that there is tremendous diversity among animals.

• • • • • • • • **DISCOVER** • • • • • • • •

Skills Focus forming operational definitions

Materials *organisms that students can safely observe such as earthworms, minnows, pill bugs, crickets, potted plants, ferns, and sponges*

Time 15 minutes

Tips Make sure students record whether or not each specimen is an animal while looking at that specimen. Ask students to give at least one reason for their choice. Invite them to discuss their decisions in small groups. Remind students to treat all living things with care.

Expected Outcome Students should recognize animals such as earthworms and minnows. They may not recognize sponges as animals.

Think It Over Students may note behavioral characteristics such as eating and movement or physical features such as mouths, hair, legs, fins, or wings.

DISCOVER • **ACTIVITY** • • •

Is It an Animal?

1. Carefully examine each of the organisms that your teacher gives you.

2. Decide which ones are animals. Think about the reasons for your decision. Wash your hands after handling each of the organisms.

Think It Over

Forming Operational Definitions What characteristics did you use to decide whether each organism was an animal?

GUIDE FOR READING

◆ What characteristics do all animals have in common?

◆ How are animals classified into groups?

Reading Tip Before you begin to read, write your own definition of *animal*. Add to it or change it as you read.

I n the waters off the north coast of Australia, a young box jellyfish floats along, looking more like a tiny transparent flower than an animal. After a time the young jellyfish will change form. As an adult, it will resemble a square bubble of clear jelly trailing bunches of long, wavy, armlike structures called tentacles.

To capture food, a box jellyfish's tentacles fire deadly venom at unlucky animals that happen to touch them. Humans are no exception. A swimmer who brushes the tentacles of a box jellyfish can die in only four minutes. In spite of their harmless appearance, adult box jellyfish have one of the strongest venoms on Earth.

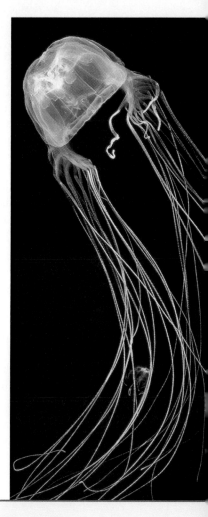

Figure 1 Don't be fooled by the delicate-looking tentacles of the Australian box jellyfish. Animals that brush against them can be killed by their venom—and become the jellyfish's next meal.

READING STRATEGIES

Reading Tip When defining the term *animal*, students may find it helpful to list some characteristics they have noticed in animals. Remind students to modify their definition as they read. Suggest that they note the subhead titles under *Characteristics of Animals* to help them add to their definition.

Study and Comprehension Have students outline the main ideas of the section. Outlines should include the characteristics of animals (multicellular, heterotroph, sexual reproduction, movement); adaptations for getting food; adaptations for escaping predators; and how animals are classified (body structure, embryo development, and DNA).

Characteristics of Animals

The box jellyfish may not look like most of the animals that you are familiar with, but it is indeed an animal. Biologists, scientists who study living organisms, have described over 1 million different animal species, and there are certainly many more. A **species** is a group of organisms that can mate with each other and produce offspring, who in turn can mate and reproduce.

All species of animals, including the beautiful but deadly box jellyfish, are similar in some important ways. **Animals are many-celled organisms that must obtain their food by eating other organisms.** In addition, most animals reproduce sexually and can move from place to place. Biologists look for these characteristics in deciding whether an organism is an animal.

How Animal Cells Are Organized All animals are multicellular; that is, their bodies are composed of many cells, the tiny working units that make up all living things. The cells of most animals are grouped together to form different kinds of tissue. A tissue is a group of similar cells that perform a specific job. For example, muscle tissue allows animals to move, while nerve tissue carries messages from one part of the body to another. Tissues may combine to form an organ, which is a group of different tissues that work together to perform a specific job that is more complex than the functions of each tissue by itself. Organs are made up of different types of tissue—your thigh bone, for example, is an organ that contains bone tissue, nerve tissue, and blood. In most animals, different organs combine to form an organ system, such as your skeletal system, shown in Figure 2.

How Animals Obtain Food Every animal is a **heterotroph** (HET ur oh trohf)—it cannot make food for itself, and must obtain food by eating other organisms. Contrast this with a green plant, which is an **autotroph** (AW toh trohf), an organism that makes its own food. Most animals take food into a cavity inside their bodies. Inside this cavity, the food is digested, or broken down into substances that the animal's body can absorb and use.

How Animals Reproduce Animals typically reproduce sexually. **Sexual reproduction** is the process by which a new organism forms from the joining of two sex cells—a tiny male sperm cell combines with a much larger female egg cell. The joining of egg and

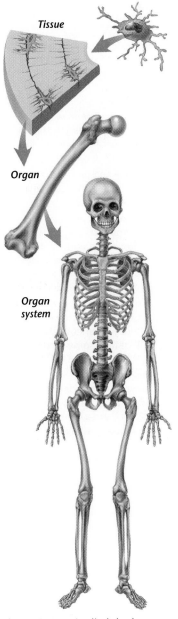

Cell

Tissue

Organ

Organ system

Figure 2 An animal's skeletal system has different levels of organization. Bone cells make up tissues, and tissues make up organs such as the thigh bone. *Classifying Is the skull best classified as an organ or as a tissue?*

2 Facilitate

Characteristics of Animals

Using The Visuals: Figure 1
Draw students' attention to the jellyfish. Then ask: **Is this a picture of an animal? How can you tell?** Elicit information on what characteristics students used to form their answer. Finally, tell students to read the caption and describe how the jellyfish obtains its food. **learning modality: visual**

Including All Students
 To provide students who need extra challenges with the opportunity to observe details of tissues and organs, give them a chicken drumstick with the thigh still attached, a dissection kit, and hand lenses. **CAUTION:** Beforehand, soak chicken overnight in dilute bleach solution; then rinse. Students should wear disposable gloves. Dissecting probes and scalpels are sharp. Urge students to use them carefully.

Remind students that muscles are part of the system that provides support for the animal. Have students carefully remove the skin and notice the fat, muscle, and connective tissue. Ask students to carefully disassemble, sketch, and count the muscles of the thigh and lower leg. Have students carefully slice through one of the larger muscles in cross section and observe the structure with a hand lens.
learning modality: visual

Portfolio Students can save sketches of their work and written observations in their portfolios.

Program Resources

◆ **Teaching Resources** 1-1 Lesson Plan, p. 17; 1-1 Section Summary, p. 18

Media and Technology

 Audiotapes English-Spanish Summary 1-1

Answers to Self-Assessment

Caption Question
Figure 2 Like the thigh bone, the skull is an organ.

Ongoing Assessment

Writing Have each student list the major characteristics of animals. (*Multicellular, heterotrophs, typically reproduce sexually, most move freely*)

Characteristics of Animals, continued

How Animals Meet Their Needs

Cultural Diversity

Help students to brainstorm a list of animals that people of cultures throughout the world use for transport. (*Samples: horse, camel, elephant, donkey, llama*) Explain that each culture uses transport animals that have specific adaptations to the climate of the region they live in. Ask students to name characteristics that help these animals survive in their environments. (*Sample: Camels can go without water for a long time in hot, dry climates.*) **learning modality: verbal**

Get Moving

Design an animal with a new and different way of moving. Your design should help your animal obtain food or get out of danger.

1. Make and label a drawing that shows how the animal would move.

2. Using clay, pipe cleaners, aluminum cans, construction paper, and whatever other materials are available, create a three-dimensional model of your animal.

3. Compare your animal to those of other classmates. What are some similarities? What are some differences?

Making Models What features of your design help your animal obtain food or escape danger?

sperm is called **fertilization.** Sperm and egg cells carry information about the characteristics of the parent that produced them—characteristics such as size and color. When sperm and egg unite, the resulting new individual has a combination of characteristics from both parents. It is something like each parent, but not exactly like either one.

Some animals can reproduce asexually as well as sexually. **Asexual reproduction** is the process by which a single organism produces a new organism identical to itself. Asexual reproduction does not involve a joining of sex cells from two individuals. Instead, the parent organism may divide to form two or more new organisms, or it may produce offspring from buds that grow on its body. A tiny animal called a hydra, for example, reproduces asexually by forming buds that eventually break off to form new hydras.

How Animals Move Animal movement can be fascinating to watch. Much of the movement is related to obtaining food, reproducing, and escaping danger. Barnacles, for example, wave feathery arms through the water to collect tiny food particles. Some geese must fly thousands of miles each spring to the place where they mate and lay eggs. And you've probably seen a cat claw its way up a tree trunk to get away from a snarling dog.

Some animals don't move from place to place. Adult oysters, sponges, and corals all stick firmly to underwater rocks and other solid surfaces. But most animals move freely at some point in their lives. For example, for its first few weeks of life, an oyster is a tiny swimmer—so tiny that you need a microscope to see it. Then the young oyster swims to a solid surface and attaches itself. It glues itself in place and undergoes changes in its form, eventually becoming an adult oyster within a shell.

☑ *Checkpoint Contrast the ways in which heterotrophs and autotrophs obtain food.*

Figure 3 Animals such as this Arabian stallion move with grace and power.

How Animals Meet Their Needs

If someone asked you to make a list of the things that you need to stay alive, you would probably write down *water*, *food*, and *oxygen*. Like all living things, animals need water because the chemical reactions that keep them alive, such as the breakdown of food, take place in water. Food provides animals with raw materials for growth and with energy for their bodies' activities, such as moving and breathing. To release that energy, the body's cells need oxygen. Some animals get oxygen from air; others absorb it from water.

Water, food, and oxygen must come from an animal's environment, or surroundings. An animal needs to be able to respond to its environment—for example, to find food and to run away from danger. Animals' bodies and behaviors are adapted for tasks such as these. An **adaptation** is a characteristic that helps an organism survive in its environment or reproduce.

Adaptations for Getting Food

Unlike plants that make their own food using sunlight, animals must obtain their food. Some animals eat plants, other animals eat animals, and still others eat both plants and animals.

Herbivores Animals that eat only plants are called **herbivores**. Grasshoppers, termites, and garden snails are some common smaller herbivores. Larger herbivores include cows, horses, and pandas. Herbivores have adaptations such as teeth with broad, flat surfaces that are good for grinding tough plants.

Carnivores Animals that eat only other animals are **carnivores**. Many carnivores are **predators** that hunt and kill other animals. Predators have adaptations that help them capture the animals

Figure 4 Animals have different adaptations for obtaining food. **A.** A carpet snake is a carnivore that feeds on lizards and other animals. **B.** A macaw is an herbivore that feeds on fruits and seeds. *Observing What feeding adaptations do you see in the photos?*

Chapter 1 **B ◆ 19**

Answers to Self-Assessment

Caption Question

Figure 4 The macaw uses its sharp claws to pick up food and bring it to its beak. It uses its heavy beak to crush fruit and seeds. The snake captures food by coiling around it and squeezing.

✓ *Checkpoint*

Heterotrophs obtain food by eating other living things. Autotrophs manufacture their own food.

Adaptations for Getting Food

Including All Students

For the benefit of students who are learning English, contrast the meanings, spellings, and pronunciations of *predator* and *prey*. You might point out that both words derive from the Latin word *praedari*, meaning "to plunder." **limited English proficiency**

Building Inquiry Skills: Problem Solving

Materials *cardboard tube* **ACTIVITY** *(half a paper towel tube or a toilet paper tube), plastic wrap, rubber band, birdseed, chopsticks, tweezers, masking tape, butter knife, plastic dropper*
Time 15 minutes
To help students investigate feeding adaptations, seal one end of the cardboard tube with plastic wrap and the rubber band. Place about 2 centimeters of birdseed in the tube. Then tape the sealed end of the tube to a table. Challenge students to find the best way to remove the birdseed using the remaining materials. Allow students to use creative methods, such as wrapping the knife in masking tape, then inserting it into the tube. Ask students to identify the real-life adaptations that their solutions stand for. (*Sample answer: The sticky masking tape is like a frog's tongue.*)
learning modality: kinesthetic

Ongoing Assessment

Oral Presentation Have each student choose an animal and give a brief oral presentation, describing its adaptations for feeding or protection.

B ◆ 19

Adaptations for Getting Food, continued

Sharpen your Skills

Inferring

Time 15 minutes

Tips Have students

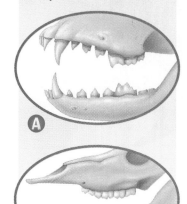

describe the shape of the teeth in each picture. Ask: **What do you think the sharp, pointed teeth in A are adapted to do?** (*Tear skin or flesh*) Then ask: **What do you think the broad, flat teeth in B are adapted to do?** (*To grind or shred plants*) Remind students that animals that eat flesh are carnivores and those that eat plants are herbivores.

Expected Outcome Students should say that the animal in A eats meat and the animal in B eats plants.

Extend Have students compare their own teeth and jaws to those shown in the pictures. Have students describe characteristics of their own teeth. (*Sample: Some of my front teeth are sharp and pointed like a carnivore's. Some of my back teeth are broad and flat like an herbivore's.*) Explain that humans, who are omnivores, share some adaptations with herbivores and carnivores.

learning modality: visual

Adaptations for Escaping Predators

Building Inquiry Skills: Classifying

Materials: *Pictures of animals from various sources*

Obtain several photographs or drawings of prey animals and predators. If pictures are not available that show both in the same picture, use separate pictures and match them up, as in lion—zebra, fox—rabbit. Divide the class into groups and distribute a set of matching pictures to each group. Have the group make a list of adaptations the prey animals have, such as big horns or long legs. They should then classify these as adaptations for getting food or adaptations for escaping predators. Then have them make a list of adaptations the predators have that allow them to capture prey.

cooperative learning

Sharpen your Skills

Inferring ACTIVITY

The pictures show the jawbones of two animals. Look at the pictures carefully, and decide what types of food each animal probably eats. List the observations on which you base your inferences.

A

B

Figure 5 Hedgehogs, like this African pygmy hedgehog, roll up into spiny balls to protect themselves from possible predators.

---

they feed upon, their **prey**. Wolves, for example, run down their prey. A wolf's adaptations include sharp claws, speed, and excellent hearing and eyesight. The teeth of most carnivores are sharp and pointed—they are adapted for cutting and stabbing.

Unlike wolves, sit-and-wait predators hide quietly and attack suddenly. Most of them blend in with their surroundings. Think of a frog sitting quietly by a pond. An insect flying by doesn't see the frog. Suddenly the frog flicks out its sticky tongue and catches the unsuspecting insect.

Omnivores Some animals eat both plants and animals; such an animal is an **omnivore**. A grizzly bear eats berries and roots, as well as insects, fish, and other small animals. Humans are also omnivores, as you know if you like hamburgers with tomato.

☑ *Checkpoint* Describe some feeding adaptations of carnivores.

Adaptations for Escaping Predators

In addition to feeding adaptations, animals have adaptations that help them avoid being eaten by predators. Some animals, such as box turtles and hedgehogs, have hard shells or spiny skins. Opossums and pill bugs "play dead" when they are attacked, so their predators lose interest. Stingers, claws, bitter-tasting flesh, or smelly sprays protect other animals. If you see a skunk, you stay far away from it. So do most predators.

Classification of Animals

Biologists classify animals in the animal kingdom into about 35 major groups, each of which is called a **phylum** (plural *phyla*). As you read this book, you will learn the characteristics of some of these phyla. Notice that in Figure 6, the phyla are arranged like the branches on a tree.

| Background |

History of Science Aristotle was among the first students of natural history to describe and classify different forms of animal life. The classification scheme that biologists use today grew out of a system developed by the Swedish botanist, Carl Linnaeus (1707–1778). In 1732, while still a student, Linnaeus undertook an expedition to the largely unexplored region of northern Scandinavia known as Lapland. His Lapland

journey helped to focus Linnaeus's attention on the need for a standard system of classification, a task which became his life's work. Linnaeus provided the system for grouping living organisms together in a manner that shed light on the relationships between different life forms. And by writing in Latin, which was the language of scholars, he made his work universally available to the learned world.

The branching tree shows how biologists think the different phyla are related. For example, from their positions on the tree, you can see that segmented worms are more closely related to arthropods than to sponges.

The tree also shows the order in which biologists think animal life has evolved, or changed over time. This evolution process has resulted in all the different phyla that exist today. Biologists do not know the exact way in which evolution took place—they can only make inferences on the basis of the best evidence available. Notice that biologists think all animals arose from unicellular, or single-celled, ancestors, as shown at the base of the tree.

Figure 6 This branching tree shows how the major animal phyla are related to one another, and the approximate order in which they evolved. *Interpreting Diagrams To which group are flatworms more closely related—roundworms or mollusks?*

B ◆ 21

Answers to Self-Assessment

Caption Question

Figure 6 Flatworms are more closely related to roundworms.

☑ *Checkpoint*

Students may note the wolf's adaptations mentioned in the text—sharp claws, speed, and keen senses. Students may also mention snakes that constrict prey or inject venom.

Classification of Animals

Using the Visuals: Figure 6

Have students read aloud the names on the limbs of the branching tree. Some of the names may be unfamiliar to students. Tell them they will learn more about these animals as they study this book. Ask: **Are insects more closely related to spiders or to mollusks?** *(spiders)* Then ask: **Which group probably arose earlier, crustaceans or echinoderms?** *(echinoderms)* Continue in this fashion with other animal groups. Explain that this family tree shows rough evolutionary relationships among the major animal groups. **learning modality: visual**

Inquiry Challenge

ACTIVITY

Explain to students that biological classification systems are ways of organizing information reasonably and realistically. To reinforce this concept, allow students to devise their own classification systems. Have each student bring to class photographs of five animals with backbones and five without backbones. Place students in cooperative groups. Ask groups to create classification systems for organizing their animals. Students should first classify the animals into two or three groups based on shared characteristics. They should continue to divide animals into subgroups until each animal is classified in a way that distinguishes it from all other animals. Student groups can create diagrams to show how their classification systems are organized. Inform students that scientists may classify the animals differently than they have, and that they will learn more about classification as they read subsequent chapters. **cooperative learning**

Ongoing Assessment

Skills Check Obtain photographs or illustrations of the teeth of animals other than those shown in Sharpen Your Skills. Have students infer whether the animals are carnivores, omnivores, or herbivores.

3 Assess

Section 1 Review Answers

1. Multicellular; obtain food by eating other organisms (heterotrophic)

2. Body structure, development of the embryo, and DNA are the major characteristics used to classify animals into groups.

3. Animals need water, food, and oxygen to survive.

4. The wolf actively pursues its prey while the frog waits in ambush. Students should name one adaptation each for the wolf and frog. The wolf has sharp, pointed teeth, keen senses, and speed. The frog blends in with its surroundings and has a long, sticky tongue that it can quickly shoot out.

Check Your Progress

CHAPTER PROJECT 1

Before students obtain their animals, group students who have researched and planned habitats for the same kind of animal. Have these students discuss plans for acquiring, housing, and caring for the animal. Visit groups and verify that all students meet the planning requirements of the project and will be able to care for the needs of their animals. After this initial approval, allow students to prepare the habitats. Check habitats for safety before allowing students to obtain their animals.

Performance Assessment

Oral Presentation Provide students with magazines or books containing photographs of animals. Ask each student to choose a photograph of an animal. Have students present their photographs to the class and describe at least two characteristics a scientist would use to classify the organism as an animal. Then show students a plant or a photograph of a plant. Ask them to explain why that organism is *not* an animal.

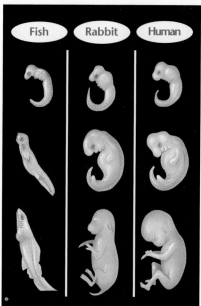

Figure 7 Biologists often study embryo development when classifying animals. *Comparing and Contrasting Compare the embryos of three vertebrates—a fish, a rabbit, and a human. Which two animals show greater similarity in their development?*

Animals are classified, or put into groups, according to how they are related to other animals. **When biologists classify an animal, they look at the structure of its body and the way it develops as an embryo at the very beginning of its life. Biologists also examine the animal's DNA, which is a chemical in cells that controls an organism's inherited characteristics.** The more similar two animals are in those characteristics, the more closely they are probably related.

For example, look at the developing embryos shown in Figure 7. You can see that a rabbit embryo is more similar to a human embryo than it is to a fish embryo. This similarity provides one piece of evidence indicating that rabbits are more closely related to humans than they are to fishes. The structure of the animals' hearts provides another piece of evidence. The hearts of rabbits and humans are similar—but are quite different from the hearts of fishes.

One important structural characteristic used to classify animals is the presence or absence of a backbone, which is a series of bones that run down the center of the back. An animal that does not have a backbone is called an **invertebrate**. Jellyfishes, worms, snails, crabs, spiders, and insects are all invertebrates. Most animal species—about 95 percent—are invertebrates. In contrast, a **vertebrate** is an animal that has a backbone. Fishes, amphibians, reptiles, birds, and mammals are all vertebrates.

Aside from having—or not having—a backbone, animals also differ in the overall shape of their bodies. Although a few animals have lopsided bodies, most do not, as you will learn in the next section.

Section 1 Review

1. Describe two characteristics that all animals share.
2. List the major characteristics that are used to classify animals into groups.
3. List three needs that all animals must meet in order to survive.
4. **Thinking Critically Comparing and Contrasting** Contrast the ways in which wolves and frogs obtain their food, and identify one food-getting adaptation of each animal.

Check Your Progress

CHAPTER PROJECT 1

By now, you should have chosen your animal and learned from library research how to meet its needs. Discuss with your teacher your plans for obtaining, housing, and caring for your animal. After preparing your animal's home and obtaining some food for it, put the animal in its new home. (*Hint:* Be sure to consider how your animal will survive holidays and weekends.)

Program Resources

◆ **Teaching Resources** 1-1 Review and Reinforce, p. 19; 1-1 Enrich, p. 20

Media and Technology

 Interactive Student Tutorial CD-ROM B-1

Answers to Self-Assessment

Caption Questions

Figure 7 The human embryo and the rabbit embryo show the greater similarity.

Figure 8 This balanced arrangement is called bilateral symmetry.

SECTION 2 Symmetry

DISCOVER  ACTIVITY

How Many Ways Can You Fold It?

1. Trace the triangle onto a sheet of paper and cut it out. Then draw a circle by tracing the rim of a glass or other round object. Cut out the circle.

2. Fold the triangle so that one half matches the other. Do the same with the circle.

3. See how many different ways you can fold each figure so that the two halves are identical.

Think It Over
Classifying Can you think of animals whose body shape could be folded in the same number of ways as the triangle? As the circle?

With its wings closed, a bright and colorful butterfly perches lightly on a flower, drinking nectar. Its delicate but strong wings are motionless as it drinks. Then, suddenly, those fragile-looking wings begin to move, and they lift the butterfly, seemingly effortlessly, into the air.

As you can see from the photo of the large copper butterfly in Figure 8, a butterfly's body has two halves, and each half looks almost like a reflection of the other. This balanced arrangement, called symmetry, is characteristic of many animals. A butterfly's symmetry contributes to its pleasing appearance. More importantly, the balanced wings help the butterfly to fly more easily.

GUIDE FOR READING

◆ What types of symmetry do complex animals exhibit?

Reading Tip Before you read, preview the illustrations in Figures 8 and 9. Predict how body shape is important to an animal.

Figure 8 If you could draw a line through this butterfly's body, it would divide the animal into two mirror-image halves. *Applying Concepts What is this balanced arrangement called?*

READING STRATEGIES

Reading Tip Have students update their predictions as they read and learn new content.

Concept Mapping Have students create concept maps using the words *bilateral symmetry, radial symmetry,* and *no symmetry.* In their concept maps, students can include examples of animals that belong in each category.

Vocabulary Point out that the word *bilateral* comes from Latin words meaning "two-sided." Ask students to list other English words that include the root *bi-* and discuss their meanings. *(Sample: Bicycle means "two-wheeled.")* Ask students to think of words similar to the word *radial. (Sample: radius, radiation)* Suggest that when students read the section, they look for a connection between these words and the definition of radial symmetry.

SECTION 2 Symmetry

Objectives

After completing the lesson, students will be able to
◆ recognize bilateral and radial symmetry in animals.

Key Terms bilateral symmetry, radial symmetry

1 Engage/Explore

Activating Prior Knowledge

Bring to class a selection of bilaterally symmetrical and asymmetrical shapes, pictures, or objects such as leaves, shells, keys, gloves, and scissors. Show students each object, then sort the objects into two groups—symmetrical and asymmetrical. Ask students what characteristic you used to group the shapes. Accept all reasonable answers. Leave the objects in their groups until after the section content has been introduced. Then make sure students understand you sorted the objects based on symmetry.

DISCOVER

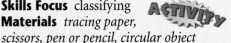

Skills Focus classifying
Materials *tracing paper, scissors, pen or pencil, circular object*
Time 10 minutes
Tips Suggest that students first determine how many ways the triangle can be folded before they attempt to fold the circle.
Expected Outcome Students should conclude that the triangle can be folded one way into identical halves, and that the circle could be folded in an infinite number of ways.
Think It Over Students may say that the body shapes of butterflies, tigers, and dogs could be folded the same number of ways as a triangle. The body shapes of a sea urchin and jellyfish could be folded the same number of ways as a circle.

2 Facilitate

The Mathematics of Symmetry

Building Inquiry Skills: Applying Concepts

Materials *magazines, tape, colored pencils, white paper*

Time 15 minutes

Tips Cut magazine pictures of symmetrical objects in half and give them to students. Objects could include such things as a basketball, a human face, a car, or a pizza. Have students tape their pictures onto pieces of paper, then use what they know about symmetry to draw the complete object. Ask students to identify the objects as radially or bilaterally symmetrical. **learning modality: visual**

 Students can save their finished pictures in their portfolios.

Including All Students

Point out that the prefix *bi-* in *bilateral* means "two," and relate this to the concept of bilateral symmetry. Ask the class to identify and define other words with the prefix *bi-*. (*Examples: bicycle, binoculars*) **limited English proficiency**

Symmetry in Animals

Using the Visuals: Figures 8 and 9

Draw students' attention to the photographs of the animals and their diagrams. Organize students in small groups and give each group a small hand mirror. Direct students to hold the mirror along the lines of symmetry and examine the mirror images produced. Ask them to predict what would happen if they held the mirror somewhere else on the drawing of the butterfly. (*The image would not exactly match the butterfly's shape.*) **cooperative learning**

Figure 9 Sea anemones have radial symmetry. A radially symmetrical object has many lines of symmetry that all go through a central point. *Observing How would you describe the shape of the sea anemone?*

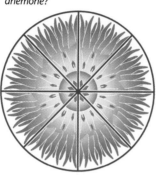

The Mathematics of Symmetry

In Figure 8, you can see that a line drawn down the middle of the butterfly produces two halves that are the same—they are mirror images. This dividing line is called a line of symmetry. An object has line symmetry, or **bilateral symmetry,** if there is a line that divides it into halves that are mirror images. A large copper butterfly has bilateral symmetry, as do an oak leaf, a spoon, and a pair of eyeglasses.

Contrast the butterfly's symmetry to that of a sea anemone. A sea anemone is circular if you look at it from the top, as in Figure 9. Any line drawn through its center will divide the sea anemone into two symmetrical halves. Like the sea anemone, many circular objects exhibit **radial symmetry**—they have many lines of symmetry that all go through a central point. Pie plates and bicycle wheels have radial symmetry.

☑ *Checkpoint* How is radial symmetry different from bilateral symmetry?

Symmetry in Animals

There are a few animals, such as most sponges, that exhibit no symmetry. These asymmetrical animals generally have very simple body plans. Sponges, for example, have no hearts, brains, kidneys, or nerve cells. **The bodies of complex animals all have either radial or bilateral symmetry.**

Animals with Radial Symmetry The external body parts of animals with radial symmetry are equally spaced around a central point, like spokes on a bicycle wheel. Because of the circular arrangement of their parts, radially symmetrical animals, such as jellyfishes, sea anemones, and sea urchins, do not have distinct front or back ends.

Animals with radial symmetry have several characteristics in common. All of them live in water. Most of them do not move very fast—they either stay in one spot, are moved along by water currents, or creep along the bottom. Few radially symmetrical animals are able to go out in search of prey. Instead, their watery environment carries food to them.

For a water animal that does not actively chase prey, the absence of a front end creates no disadvantage. Animals with radial symmetry learn about their environment primarily through senses of touch and taste, which function on the surfaces of their bodies. Because the animals are able to sense their environment in all directions, they can be ready to grab food coming from any direction.

Background

Facts and Figures There are three basic kinds of symmetry among living things—spherical, radial, and bilateral. Animals that lack these basic symmetries, such as sponges, are said to be asymmetrical.

Spherical symmetry is rare and is typical of free-floating organisms that do not move under their own power, such as protozoans. Amebas become spherical when at rest.

The octopus has an unusual symmetry. It is basically bilaterally symmetrical, but its arms are arranged radially around its mouth. Its body is streamlined so that when the octopus swims rapidly, its head follows along behind.

No one kind of symmetry is better or more advanced than any other. Each has advantages and disadvantages, depending on the animal's habits and environment.

Animals with Bilateral Symmetry Most animals you are familiar with have bilateral symmetry. For example, a fish has only one line of symmetry that divides it into mirror images. Each half of a fish has one eye, one nostril, half of a mouth, and one of each of the fish's pairs of fins. Your body also has bilateral symmetry.

In general, bilaterally symmetrical animals are larger and more complex than those with radial symmetry. Animals with bilateral symmetry have a front end that goes first as the animal moves along. These animals move more quickly and efficiently than most animals with radial symmetry. This is partly because bilateral symmetry allows for a streamlined, balanced body. In addition, most bilaterally symmetrical animals have sense organs in their front ends that pick up information about what is in front of them. Swift movement and sense organs help bilaterally symmetrical animals get food and avoid enemies.

Figure 10 Radially symmetrical animals, like the sea urchin at left, have no distinct front or back ends. In contrast, bilaterally symmetrical animals, like the tiger above, have a front end with sense organs that pick up information. Because of its balanced body plan, a tiger can also move quickly.

 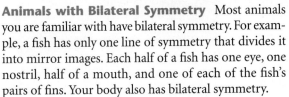

Section 2 Review

1. What two types of symmetry do complex animals exhibit? Describe each type.
2. How can bilateral symmetry be an advantage to a predator?
3. Draw a view of a bilaterally symmetrical animal to show its symmetry. Draw the line of symmetry.
4. **Thinking Critically** **Applying Concepts** Which capital letters of the alphabet have bilateral symmetry? Radial symmetry?

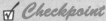
Science at Home

With a family member, observe as many different animals as possible in your yard or at a park. Look in lots of different places, such as in the grass, under rocks, and in the air. Explain to your family member the advantage to an animal of having a distinct front end. What is this type of body arrangement called?

Answers to Self-Assessment

Caption Question

Figure 9 The sea anemone is circular when viewed from the top.

☑ *Checkpoint*
A radially symmetrical shape has many lines of symmetry. A bilaterally symmetrical shape has one line of symmetry.

3 Assess

Section 2 Review Answers

1. Complex animals exhibit bilateral or radial symmetry. An object has bilateral symmetry if one line can be drawn that divides it into two symmetrical halves. It has radial symmetry if any line drawn through the center divides it into two symmetrical halves.
2. Bilateral symmetry allows animals to have balanced body plans with distinct front and back ends. This body plan enables fast, purposeful movement.
3. Students' drawings should show a bilaterally symmetrical animal with the line of symmetry marked.
4. Bilaterally symmetrical capital letters are A, B, C, D, E, H, I, K, M, T, U, V, W, and Y. Radially symmetrical capital letters are O and X.

Science at Home

Ask a volunteer to read *Science at Home* aloud to the class. Direct students' attention to the paragraph that explains the advantages of having a distinct front end. Ask students to list these advantages. (*Animals move more quickly because of streamlined, balanced bodies. Sense organs in the front end pick up information about what is in front of the animal, such as food or predators.*) Suggest students show their lists to a family member when explaining bilateral symmetry. When observing animals at home, students can sketch the animals they see.

Performance Assessment

Drawing Have each student sketch two familiar objects or living things in the classroom. One should be bilaterally symmetrical, the other radially symmetrical. Ask students to mark the line of bilateral symmetry on the first sketch and the center point on the second sketch.

 Students can save their sketches in their portfolios.

You Solve the Mystery

A Tale Told by Tracks

Preparing for Inquiry

Key Concept Animal behavior can be inferred by studying animal tracks.

Skills Objectives Students will be able to
◆ observe tracks left by animals;
◆ infer animal behavior from the tracks.

Time 30 minutes

Advance Planning
◆ If you have not yet taught the skills of observing and inferring, see page 184 of the Skills Handbook.

Alternative Materials Allowing students to examine photographs or drawings of additional animal tracks, which can often be found in field guides, will reinforce and enrich this lab.

Guiding Inquiry

Invitation
◆ Prior to the lab, prepare an outdoor area with damp sand or soil, or undisturbed snow. The area should be about 2 to 3 meters wide and 5 meters long. Invite one student to walk through that area before the class arrives. Then lead the rest of the students to the area.
◆ Have students examine the tracks. Ask: **What observations can you make about these tracks?** (*Sample: The tracks were made by two feet, the feet were a certain size, and the feet were going in a certain direction.*) Next, have students run and hop through the same area. Ask: **How can you tell running tracks from walking tracks? Running tracks from hopping tracks?** (*Accept all reasonable descriptions. The depth and shape of the tracks will be different.*)

Introducing the Procedure
◆ Before students begin the procedure, suggest they make a list of their own questions about the illustrations such as: "How many animals were there?" and "What were the animals doing in each section?"

A TALE TOLD BY TRACKS

Suppose that, on a chilly winter day, you hike through a park. You suspect that many animals live there, but you don't actually see any of them. Instead, you see signs that the animals have left behind, such as mysterious tracks in the snow. These tracks are evidence you can use to draw inferences about the animals, such as what size they are and what they were doing. Inferences are interpretations of observations that help you to explain what may have happened in a given situation.

Problem

What can you learn about animals by studying their tracks?

Skill Focus

observing, inferring

Procedure

1. Copy the data table into your notebook.
2. The illustration at the top of the next page shows the tracks, or footprints, left in the snow by animals living in a park. The illustration has been divided into three sections. Focus in on the tracks in Section 1.
3. Make two or more observations about the tracks and record them in your data table.
4. For each observation you listed, write one or more inferences that could be drawn from that observation.

DATA TABLE		
Section	Observations	Inferences
Section 1		
Section 2		
Section 3		

Troubleshooting the Experiment
◆ Students may have difficulty distinguishing observations and inferences.
◆ Students may think there is only one "correct" inference for an observation. Give examples of different, even conflicting, inferences that can be made from a given observation.

Expected Outcome

Students should observe that there are different sets of tracks, probably made by three different animals. Since the tracks and strides are the same, the animals are probably about the same size. They should infer that two of the animals interacted in some way, probably as predator and prey.

Analyze and Conclude

1. Three animals
2. Answers will vary. Sample: All the animals appear to be approximately similar in size.
3. Answers will vary. Sample: The animal entering from the upper left (pink circle) appears to be walking, then it turns direction and begins to run (longer distances between

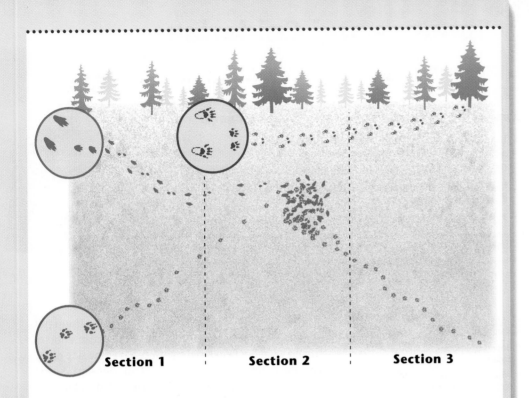

Section 1   **Section 2**   **Section 3**

5. Now look at the tracks in Section 2. Write two or more observations in the data table. For each observation, write one or more inferences.

6. Study the tracks in Section 3. Write two or more observations in the data table. Write at least one inference for each observation.

Analyze and Conclude

1. How many types of animals made the tracks shown in the illustration? Explain.

2. What inferences, if any, can you make about the relative sizes of the animals based on their tracks? Explain.

3. What can you infer about the speed of the animals' movements? Are they walking? Running? How can you tell?

4. In a paragraph, explain what you think happened to the animals and the order in which the events happened.

5. What inference do you feel most confident about and why? Which inference do you feel least confident about and why?

6. **Apply** How might making inferences be important in the work of a real detective? Explain.

More to Explore

Take a walk around your community looking for indirect evidence of animal life such as tracks, feathers, empty nests, and holes in the ground or in dead trees. For each discovery, record its location, at least two observations, and one or more inferences to explain each observation.

prints); then it encounters another animal. The animal entering from the lower left (green circle) appears to walk, then run, before the encounter; it then walks away. The third animal appears to be walking the whole time (small, evenly spaced distances between prints) and was not present during the encounter.

4. Answers will vary. See previous answer.

5. Answers will vary. Sample: Most confident: the predator caught its prey because the tracks of the other animal end. Least confident: deciding what the third animal was doing because the tracks don't provide enough information.

6. Answers will vary. Sample: Making inferences from clues helps a detective figure out what happened during a past event.

Extending the Inquiry

More to Explore Provide field guides to aid student observation, and suggest that students bring a field notebook along with them for quick notes and drawings. Encourage students to make a written record of their findings to bring to class. You may want to put up a map of your community and have students mark and label where they went and what they saw.

Sample Data Table

Section	Observations	Inferences
Section 1	two sets of footprints	Two animals don't see each other
Section 2	three sets of footprints; two sets come together	Two animals meet
Section 3	two sets of footprints	One animal was eaten

Program Resources

◆ **Teaching Resources** Chapter 1 Real-World Lab blackline masters, pp. 33–34
◆ **Inquiry Skills Activity Book** Provides teaching and review of all inquiry skills

Safety

Make sure students are appropriately dressed for the outdoor activity in the Invitation. Review the safety guidelines in Appendix A.

SECTION 3 Sponges and Cnidarians

Objectives

After completing the lesson, students will be able to
- describe the organization of a sponge's body;
- identify the main characteristics of cnidarians;
- describe life on a coral reef.

Key Terms larva, cnidarian, polyp, medusa

1 Engage/Explore

Activating Prior Knowledge

Bring in a basin of water and a sponge. Ask students to tell you ways sponges are used around the house. *(Mopping floors, wiping up spills, washing dishes)* Ask: **What feature of sponges makes them useful?** *(They soak up liquids.)* Inform students that natural sponges were once live animals, and that divers have harvested sponges for thousands of years.

········ DISCOVER ········

Skills Focus observing

Materials *natural sponges, synthetic kitchen sponges, scissors, hand lens or microscope*

Time 20 minutes

Tips Provide students with specimens of sponges to examine. Natural sponges can often be found in cosmetic departments or ordered from a biological supply house. Direct students' attention to the pores on the surfaces of the sponges. Tell them that pores in a natural sponge are the openings of pathways through the sponge. Openings on a synthetic sponge are not connected by regular pathways. Students can draw diagrams to compare and contrast features of natural and synthetic sponges.

Expected Outcome Students will observe similarities and differences between natural and artificial sponges.

Think It Over Both have pores, hold liquid, and are soft. They are different in material, color, texture, and shape.

SECTION 3 Sponges and Cnidarians

▶ DISCOVER ●●●●●●●●●●●●●●●●●●●●●●●●●●●●●●●● ACTIVITY

How Do Natural and Synthetic Sponges Compare?

1. Examine a natural sponge, and then use a hand lens or a microscope to take a closer look at its surface. Look carefully at the holes in the sponge. Draw what you see through the lens.

2. ✂ Cut out a small piece of sponge and examine it with a hand lens. Draw what you see.

3. Repeat Steps 1 and 2 with a synthetic kitchen sponge.

Think It Over

Observing What are three ways a natural and synthetic sponge are similar? What are three ways they are different?

GUIDE FOR READING

- **How is the body of a sponge organized?**
- **What are the main characteristics of cnidarians?**

Reading Tip Before you read, preview *Exploring a Sponge* on page 29. Then write a brief description of a sponge.

E agerly but carefully, you and the others in your group put on scuba gear, preparing to dive into the ocean and see firsthand what lies beneath the surface. Over the side of the boat you go; the salty ocean water feels cool on your skin. As you slowly descend, you notice that you are surrounded by animals. You see many kinds of fishes, of course, but as you get to the ocean bottom, you notice other animals, too, some as strange as creatures from a science fiction movie. Some of these strange creatures may be sponges.

Sponges live all over the world—mostly in oceans, but also in freshwater rivers and lakes. Sponges are attached to hard surfaces underwater, and they are well adapted to their watery life. Moving currents carry food and oxygen to them, and these same currents take away their waste products. Water plays a role in their reproduction and helps their young find new places to live.

Sponges

Sponges don't look or act like most animals you know. In fact, they are so different that for a long time, people thought that sponges were plants. Like plants, adult sponges stay in one place. But unlike most plants, sponges take food into their bodies, which qualifies them for membership in the animal kingdom. These strange animals have been on Earth for about 540 million years.

◀ Pink sponges on a Caribbean coral reef

READING STRATEGIES

Reading Tip As students examine *Exploring a Sponge,* make sure they understand that the enlargement feature on the diagram helps them to better see the collar cells and spikes. Have students note the arrows and describe what they indicate. *(The path of water through the sponge)*

Study and Comprehension Have students write a description of cnidarians after they finish reading the last half of the lesson. Then have them compare this description with the description of sponges they wrote for the Reading Tip. Direct them to underline the main characteristics of sponges and cnidarians, then list any differences.

The bodies of most sponges have irregular shapes, with no symmetry. While some of their cells do specialized jobs, sponges lack the tissues and organs that most other animals have.

The Structure of a Sponge You might use a brightly colored, synthetic sponge to mop up a spill. That sponge is filled with holes, and so are the animals called sponges. **The body of a sponge is something like a bag that is pierced all over with openings called pores.** In fact, the name of the phylum to which sponges belong—phylum Porifera—means "having pores." Notice the many pores in the sponge in *Exploring a Sponge.*

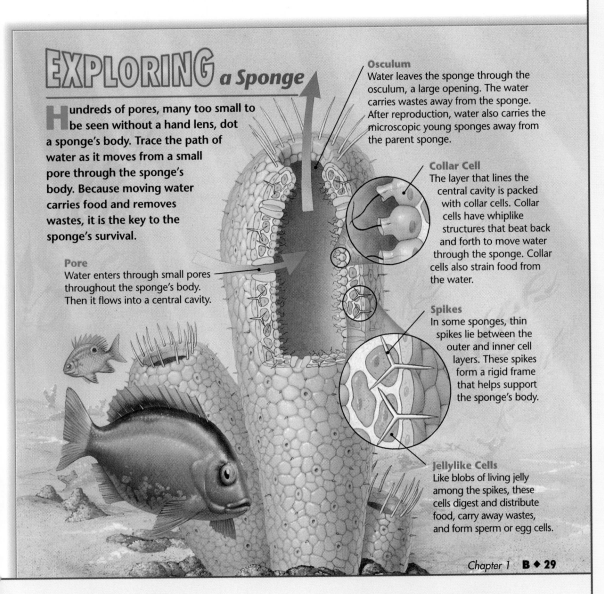

EXPLORING a Sponge

Hundreds of pores, many too small to be seen without a hand lens, dot a sponge's body. Trace the path of water as it moves from a small pore through the sponge's body. Because moving water carries food and removes wastes, it is the key to the sponge's survival.

Pore
Water enters through small pores throughout the sponge's body. Then it flows into a central cavity.

Osculum
Water leaves the sponge through the osculum, a large opening. The water carries wastes away from the sponge. After reproduction, water also carries the microscopic young sponges away from the parent sponge.

Collar Cell
The layer that lines the central cavity is packed with collar cells. Collar cells have whiplike structures that beat back and forth to move water through the sponge. Collar cells also strain food from the water.

Spikes
In some sponges, thin spikes lie between the outer and inner cell layers. These spikes form a rigid frame that helps support the sponge's body.

Jellylike Cells
Like blobs of living jelly among the spikes, these cells digest and distribute food, carry away wastes, and form sperm or egg cells.

Chapter 1 **B ◆ 29**

Sponges

EXPLORING
a Sponge

Begin your discussion of the illustration by making certain that students understand what each enlargement shows. Ask a volunteer to describe the structure of a collar cell. Students should observe that a whiplike flagellum is part of the cell. Then have students trace the path of water through the sponge. Help students understand that water enters only through pores, not through the osculum.

After students have examined the illustration, ask: **How do pores help a sponge feed?** (*They allow water into the sponge; the water contains food.*) **How do collar cells help a sponge feed?** (*Move water through the sponge*) **What is the function of the osculum?** (*Allows water to leave the sponge*) **learning modality: visual**

Program Resources

◆ **Teaching Resources** 1-3 Lesson Plan, p. 25; 1-3 Section Summary, p. 26

Media and Technology

 Audiotapes English-Spanish Summary 1-3

 Transparencies "Exploring a Sponge," Transparency 2

Ongoing Assessment

Oral Presentation Ask students to compare and contrast the pores and osculum of a sponge. (*Water enters the sponge through pores and exits through the larger osculum.*)

Sponges, continued

Integrating Chemistry

Materials *large plastic beaker, water, plastic dropper, food coloring, clock or watch*

Time 20 minutes

Tips Place students in groups and invite them to investigate how oxygen in the water diffuses into a sponge's cells. First have them fill a beaker three-quarters full of water and allow the water to stand for 2 minutes. Then put eight drops of food coloring into the water. Ask students to describe what the food coloring looks like as it enters the water. *(The food coloring is dark and concentrated at the point it enters the beaker.)* Have students observe the water every 2 minutes over a 10-minute period. Ask: **What happened to the food coloring?** *(The food coloring spread evenly throughout the water.)* Tell students the way the food coloring spreads throughout the water is diffusion, and is similar to the way oxygen in water diffuses into a sponge's cells. **learning modality: visual**

Language Arts
CONNECTION

Organize students into small groups. Ask students to make lists of familiar animals and their characteristics. Then have students choose a characteristic, and name several objects or processes that also have this characteristic. Direct students to write a simile about the animal they chose, comparing it to what they named. *(Samples: The cheetah runs as fast as lightning. An elephant's back is as broad as a barn.)* After students make similes for several animals, have them share with group members. Groups can share similes with the class.

cooperative learning

In Your Journal In addition to recording the similes they wrote with their groups, students can look for similes in their favorite books about animals and share them with the class.

Portfolio Students can save their similes in their portfolios.

Language Arts
CONNECTION

In the paragraph that describes how sponges defend themselves, notice how the author says that a sponge dinner would be "like a sandwich made of thorns, sand, and cement, with a little awful-tasting goo mixed in." The author's description is a simile, which is a comparison using the word *like* or *as*. Writers use similes to paint lively word pictures and create vivid impressions.

In Your Journal

You can use similes in your own writing. For instance, you might say that a racehorse launches itself from the starting line like a rocket. Choose three different animals and write a simile describing each one. For each simile, identify the characteristic that you are trying to convey.

Getting Food and Oxygen from Water Sponges feed by straining food particles from water. As water enters a sponge, it carries tiny organisms such as bacteria and protists. Collar cells on the inside of the central cavity trap these food particles and digest them. Sponges are very efficient at removing food particles from water. A sponge the size of a teacup is able to remove food from 5,000 liters of water per day. That's enough water to fill a truckload of two-liter soft-drink bottles!

INTEGRATING CHEMISTRY A sponge gets its oxygen from water too. The water contains oxygen, which moves from the water into the sponge's cells in a process known as diffusion. In diffusion, molecules of a substance move from an area in which they are highly concentrated to an area in which they are less concentrated. Oxygen is more highly concentrated in the water than it is in the sponge's cells. So the oxygen moves from the water into the sponge. Diffusion also carries waste products from the sponge's cells into the water.

Spikes The soft bodies of most sponges are supported by a network of spikes. Those spikes can be as sharp as needles, as anyone who has touched a live sponge knows. In addition, many sponges are tougher than wood, and some produce irritating substances. Even so, some fish eat sponges. A sponge dinner is probably like a sandwich made of thorns, sand, and cement, with a little awful-tasting goo mixed in.

Sponge Reproduction Sponges reproduce both asexually and sexually. Budding is one form of asexual reproduction in sponges. In budding, small new sponges grow from the sides of an adult sponge. Eventually these tiny sponges detach and begin life on their own. Sponges reproduce sexually too. Sponges do not have separate sexes—a single sponge forms eggs at one time of the year and sperm at a different time. At any one time of the year, some sponges are producing eggs and others are producing sperm. When a sponge produces sperm, the water currents that move through the sponge carry sperm from the sponge into the open water. The sperm may then enter the pores of another sponge and fertilize egg cells in that sponge.

After fertilization, a larva develops. A **larva** (plural *larvae*) is the immature form of an animal that looks very different from the adult. A sponge larva is a hollow ball of cells that swims through the water. Eventually the larva attaches to a surface and develops into a nonmoving adult sponge.

✓ *Checkpoint* As water flows through a sponge's body, what functions does it enable the sponge to perform?

Background

Facts and Figures If a sponge is ground up in a food processor, the individual sponge cells are capable of living independently. When large numbers of sponge cells come near each other, they tend to join together to form new sponges. If cells of several species of sponges are mixed together in the same water, sponge cells will join only with other cells of the same species to form new sponges.

Program Resources

◆ **Interdisciplinary Exploration Series** "Where River Meets Sea," pp. 33–34

Science Explorer Series *Chemical Building Blocks*, Chapter 2, covers diffusion

Cnidarians

Some other organisms you might notice on an underwater dive are jellyfishes, sea anemones, and corals. At first glance, those animals look like they could be creatures from another planet. Most jellyfishes look like transparent bubbles that trail curtains of streamerlike tentacles. Sea anemones look like odd, underwater flowers. Some corals have branches that make them look like trees. Jellyfishes, sea anemones, and corals are **cnidarians** (nih DAIR ee uhnz), animals that have stinging cells and take their food into a hollow central cavity. **Members of the phylum Cnidaria are carnivores that use their stinging cells to capture their prey and defend themselves.** The stinging cells are located on the long, wavy tentacles.

Unlike sponges, cnidarians have specialized tissues. For example, because of muscle-like tissues, many cnidarians can move in interesting ways. Jellyfishes swim through the water, and hydras turn slow somersaults. Anemones stretch out, shrink down, and bend slowly from side to side. These movements are directed by nerve cells that are spread out like a spider web, or net. This nerve net helps the cnidarian respond quickly to danger or the presence of food.

Cnidarian Body Plans Cnidarians have two different body plans, both with radial symmetry. As you read about these two body plans, refer to Figure 12. A **polyp** (PAHL ip), such as a hydra, sea anemone, or coral, is shaped something like a vase, with the mouth opening at the top. Most polyps do not move around; they are adapted for a life attached to an underwater surface. In contrast, the bowl-shaped

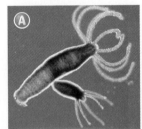
Figure 11 All cnidarians live in watery environments. **A.** Hydras live in freshwater ponds and lakes, where they reproduce by budding. **B.** The Portuguese man-of-war is actually a colony of cnidarians living together. **C.** Sea anemones are large cnidarians that often live in groups in the ocean. *Comparing and Contrasting What characteristics do these three cnidarians share?*

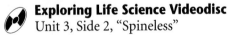

Answers to Self-Assessment

Caption Question

Figure 11 All the cnidarians are carnivores and have a mouth and tentacles with stinging cells. Cnidarians also have a hollow, central cavity and specialized tissues. They live in water.

✓ Checkpoint

The water enables a sponge to feed, get oxygen, discharge waste, and reproduce.

Demonstration

Materials *large jar such as a mayonnaise jar, 50% solution of bleach, natural dried sponge, microscope*

Time 10 minutes for setup, 1 or 2 days to complete demonstration

Tips Prepare about 600 mL of bleach solution by pouring bleach into an equal amount of water. **CAUTION:** *Bleach can damage eyes and clothing. Wear goggles and a lab apron while preparing the bleach solution.*

Fill the jar with the bleach solution and place a sponge in the jar. Seal the jar and let it stand overnight or over a weekend. The bleach will dissolve most of the sponge, leaving the spikes in a gel on the bottom of the jar. Carefully pour the liquid from the jar, making sure not to pour out the gel containing the spikes. Place some of the gel under a binocular microscope and allow students to examine the spikes. To increase learning, students can draw the shapes of the spikes they observe. **learning modality: visual**

Cnidarians

Including All Students

Students may have difficulty remembering that the *c* in cnidarians is silent. Pair students whose first language is not English with native English speakers. Instruct each pair to find three other English words that begin with a silent consonant, such as *knot, know,* and *knuckle.* Pairs can make a table of the words and their pronunciations, and share tables with the class. **limited English proficiency**

Ongoing Assessment

Skills Check Have students compare and contrast how jellyfishes, sea anemones, corals, and hydras move.

Cnidarians, continued

TRY THIS

Skills Focus classifying
Materials *live hydra,*
small glass bowl or petri dish, hand lens or
microscope, toothpicks
Time 25 minutes
Tips You can order hydras from a
biological supply house. Guide students
to observe characteristics of a cnidarian.
Expected Outcome The hydras will
respond by wrapping their tentacles
around the toothpick.
Classifying A hydra is a polyp. It moves
from place to place in a somersaulting
fashion.
Extend Ask if anyone sees a hydra with a
bulb or bud developing on its stalk. If so,
explain that the hydra is reproducing
asexually. **learning modality: visual**

Life on a Coral Reef

Including All Students

Materials *balloon,*
newspaper strips, flour,
water, bowl, straight pins
Time 20 minutes on 2 days
Tips Some students may need extra help
understanding how coral reefs form. To
help these students visualize the process,
allow them to model a reef by covering
balloons with papier mâché. Provide
each student with a balloon, newspaper
strips, and a flour and water paste made
by mixing 3 parts water to 2 parts flour.
Direct students to dip newspaper strips
into a bowl of paste, then cover the
balloon with strips except for a circle
about 1 inch in diameter at one end.
Students can let the strips dry for one
day, then apply another layer and allow
to dry for one more day. Ask: **If the**
balloon represents the soft coral polyp,
what does the newspaper shell
represent? *(The coral's hard skeleton)* To
model the building of a coral reef,
students stack their balloons together
while the second layer is wet. Students
can demonstrate what happens when the
coral polyp dies by popping the balloons
with the pins. **CAUTION:** *Pins are a*
safety hazard. **learning modality:**
kinesthetic

TRY THIS

Hydra Doing?

In this activity,
you will observe
hydras in action.

1. Put a drop of water
   that contains hydras in
   a small unbreakable bowl
   or petri dish. Allow it to sit
   for about 15 minutes.
2. Use a hand lens to examine
   the hydras as they swim.
   Then gently touch the
   tentacles of a hydra with
   the end of a toothpick.
   Watch what happens.
3. Return the hydras to your
   teacher, and wash your hands.

Classifying Is a hydra a polyp
or a medusa? Describe its
method of movement.

medusa (muh DOO suh), such as a jellyfish, is adapted for a free-swimming life. Medusas, unlike polyps, have mouths that open downward. Some cnidarians go through both a polyp stage and a medusa stage during their lives. Others are polyps or medusas for their whole lives.

How Cnidarians Feed A cnidarian captures its prey by using its stinging cells to inject venom, a poisonous substance that paralyzes fish and other prey. Then the cnidarian's tentacles pull the prey animal to its mouth. From there the food passes into a body cavity where it is digested. Because cnidarians have a digestive system with only one opening, undigested food is expelled through the mouth.

Cnidarian Reproduction Cnidarians reproduce both asexually and sexually. For polyps, such as the hydra in Figure 11, budding is the most common form of asexual reproduction. Amazingly, in some polyps the entire animal splits into pieces. Each piece then forms a new polyp. Both kinds of asexual reproduction allow the numbers of cnidarians to increase rapidly in a short time.

Sexual reproduction in cnidarians occurs in a variety of ways. Some species of cnidarians have both sexes within one individual. In others, the sexes are in separate individuals, as in humans.

☑ *Checkpoint* *How does a cnidarian obtain and digest food?*

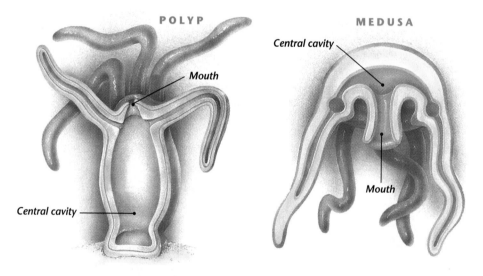

Figure 12 Cnidarians have two basic body forms, the vase-shaped polyp and the bowl-shaped medusa. *Comparing and Contrasting* *Contrast the location of the mouth in the polyp and the medusa.*

Background

Facts and Figures Cnidarians that live in colonies, such as the Portuguese man-of-war, can be surprisingly complex. The colony consists of polyps and medusas that are specialized for certain functions. Some polyps capture and digest prey, while others produce reproductive cells. Other individuals within the colony act as swimming organs that can contract rhythmically to propel the colony, or as with the Portuguese man-of-war, act as a float, or air-filled sac.

This form of colony is rarely found in animals. Because the fossils of soft bodied animals are so rare, scientists do not know precisely when the Portuguese man-of-war first formed this unusual colonial relationship. However, the Portuguese man-of-war remains a fascinating example of how specialized function can be an advantage to colonial organisms.

Life on a Coral Reef

In some warm, shallow ocean waters, just below the surface, you can find one of the most diverse ocean environments—a coral reef. Coral reefs seem to be made of stone. But in fact, coral reefs are built by cnidarians. At the beginning of its life, a free-swimming coral larva attaches to a solid surface. A broken shell, a sunken ship, or the skeleton of a once-living coral animal will do just fine.

The coral polyp reproduces asexually, and then its offspring reproduce asexually, too. The coral polyp then produces a hard, stony skeleton around its soft polyp body. Over time, that polyp may give rise to thousands of polyps, each with a hard skeleton. When the coral polyps die, their skeletons remain behind. Over thousands of years, as live corals add their skeletons to those that have died, rocklike masses called reefs grow up from the sea floor. Coral reefs can become enormous. The Great Barrier Reef off the coast of Australia is about 2,000 kilometers long.

Coral reefs, like the one in Figure 13, are home to more species of fishes and invertebrates than any other environment on Earth. Hundreds of sponge species live among the corals, constantly filtering water through their bodies. Worms burrow into the coral reef. Giant clams lie with their huge shells slightly open. Shrimp and crabs edge out of hiding places below the corals. At night, bright blue damsel fish settle into pockets in the coral. At dawn and dusk, sea turtles, sea snakes, and sharks all visit the reef, hunting for prey. These living things interact in complex ways, creating an environment that is rich and beautiful.

Figure 13 Coral reefs provide homes and hunting grounds for a vast variety of sea animals. The bottom photo is a close-up of a group of individual coral polyps.

Section 3 Review

1. Describe the structure of a sponge's body.
2. Explain how cnidarians capture prey and defend themselves. In your explanation, refer to specific body structures.
3. Draw a diagram to show how water travels through a sponge. Show the path with an arrow.
4. **Thinking Critically** **Classifying** Why is a sponge classified as an animal?

Check Your Progress
CHAPTER PROJECT 1
You should be observing your animal every day and writing your observations in your journal. Record how the animal looks, feeds, and behaves. Note any changes in the animal. Talk to your teacher before making any changes to your animal's home, feeding schedule, or other living conditions.

Program Resources

◆ **Teaching Resources** 1-3 Review and Reinforce, p. 27; 1-3 Enrich, p. 28

Media and Technology

 Interactive Student Tutorial CD-ROM B-1

Answers to Self-Assessment

Caption Question

Figure 12 Polyps have mouths that face upward; medusas have mouths that face downward.

☑ *Checkpoint*

A cnidarian injects venom into its prey. Then it uses its tentacles to pull the food into its mouth. Digestion occurs in the body cavity.

3 Assess

Section 3 Review Answers

1. The body of a sponge is shaped like a hollow bag. Its sides are pierced with openings called pores that lead to a central cavity.
2. Cnidarians obtain food and defend themselves with tentacles covered with stinging cells.
3. Diagrams should show water passing through the pores in the sides of the sponge into a central cavity, then exiting through the osculum at the top of the sponge.
4. Sponges have the characteristics of animals. They are multicellular, take food into their bodies, can reproduce sexually, and are mobile during the early stages of their lives.

Check Your Progress
CHAPTER PROJECT 1
Give students time in class to study their animal and write down their observations. Suggest that students keep their journal notes in a loose-leaf project notebook so that they can insert drawings and photographs. Review students' observation records on a regular basis. Be sure students include details of any changes in the health and behavior of their animals. Check the health of the animals periodically.

Performance Assessment

Writing Ask students to write two diary entries, the first from the viewpoint of a sponge, and the second from the viewpoint of a cnidarian. Entries should include what and how the animals eat, and a description of the animals' physical features.

 Students can save their diary entries in their portfolios.

Coral Reefs in Danger

Purpose

To provide students with an understanding of the issues involved in diving into coral reefs.

Debate

Time one class period for research and preparation, 30 minutes to conduct the debate

- Explain to students that they will be debating the proposition that "Diving near coral reefs should be banned to protect the reefs from ecological damage."
- Separate the class into two groups: one to support the proposition, the other to oppose it. Have groups review and investigate the issue from their respective points of view.
- Encourage students in the pro-diving group to explore ideas such as education and environmental awareness as an alternative to banning diving. Encourage students in the other group to think realistically and offer alternatives for those affected by a diving ban.

Extend Have students contact a local aquarium, university biology department, or diving organization to obtain relevant background information. Encourage students to prepare questions in advance.

You Decide

Have groups of students complete Steps 1 and 2 before the debate to prepare their arguments. After the debate, direct students to write their editorials using the points they raised during the debate. Give them examples of newspaper editorials to use as models. Consider submitting the most polished articles to a local or school newspaper for possible publication.

Portfolio Students can save their editorials in their portfolios.

Coral Reefs in Danger

Coral reefs off the coasts of many nations are endangered, damaged, or threatened with destruction. Reefs house and protect many species of sea animals, including sponges, shrimp, sea turtles, and fishes. In addition, reefs protect coastlines from floods caused by ocean storms.

Although coral reefs are hard as rocks, the coral animals themselves are quite delicate. Recreational divers can damage the fragile reefs. Is it possible to protect the reefs while still allowing divers to explore them?

The Issues

What's the Harm in Diving? About 3.5 million recreational divers live in the United States. With so many divers it is hard to guarantee that no harm will occur to the coral reefs. In fact, divers can cause significant damage by standing on or even touching these fragile reefs. Carelessly dropping a boat anchor can crush part of a reef. Although most divers are careful, not all are, and accidents can always happen.

Harm to the reefs is even more likely to occur when divers collect coral for their own enjoyment or to sell for profit. You can see brightly colored coral from the sea in jewelry and in decorations.

Should Reefs Be Further Protected? The United States government has passed laws making it illegal, under most circumstances, to remove coral from the sea. Because a few divers break these laws, some people want to ban diving altogether. However, many divers say it's unfair to ban diving just because of a few lawbreakers.

Many divers consider coral reefs the most exciting and beautiful places in the ocean to explore. As recreational divers, photographers, scientists, and others visit and learn more about these delicate coral reefs, they increase their own and other's awareness of them. Public awareness may be the best way to ensure that these rich environments are protected.

More Than a Diving Issue Coral reefs in the Western Atlantic—such as those in Bermuda, the Bahamas, the Caribbean Islands, and Florida—are major tourist attractions that bring money and jobs to people in local communities. If diving were banned, local businesses would suffer significantly. Also, although divers can harm coral reefs, other human activities, such as ocean pollution, oil spills, and fishing nets, can also cause harm. In addition, natural events, such as tropical storms, changes in sea level, and changes in sea temperature, can also damage the fragile reefs.

You Decide

1. Identify the Problem

In your own words, explain the controversy surrounding diving near coral reefs.

2. Analyze the Options

List the arguments on each side of the issue. Note the pros and cons. How well would each position protect the reefs? Who might be harmed or inconvenienced?

3. Find a Solution

Write a newspaper editorial stating your position on whether diving should be allowed near coral reefs. State your position and reasons clearly.

Background

Facts and Figures Coral reefs have extremely high levels of animal diversity—nowhere else in the ocean can you find so many kinds of fish and invertebrates. Like rain forests, coral reefs contain many animals and plants that produce potentially valuable chemicals. For this reason, it is important to protect the reefs from damage from the environment.

But reefs are in danger from natural disasters and from humans. Natural forces, such as water that is too warm, can kill corals and produce a phenomenon called coral bleaching. Organisms that eat living corals, such as the crown-of-thorns sea star, can greatly damage reefs.

In addition to the destruction they cause when diving, people can harm reefs through construction projects on islands near coral reefs.

DISCOVER •••••••••••••••••••••••••••• ACTIVITY ••••

What Can You Learn About a Flatworm by Looking at It?

1. Your teacher will give you a planarian, a kind of flatworm. Pick the worm up with the tip of a small paintbrush. Place it carefully in a small, transparent container. Use a dropper to cover the planarian with spring water.

2. Observe the planarian with a hand lens for a few minutes. Look for a head and tail region. Look for two spots in the head region. Draw a picture of the planarian.

3. Observe and describe how the planarian moves.

4. Gently touch the planarian with a toothpick and observe how it behaves. Then return the planarian to your teacher, and wash your hands.

Think It Over
Observing What are some ways in which a planarian is different from a sponge?

Y ou might think that all worms are small, slimy, and wriggly. But many worms do not fit that description. Some worms are almost three meters long and are as thick as your arm. Others look like glowing, furry blobs. Worms can flutter and glide or climb around with paddle-like bristles. Still others are very small and live in white tubes cemented to rocks.

What Worms Have in Common

It's hard to say exactly what worms are, because there are many kinds of worms, all with their own characteristics. **Biologists classify worms into several phyla—the three major ones are flatworms, roundworms, and segmented worms.** Flatworms belong to the phylum Platyhelminthes (plat ee HEL minth eez);

> ### GUIDE FOR READING
> ◆ What are the three main groups of worms?
> ◆ What are the characteristics of each group of worms?
>
> *Reading Tip* As you read, list the characteristics of flatworms, roundworms, and segmented worms.

Figure 14 The ocean flatworm, left, and the segmented Christmas tree worm, right, show some of the wide variety of ocean worms.

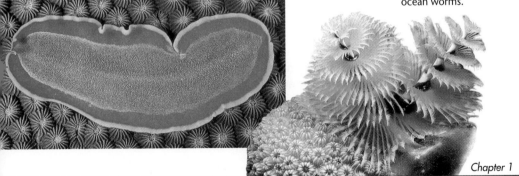

Chapter 1 **B ◆ 35**

READING STRATEGIES

Reading Tip Sample list of worm characteristics: (1) All worms: invertebrates with bilateral symmetry, narrow bodies, specialized organs and tissues. (2) Flatworms: flat, some are parasites, digestive system with only one opening. (3) Roundworms: cylindrical body with a one-way digestive system. (4) Segmented worms: segments, one-way digestive system, closed circulatory system.

Concept Mapping Encourage students to use the lists they developed to create a concept map. Pair students so they can compare maps and correct or enhance them.

Objectives

After completing the lesson, students will be able to
◆ identify the three main groups of worms;
◆ identify the characteristics of each group of worms.

Key Terms regeneration, parasite, host, anus

1 Engage/Explore

Activating Prior Knowledge

Ask students if they have ever:
◆ used worms as fishing bait;
◆ dug up worms in a garden.
Encourage students to share any observations they have made about the appearance and behavior of worms. Then ask them what words they would use to describe worms. (*Sample: slimy, creepy, crawly*) Inform students that in this section, they learn about the characteristics and nature of worms.

•••••••• DISCOVER ••••••••

Skills Focus observing
Materials *live planarian, small paintbrush, small transparent container or petri dish, plastic dropper, bottled water, hand lens, toothpick*
Time 15 minutes
Tips Ask students to discuss what the planarians do and how they behave. Direct them to sketch the planarian and make notes of what they see. Check students' sketches and ask them about their observations. Verify that students note the bilateral symmetry of planarians.
Expected Outcome Planarians should visibly react to being touched by recoiling from the toothpick.
Think It Over Suggest students refer back to Section 3 to help them answer this question. Planarians have bilateral symmetry and distinct head and tail ends. Sponges are asymmetrical and do not have head and tail ends.

2 Facilitate

What Worms Have in Common

Using the Visuals: Figure 15

For students who have difficulty understanding how the worm in Figure 15 could be an animal, ask: **If you didn't know this was an animal, how could you figure it out?** *(Sample: If the organism can move by itself, it is probably an animal.)* **learning modality: visual**

Including All Students

Point out that the terms *flatworm*, *roundworm*, and *segmented worm*, which were introduced on page 35, all describe major visible characteristics of the groups—all flatworms have flat bodies, and so forth. If students know the meanings of the words *flat*, *round*, and *segmented*, they will also know the major distinguishing characteristics of each group. **limited English proficiency**

Inquiry Challenge

Materials *planarians, small flashlights, transparent containers, bottled water, dark paper or foil*

ACTIVITY

Time 30 minutes

Tips This activity may also be done as a demonstration. It will work better in a partially darkened room. Divide the class into groups and distribute a petri dish (or other small transparent container) to each group. Place a planarian in each dish and cover it with a few drops of water. Have students predict how the planarians will react to light and record their prediction. Have students cover half the container with paper or foil and then shine the flashlight on the container. Students should observe that the planarians move out of the light.

cooperative grouping

Portfolio Students can save their observation notes in their portfolios.

Figure 15 As you can tell from this spectacular spaghetti worm, not all worms are gray and tube shaped.

roundworms belong to the phylum Nematoda; segmented worms belong to the phylum Annelida.

All worms have some characteristics in common. All worms are invertebrates, and they all have long, narrow bodies without legs. In addition, all worms have tissues, organs, and organ systems. Also, all worms have bilateral symmetry. Unlike sponges or cnidarians, worms have head and tail ends.

Worms are the simplest organisms with a brain, which is a knot of nerve tissue located in the head end. Because a worm's brain and some of its sense organs are located in its head end, the worm can detect objects, food, mates, and predators quickly, and it can respond quickly, too. Sense organs, such as organs sensitive to light and touch, pick up information from the environment. The brain interprets that information and directs the animal's response. For example, if an earthworm on the surface of the ground senses a footstep, the worm will quickly return to its underground burrow.

Both sexual and asexual reproduction are found in the worm phyla. In many species of worms, there are separate male and female animals, as in humans. In other species each individual has both male and female sex organs. A worm with both sexes does not usually fertilize its own eggs. Instead, two worms mate and exchange sperm. Many worms reproduce asexually by methods such as breaking into pieces. In fact, if you cut some kinds of worms into several pieces, a whole new worm will grow from each piece. Earthworms cannot do this, but if you cut off the tail end of an earthworm, the front end will probably grow a new tail. This ability to regrow body parts is called **regeneration.**

☑ *Checkpoint* *What type of symmetry do worms exhibit?*

Flatworms

As you'd expect from their name, flatworms are flat. The bodies of flatworms, such as planarians, flukes, and tapeworms, are soft as jelly. Although tapeworms can grow to be 10 to 12 meters long, other flatworms are almost too small to be seen.

Most flatworms are parasites that obtain their food from their hosts. Instead of living on its own, a **parasite** is an organism that lives inside or on another organism. The parasite takes its food from the organism in or on which it lives, called the **host**. Parasites may rob their hosts of food and make them weak. They

Facts and Figures The longest animal on Earth is an ocean-dwelling worm called a ribbon worm. The longest ribbon worm measured 54 meters. It was found living in the ocean near Scotland. Some of the smallest animals on Earth are also worms. Turbellarian flatworms are less than 1 centimeter long. They live in the deep mud of oceans and some freshwater lakes.

Trichinella roundworms are among the smallest worms that are parasitic in humans. The mature male is only 1.5 millimeters long. The female Trichinella, which is about 3 to 4 millimeters long, gives birth to between 1,000 to 2, 000 larvae. These larvae measure only 7 by 120 microns. (A micron is one-thousandth of a millimeter.)

may injure the host's tissues or organs. Sometimes a parasite will kill its host, but usually the host survives.

Tapeworms Tapeworms are one kind of parasitic flatworm. A tapeworm's body is adapted to absorbing food from the host's digestive system. Some kinds of tapeworms can live in human hosts. Many tapeworms live in more than one host during their lifetime. Notice that in *Exploring the Life Cycle of a Dog Tapeworm*, the tapeworm has two different hosts—a rabbit and a dog.

EXPLORING the Life Cycle of a Dog Tapeworm

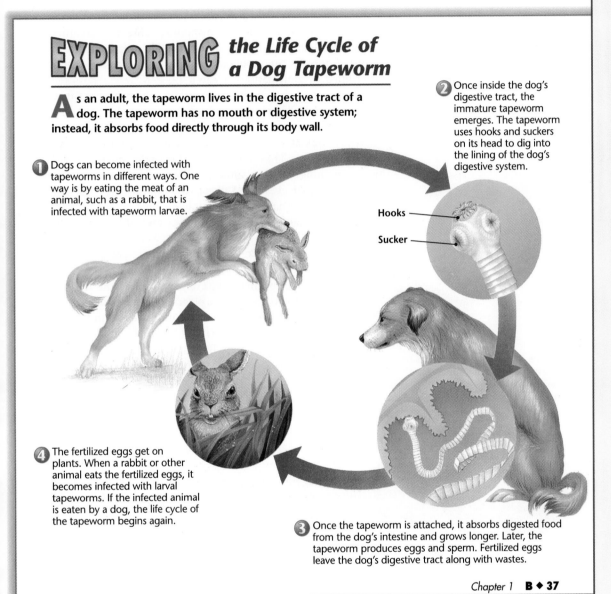

As an adult, the tapeworm lives in the digestive tract of a dog. The tapeworm has no mouth or digestive system; instead, it absorbs food directly through its body wall.

1 Dogs can become infected with tapeworms in different ways. One way is by eating the meat of an animal, such as a rabbit, that is infected with tapeworm larvae.

2 Once inside the dog's digestive tract, the immature tapeworm emerges. The tapeworm uses hooks and suckers on its head to dig into the lining of the dog's digestive system.

Hooks

Sucker

4 The fertilized eggs get on plants. When a rabbit or other animal eats the fertilized eggs, it becomes infected with larval tapeworms. If the infected animal is eaten by a dog, the life cycle of the tapeworm begins again.

3 Once the tapeworm is attached, it absorbs digested food from the dog's intestine and grows longer. Later, the tapeworm produces eggs and sperm. Fertilized eggs leave the dog's digestive tract along with wastes.

Chapter 1 **B ◆ 37**

Program Resources

◆ **Teaching Resources** 1-4 Lesson Plan, p. 29; 1-4 Section Summary, p. 30

Media and Technology

 Audiotapes English-Spanish Summary 1-3

 Transparencies "Exploring the Life Cycle of the Dog Tapeworm," Tr. 3

Answers to Self-Assessment

☑ *Checkpoint*
Worms exhibit bilateral symmetry.

Flatworms

EXPLORING
the Life Cycle of a Dog Tapeworm

Discuss each stage in the tapeworm life cycle with students. Remind students that eating a rabbit is only one way a dog can become infected. Have students identify the parasite and the hosts. *(Parasite: tapeworm; hosts: dog and rabbit)* Ask: **Why are the pictures arranged in a cycle?** *(To emphasize that the sequence of events is continuous.)* **Why do you think the tapeworm must attach itself to the dog's digestive system?** *(Its body is adapted to absorbing digested food)* **learning modality: visual**

Building Inquiry Skills: Predicting

Ask students to predict what might happen to a host animal that was infected with tapeworms. *(Sample: Since tapeworms absorb digested food from their host's intestine, the animal might become weak because it is not getting enough food.)* **learning modality: logical/mathematical**

Real-Life Learning

Veterinarians regularly treat household pets for tapeworm infections. Invite a local veterinarian to visit. Prior to the visit, have each student prepare one question to ask the veterinarian. **learning modality: verbal**

Portfolio Students can save their questions and the veterinarian's answers in their portfolio.

Ongoing Assessment

Writing Ask students to list the distinguishing characteristics of flatworms. *(Bilateral symmetry; a brain; flat bodies; most are parasitic; some are predators)*

Flatworms, continued

Inquiry Challenge

Materials *petri or small plastic dish, bottled water, ground meat, lettuce, live planarian, soft paintbrush, hand lens*

ACTIVITY

Time 50 minutes

Tips Have students observe planarians to draw conclusions about which food they prefer. Withhold feeding for a day before the class activity to make sure the planarians are hungry at the start of the activity. To begin the activity, have students pour water into the dish until the bottom is completely covered. Then, they should place a small piece of ground meat and a piece of lettuce in one side of the dish about 1 inch apart. Students can then use the paintbrush to carefully place the planarian at the other side of the dish. Have students observe how long it takes a planarian to start moving and whether it moves toward the lettuce or the meat. (Planarians are mainly carnivorous and probably will move toward meat rather than lettuce.) If the planarians are slow to respond, place a dark cover over the dish to reduce the light in the environment. Leave it on for about 10 minutes. Then remove the cover and observe any movement. Students should wash their hands after they finish.

Extend Ask: **How did the planarian locate the food?** (*It used its sense of smell.*) **Where are its sense organs are located?** (*In its front end of its body*) **Is having sense organs at the front end of its body related to the type of symmetry the planarian has?** (*Yes. Planarians are bilaterally symmetrical. Most bilaterally symmetrical animals have their sense organs at the front ends of their bodies.*)

learning modality: visual

Figure 16 Planarians are flatworms that live in ponds, streams, and oceans. The eyespots on the planarian's head can distinguish between light and dark. *Inferring How is having a distinct head end an advantage to a planarian?*

Planarians

Planarians Some flatworms are nonparasitic, or free-living. Unlike parasites, free-living organisms do not live in or on other organisms. Small free-living flatworms glide over the rocks in ponds, slide over damp soil, or swim slowly through the oceans like ruffled, brightly patterned leaves.

Planarians, such as the one in Figure 16, are scavengers—they feed on dead or decaying material. But they are also predators and will attack any animal smaller than they are.

If you look at a planarian's head, you can see two big dots that look like eyes. These dots are called eyespots, and they function something like eyes, although they cannot see a specific image like human eyes can. A planarian's head also has cells that pick up odors. Planarians rely mainly on smell to locate food. When a planarian smells food, it moves toward the food and glides onto it.

A planarian feeds like a vacuum cleaner. The planarian inserts a feeding tube into its food. Digestive juices flow out into the food, where they begin to break down the food while it is still outside the worm's body. Then the planarian sucks up the partly-digested bits of food. Digestion is then completed within a cavity inside the planarian. Food is distributed to body cells by diffusion. Like cnidarians, planarians have one opening in their digestive system. Undigested wastes exit through the feeding tube.

Figure 17 The transparent bodies of these roundworms have been stained for better viewing under a microscope.

Roundworms

The next time you walk along a beach, consider that about a million roundworms live in each square meter of damp sand.

Roundworms can live in nearly any moist environment—including forest soils, Antarctic sands, and even pools of super-hot water. Most are tiny and hard to see, but roundworms may be the most abundant animals on Earth.

Unlike flatworms, roundworms have cylindrical bodies. As you can see in Figure 17, they look like tiny strands of cooked spaghetti that are pointed at each end. If you look at roundworms under a microscope, you'd see their bodies thrashing from side to side.

Background

Facts and Figures Parasitic flatworms and roundworms are major causes of serious disease in humans and livestock. One parasitic roundworm, *Trichinella*, lives in the muscle tissue of pigs and game animals. Humans can become a host for this roundworm if they eat undercooked meat. When a human eats meat that contains Trichinella larvae, the larvae pass in the circulatory system to all parts of the body. Once in the muscle tissue, the larvae enclose themselves in a capsule, where they can remain inactive for a long time. The meat industry has been successful in controlling the spread of this parasite in animals raised for food. However, pork and game should always be thoroughly cooked.

While many roundworms are carnivores or herbivores, others are parasites. Have you given worm medicine to a pet dog or cat? The medicine was probably meant to kill roundworm parasites, such as hookworms.

Unlike cnidarians or flatworms, roundworms have a digestive system that is like a tube, open at both ends. Food enters at the animal's mouth and wastes exit through an opening, called the **anus,** at the far end of the tube. Food travels in one direction through the roundworm's digestive system, as it does in most complex animals.

A one-way digestive system has certain advantages. It is something like an assembly line, with a different part of the digestive process happening at each place along the line. Digestion happens in orderly stages. First food is broken down by digestive juices. Then the digested food is absorbed into the animal's body. Finally wastes are eliminated. The advantage of this type of digestive process is that it enables the animal's body to use foods efficiently, by enabling it to absorb a large amount of the needed substances in foods.

☑ *Checkpoint* *You are using a microscope to look at a tiny worm. What would you look for to tell whether it is a roundworm?*

Segmented Worms

If you have ever dug in a garden in the spring, you have probably seen earthworms wriggling through the moist soil. Those familiar soil inhabitants are segmented worms. So are the exotic sea-floor worms that you see in Figure 18. Parasitic blood-sucking leeches are also segmented worms. Since their bodies are long and narrow, some segmented worms look a bit like flatworms and roundworms. But segmented worms may be more closely related to crabs and snails.

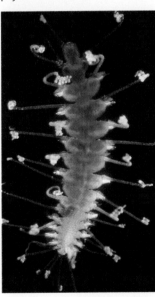
Figure 18 These segmented sea-floor worms belong to the same phylum as earthworms.

Media and Technology

 Exploring Life Science Videodisc
Unit 3, Side 2, "Spineless"

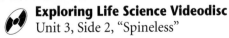
Chapter 2

Answers to Self-Assessment

Caption Question

Figure 16 Having a distinct head end is an advantage because the planarian can pick up information about what is in front of it and move forward.

☑ *Checkpoint*

To determine whether a worm is a roundworm, you would look for a cylindrical body that thrashes from side to side.

Roundworms

Including All Students

Some students may need extra help to understand **ACTIVITY** the difference between digestive systems with one or two openings. Show students two cardboard tubes, one open at both ends, the other sealed at one end. Ask: **What animal's digestive system could the sealed tube represent?** *(planarian, cnidarian)* **What animal's digestive system could the open tube represent?** *(roundworm, human, dog)* Show students marbles or small pebbles and tell them these items represent food. Fill the sealed tube with "food." Then pass "food" through the open tube. Lead students to understand that one advantage of a digestive system with two openings is that the animal can continue to eat while food eaten earlier passes through its digestive tract. **learning modality: kinesthetic**

Segmented Worms

Using the Visuals: Figures 16, 17, and 18

Direct students to compare and contrast the worms in the figures. Ask: **How are these worms similar?** *(They are all long and slender.)* **How are the worms in Figure 18 different from the other worms?** *(They are made up of many similar sections.)* **learning modality: visual**

Ongoing Assessment

Oral Presentation Have students Identify the distinguishing characteristics of roundworms and contrast roundworms to flatworms. *(Roundworms have cylindrical bodies and a one-way digestive system; in contrast, flatworms have flat bodies and a digestive system in which food and wastes move through the same opening.)*

Segmented Worms,
continued

Sharpen your Skills

Observing

Materials *earthworm, transparent container, construction paper, soil*

Time 15 minutes per day over several days

Tips Fill the container with loose, moist soil. Mist the soil if it starts to dry out. Keep the container out of direct sunlight. Have students wrap the jar walls with dark construction paper. That way the worms, which naturally avoid the light, may burrow along the outside wall of the jar. Have students note the earthworm's location in the soil. Ask: **When the segments at the front end of the worm contract, do the segments at the back end contract at the same time?** *(No, segments contract independently.)*

Expected Outcome Students may say that an earthworm's tunneling behavior is adaptive to the environment because tunneling helps the worm find food.

Extend If feasible, suggest that students raise earthworms in the classroom. They will need to add a food source to the soil such as vegetable waste or leaf litter.

learning modality: visual

Integrating Earth Science

Materials *transparent container, potting soil, light-colored sand, drinking straw*

Time 15 minutes

 Have students place a layer of potting soil, then a layer of sand, in the container. Instruct students to stick the straw through the layers to the bottom of the container. Then cover the upper opening of the straw with a finger and withdraw the straw. Remove the finger from the straw and allow the contents to pile up on the surface of the sand. Repeat several times. Ask: **What kind of earthworm behavior does this model?** *(As earthworms move through the soil, they mix it up and loosen it.)* **learning modality: kinesthetic**

Sharpen your Skills

Observing ACTIVITY

 Observe earthworms in a container filled with soil. Make your observations on several different days—if possible, at different times in the day. Note the worms' general sizes, colors, and appearances. Also observe their behavior—for example, how the worms move and how they tunnel through the soil. How is an earthworm's behavior adapted to surviving in its environment?

Figure 19 An earthworm's body is divided into over 100 segments. Some organs are repeated in most of those segments; others exist in only a few. *Interpreting Diagrams How does blood move through an earthworm's body?*

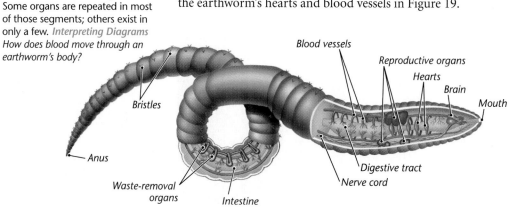

Blood vessels
Reproductive organs
Hearts
Brain
Mouth
Bristles
Anus
Waste-removal organs
Intestine
Digestive tract
Nerve cord

Segmented worms occupy nearly all environments, and most live in burrows or tubes. The burrow helps the worm hide both from possible predators and from possible prey. Many segmented worms are sit-and-wait predators that leap out of their burrows to attack animals that come too close.

Segmentation When you look at an earthworm, you notice that its body seems to consist of a series of rings separated by grooves, something like a vacuum-cleaner hose. **Earthworms and other segmented worms have bodies made up of many linked sections called segments.** An earthworm usually has more than 100 segments. On the outside, the segments look nearly identical. On the inside, some organs are repeated in most segments. For example, each segment has tubes that remove wastes . Other organs, however, such as the worm's reproductive organs, are found only in some segments. Nerve cords and a digestive tube run along the length of the worm's body. Like roundworms, earthworms have a one-way digestive system with two openings.

A Closed Circulatory System Segmented worms have a closed circulatory system. In a closed circulatory system, like your own, blood moves only within a connected network of tubes called blood vessels. In contrast, some animals, such as insects, have an open circulatory system in which blood leaves the blood vessels and sloshes around inside the body. A closed circulatory system can move blood around an animal's body much more quickly than an open circulatory system can. Blood quickly carries oxygen and food to cells. Because of this, an animal with a closed circulatory system can be larger and more active than one with an open circulatory system.

In segments 9 through 13, an earthworm has five paired pumping organs that act like hearts. They pump blood through large blood vessels that run the length of the worm's body. Find the earthworm's hearts and blood vessels in Figure 19.

Background

Facts and Figures Doctors sometimes use leeches, a type of segmented worm, to stimulate blood flow or to keep blood from clotting during surgery. Leeches have a chemical in their saliva called hirudin that prevents blood clotting. In nature, if the blood of the host organism were to clot, the leech could not continue to feed.

Program Resources

◆ **Integrated Science Laboratory Manual** B-1, "Observing Flatworms and Roundworms"

How Earthworms Live Earthworms tunnel for a living. They are scavengers that eat decayed plant and animal remains in the soil. On damp nights earthworms come up out of their burrows. They crawl on the surface of the ground, seeking leaves and soft fruits to drag underground and eat.

Night is a safe time for an earthworm to crawl on the surface, because many worm predators are asleep then. At night the air is damp, and this dampness helps keep the worm's skin moist. If a worm dries out, it will die, because it obtains oxygen through moisture on its skin.

Well-developed muscles let an earthworm move through its burrow. Stiff bristles stick out from each of the worm's segments. To crawl forward, an earthworm sticks its bristles in the ground and pulls itself along, much as a mountain climber uses an ice ax. Mountain climbers drive ice axes into a slippery slope and then pull themselves up.

Earthworms and Soil Earthworms are among the most **INTEGRATING EARTH SCIENCE** helpful inhabitants of garden and farm soil. They benefit people by improving the soil in which plants grow. Earthworm droppings make the soil more fertile. Earthworm tunnels loosen the soil and allow air, water, and plant roots to move through it. You have probably seen an earthworm tunnel entrance without realizing what it was—they are extremely common in lawns. To find one, look for a small, round hole in the ground with little lumps of soil next to it.

Section 4 Review

1. List the three major phyla of worms and give an example of each.
2. How does a dog tapeworm obtain its food?
3. Contrast a roundworm's digestive system to that of a planarian.
4. Describe the structure of an earthworm's body.
5. **Thinking Critically** Relating Cause and Effect If a dog is kept on a leash whenever it is outside, is it likely to get a tapeworm? Explain.

Check Your Progress
CHAPTER PROJECT 1
Begin to analyze what you have learned about your animal from your observations. Did you see a daily pattern to the animal's behavior? Think about what each kind of behavior accomplishes—whether it helps the animal obtain food or escape from danger, for example. Choose how you are going to present what you have learned—a written report, a talk, captioned illustrations, or some other method. Prepare charts or other visual aids.

Program Resources

◆ **Teaching Resources** 1-4 Review and Reinforce, p. 31; 1-4 Enrich, p. 32

Media and Technology

Interactive Student Tutorial CD-ROM B-1

Transparencies "Earthworm Anatomy," Transparency 4

Answers to Self-Assessment

Caption Question

Figure 19 Five paired pumping organs push blood through large vessels, down the length of the worm, and back to the pumping organs.

3 Assess

Section 4 Review Answers

1. Flatworms: planarians, tapeworms; roundworms: hookworms; segmented worms: earthworms.
2. The tapeworm lives in the dog's intestine where it is bathed in food. It absorbs the food.
3. A roundworm has a one-way digestive system in which food enters through a mouth and wastes exit through an anus. A planarian has a digestive system in which undigested wastes exit through its feeding tube.
4. An earthworm's body is divided into many segments. Some organs, such as those that dispose of waste material, are present in each segment. Others, such as the heart and reproductive organs, occupy only specialized segments. Organs such as those in the digestive and nervous systems run the length of the earthworm's body.
5. If a dog is kept on a leash, it is less likely to kill and eat a rabbit but might become infected some other way.

Check Your Progress
CHAPTER PROJECT 1
Tell students that analyzing their data means summarizing their observations, looking for patterns of behavior, then deciding what the patterns tell them about the animal.

Performance Assessment

Drawing Ask students to draw a flatworm, a roundworm, and a segmented worm. Have them label:
◆ the characteristics shared by all worms; *(Brain, bilateral symmetry)*
◆ the characteristics found only in flatworms; *(Flat body, feeding tube)*
◆ the main characteristics of roundworms; *(Cylindrical body, one-way digestive system)*
◆ the unique characteristics of segmented worms. *(Segmentation, closed circulatory system, bristles)*

Developing a Hypothesis

Earthworm Responses

Preparing for Inquiry

Key Concept A hypothesis is a prediction about the outcome of an experiment.

Skills Objective Students will be able to
◆ develop hypotheses.

Time 30 minutes

Advance Planning You can get worms from a biological supply company, a bait shop, or loose garden soil. Keep earthworms moist at all times. You may want to try this experiment before class to anticipate and understand the possible results.

Alternative Materials Cake pans can be used for trays. Do not substitute tissues for paper towels; they are too absorbent and will not last.

Guiding Inquiry

Invitation To help students form a hypothesis, ask: **Think about the places you are likely to see an earthworm. Would these places likely be dry or moist?** *(moist)* **Light or dark?** *(dark)*

Introducing the Procedure

◆ Give students time to read through the procedure and ask questions to clarify any steps they do not understand.

◆ Invite students to look at and thoroughly examine their earthworms on the paper towels before they begin to write a hypothesis.

◆ Have students review the diagram of the setup so they understand how to position the worms.

◆ Suggest that students conduct a trial one time before they actually collect data.

Earthworm Responses

I n this lab, you will practice the skill of making hypotheses to learn more about earthworms.

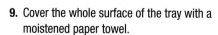

Earthworms
Wet paper towel
Dry paper towel
Tray

Problem

Do earthworms prefer dry or moist conditions? Do they prefer light or dark conditions?

Materials

plastic dropper	water	cardboard
clock or watch	paper towels	flashlight
2 earthworms	storage container	tray

Procedure

1. Which environment do you think earthworms prefer—dry or moist? Record your hypothesis in your notebook.

2. Use the dropper to sprinkle water on the worms. Keep the worms moist at all times.

3. Fold a dry paper towel and place it on the bottom of one side of your tray. Fold a moistened paper towel and place it on the other side.

4. Moisten your hands. Then place the earthworms in the center of the tray. Make sure that half of each earthworm's body rests on the moist paper towel and half rests on the dry towel. Handle the worms gently.

5. Cover the tray with the piece of cardboard. After five minutes, remove the cardboard and observe whether the worms are on the moist or dry surface. Record your observations.

6. Repeat Steps 4 and 5.

7. Return the earthworms to their storage container. Moisten the earthworms with water.

8. Which do you think earthworms prefer—strong light or darkness? Record your hypothesis in your notebook.

9. Cover the whole surface of the tray with a moistened paper towel.

10. Place the earthworms in the center of the tray. Cover half of the tray with cardboard. Shine a flashlight onto the other half.

11. After five minutes, note the locations of the worms. Record your observations.

12. Repeat Steps 10 and 11.

13. Moisten the earthworms and put them in the location designated by your teacher. Wash your hands after handling the worms.

Analyze and Conclude

1. Which environment did the worms prefer—moist or dry? Bright or dark? Did the worms' behavior support your hypotheses?

2. Use what you know about earthworms to explain how their responses to moisture and light help them survive.

3. **Think About It** What knowledge or experiences helped you make your hypotheses at the start of the experiments?

Design an Experiment

Do earthworms prefer a smooth or rough surface? Write your hypothesis. Then design an experiment to answer the question. Check with your teacher before carrying out your experiment.

Troubleshooting the Experiment

◆ Worms are delicate animals. Be sure they are handled gently. Rough handling can harm the worms and prevent them from moving.

◆ The dry paper towel may absorb some water if the wet paper towel is too wet. Have students check to make sure their dry paper towel remains dry. If a dry paper towel becomes damp, have the student replace it with another dry towel.

Safety

◆ Handle the earthworms gently.

◆ Keep the earthworms from drying out by misting them frequently with cool water in a spray bottle.

◆ Do not leave the earthworms unattended. Return them to their container when you are finished with them.

◆ Wash your hands after the experiment.

◆ Review the safety guidelines in Appendix A.

SECTION 1 What Is an Animal?

Key Ideas

◆ Animals are multicellular organisms that obtain food by eating other organisms. Animals can move. Most reproduce sexually.

◆ Animals need water, food, and oxygen to survive. Some animals are carnivores, or meat eaters. Others are herbivores, or plant eaters. Omnivores eat both plants and animals.

◆ When biologists classify an animal, they look at the structure of its body, its DNA, and the way its embryo develops. Some animals are vertebrates; most animal species are invertebrates.

Key Terms

species	heterotroph
autotroph	sexual reproduction
fertilization	asexual reproduction
adaptation	herbivore
carnivore	predator
prey	omnivore
phylum	invertebrate
vertebrate	

SECTION 2 Symmetry

INTEGRATING MATHEMATICS

Key Ideas

◆ The bodies of complex animals all have either radial or bilateral symmetry.

◆ Animals with radial symmetry have body parts arranged around a central point. They do not have distinct front ends.

◆ Animals with bilateral symmetry have one line that divides them into two mirror images. These animals, which usually have a distinct front end, are generally more complex than radially symmetrical animals.

Key Terms
bilateral symmetry
radial symmetry

SECTION 3 Sponges and Cnidarians

Key Ideas

◆ A sponge obtains food by straining water taken in through its pores. Sponges have no tissues or organs.

◆ Cnidarians, which include jellyfishes and hydras, are carnivores with stinging cells that help capture prey. Cnidarians have two body plans—polyp and medusa.

◆ Corals are cnidarians with hard skeletons around their soft bodies. Over time, the skeletons of corals form coral reefs.

Key Terms
larva
cnidarian
polyp
medusa

SECTION 4 Worms

Key Ideas

◆ The three major worm phyla are flatworms, roundworms, and segmented worms.

◆ Most flatworms are parasites that obtain food from their hosts. Planarians are nonparasitic flatworms.

◆ Roundworms have a digestive system that is a tube open at both ends.

◆ Segmented worms have bodies made up of many segments. Segmented worms have a closed circulatory system in which blood is contained in blood vessels.

◆ Earthworms help farmers and gardeners by loosening and fertilizing the soil.

Key Terms

regeneration	parasite	host
anus		

USING THE INTERNET
ACTIVITY
www.science-explorer.phschool.com

Chapter 1 **B ◆ 43**

Expected Outcome

◆ The worms generally prefer the moist towel and move toward it, though some worms may move to the dry towel. Students should record all the data and represent the number of times the worm moved towards the moist towel as a percent.

◆ Worms usually prefer a dark environment and move toward it.

Analyze and Conclude

1. Moist; dark; if students predicted these results, their hypotheses were supported.
2. Answers will vary. Sample: Earthworms live in dark, moist soil. They will dry out without water. For an earthworm, light usually means it is in the sun where it could dry out.
3. A typical response might suggest that earthworms are usually found in dark, moist places.

Extending the Inquiry

Design an Experiment Remind students that a hypothesis is a prediction about the outcome of an experiment. For example, if earthworms can move to either a rough or smooth surface, they will move to the rough surface. To test this hypothesis, students might suggest using a rough surface such as sandpaper on one side of a tray and a smooth surface such as ceramic tile on the other. Remind students they must make sure other factors (variables) such as temperature are consistent on the different sides of the tray. Their experiment must only test one factor at a time.

Sample Data Table for Entire Class

Trial Number	Minutes	Moved to Moist Towel	Moved to Dry Towel	% of worms that prefer the moist towel
1	5	16	4	80%
2	5	17	3	85%

Program Resources

◆ **Teaching Resources** Skills Lab blackline masters, pp. 34–37.

Reviewing Content:
Multiple Choice
1. b 2. b 3. b 4. b 5. a

True or False
6. true
7. true
8. bilateral symmetry
9. sponges
10. segmented worms

Checking Concepts

11. A cell is the smallest working unit of a living thing. Tissues are made up of similar cells that work together to perform a specific job. Organs are made up of different types of tissues.

12. The oxygen molecule diffused into the sponge's cell from the water. In diffusion, molecules of a substance move from an area where they are highly concentrated to an area where they are less concentrated.

13. Sample answer: A polyp is usually attached to a surface. Its mouth is at the top of its body. A medusa is free swimming. Its mouth is at the bottom of its body. Polyps and medusas are similar in that they are both radially symmetrical.

14. Humans are free-living animals because they do not live on or in the bodies of other organisms and take food from them.

15. There would probably be more roundworms—they are very abundant in soil.

16. Responses may vary. Accept any response that states there would be a wide variety of animals—from corals, sponges, and worms to shrimp, crabs, and fish. Dangers to watch out for include predators such as larger fish.

Thinking Visually

17. a. Whiplike structures on collar cells beat to move water through the sponge. Collar cells also strain food from the water. Oxygen from the water diffuses into the sponge's cells.
b. Water leaves the sponge through the osculum, carrying waste products.

Reviewing Content

For more review of key concepts, see the Interactive Student Tutorial CD-ROM.

Multiple Choice
Choose the letter of the best answer.

1. Organisms that make their own food are called
   a. omnivores.
   b. autotrophs.
   c. heterotrophs.
   d. carnivores.

2. Which of the following is *not* one of the major characteristics that biologists use to classify an animal?
   a. the structure of its body
   b. its height or length
   c. the development of its embryo
   d. its DNA

3. An animal with many lines of symmetry
   a. is bilaterally symmetrical.
   b. is radially symmetrical.
   c. has no symmetry.
   d. has line symmetry.

4. Which animal is a medusa?
   a. coral
   b. jellyfish
   c. planarian
   d. sea anemone

5. Which animal has a one-way digestive system?
   a. earthworm
   b. planarian
   c. sponge
   d. jellyfish

True or False
If the statement is true, write true. If it is false, change the underlined word or words to make the statement true.

6. <u>All</u> animals are made up of many cells.
7. <u>Sexual</u> reproduction produces offspring that are not exactly like either parent.
8. Fish have <u>radial symmetry</u>.
9. The bodies of <u>cnidarians</u> contain many pores.
10. The bodies of <u>roundworms</u> are segmented.

Checking Concepts

11. Explain the relationship among cells, tissues, and organs.

12. An oxygen molecule has just passed into a sponge's cell. Describe how it got there.

13. Compare a medusa and a polyp.

14. Are humans parasitic or free-living animals? Explain.

15. You dig up a handful of damp soil from the forest and examine it with a microscope. What kind of animal would probably be there in the greatest numbers? Explain.

16. Writing to Learn You are a small fish visiting a coral reef for the first time. What interesting sights would you see? Are there dangers to watch out for? In a paragraph, describe your adventures at the coral reef.

Thinking Visually

17. Flowchart The partially completed flowchart below shows how water travels through a sponge. Copy the flowchart onto a separate sheet of paper. Then complete it and add a title. (For more on flowcharts, see the Skills Handbook.)

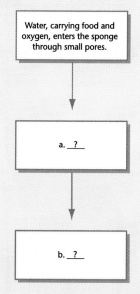

Water, carrying food and oxygen, enters the sponge through small pores.

a. _?_

b. _?_

Applying Skills

18. The manipulated variable is whether the field is treated with pesticide or not. The responding variable is the number of worms in the soil.

19. The average number of worms per cubic meter in the treated fields is 436.4. The average number in the untreated field is 722.4.

20. The number of worms in the soil goes down when the soil is treated with pesticide.

Thinking Critically

21. Collar cells in the sponge trap food and digest it. A planarian spits out digestive juice on its food, sucks up the partially digested bits of food, and absorbs the food. A roundworm has a one-way digestive system. The food is digested and absorbed along the way.

22. This predator would probably be orange because most sit-and-wait predators blend in with their surroundings.

23. Answers may vary. Sample: Although there may be fewer insects eating the plants, the

Applying Skills

A scientist used a pesticide on one field and left a nearby field untreated. Next, she marked off five plots of equal size in each field. Then she dug up a cubic meter of soil beneath each plot, and counted the earthworms in the soil. The table below shows her data. Use the table to answer Questions 18–20.

Field with Pesticide		Untreated Field	
Plot	Worms per cubic meter	Plot	Worms per cubic meter
A	730	F	901
B	254	G	620
C	319	H	811
D	428	I	576
E	451	J	704

18. **Controlling Variables** Identify the manipulated and responding variables in this experiment.

19. **Calculating** Calculate the average number of worms per cubic meter in the treated field. Then do the same for the untreated field.

20. **Drawing Conclusions** How did this pesticide affect the population of worms in the soil?

Thinking Critically

21. **Comparing and Contrasting** Compare the ways in which a sponge, a planarian, and a roundworm digest their food.

22. **Predicting** The sand in a desert is bright orange. What color would sit-and-wait predators in that desert probably be? Explain.

23. **Relating Cause and Effect** If a pesticide killed off many of the earthworms in a garden, how might that affect the plants growing in that soil?

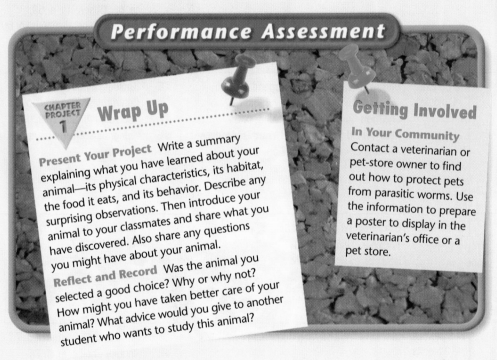

Performance Assessment

Wrap Up
CHAPTER PROJECT 1

Present Your Project Write a summary explaining what you have learned about your animal—its physical characteristics, its habitat, the food it eats, and its behavior. Describe any surprising observations. Then introduce your animal to your classmates and share what you have discovered. Also share any questions you might have about your animal.

Reflect and Record Was the animal you selected a good choice? Why or why not? How might you have taken better care of your animal? What advice would you give to another student who wants to study this animal?

Getting Involved

In Your Community Contact a veterinarian or pet-store owner to find out how to protect pets from parasitic worms. Use the information to prepare a poster to display in the veterinarian's office or a pet store.

---

plants may be less healthy because there are fewer earthworms. The earthworms break up the soil so that air, water, and plant roots can more easily move through it. They also fertilize the soil.

Performance Assessment

Wrap Up
CHAPTER PROJECT 2

Present Your Project Some students may be shy about presenting their projects to the class. Tell them all they have to do is to thoughtfully write their summaries and then share their summaries with the class. As students give their reports, ask their classmates to take brief notes, writing down the major characteristics of each animal. After students complete their presentations, have them turn in any written work you require. They should also move the animals to their new homes.

Reflect and Record After all presentations have been made, have students evaluate their projects. Students should decide what animals were best for the projects and what were the best methods for taking care of the animals.

Media and Technology

 Interactive Student Tutorial CD-ROM B-1

 Computer Test Bank Chapter 1 Test

Program Resources

◆ **Teaching Resources** Chapter 1 Project Teacher's Notes, pp. 10–11; Chapter 1 Project Student Materials, pp. 12–15; Chapter 1 Project Scoring Rubric, p. 16; Chapter 1 assessments, pp. 168–172

◆ **Inquiry Skills Handbook** Provides teaching and review of all inquiry skills

Getting Involved

Consider contacting veterinarians or pet store owners in advance to find those who are willing to participate in the activity. Create a list of addresses and phone numbers of the willing experts. Group students according to the length of the list. Have them work together to find the information and make the poster.

B ◆ 45

CHAPTER 2 Mollusks, Arthropods, and Echinoderms

Sections	Time	Student Edition Activities	Other Activities	
CHAPTER PROJECT 2 **Going Through Changes** p. 47	Ongoing (3–4 weeks)	Check Your Progress, pp. 61, 67, 76 Wrap Up, p. 79	TE	Chapter 2 Project Notes, pp. 46–47
1 Mollusks pp. 48–53 ◆ Describe the main characteristics of mollusks, and indicate evidence of early mollusks. ◆ Identify the major groups of mollusks.	3 periods/ 1–2 blocks	**Discover** How Can You Classify Shells? p. 48 **Sharpen Your Skills** Classifying, p. 50 **Science at Home** p. 52 **Skills Lab: Measuring** A Snail's Pace, p. 53	TE TE TE TE IES	Integrating Earth Science, p. 49 Exploring a Snail, p. 51 Building Inquiry Skills: Observing, p. 51 Integrating Physics, p. 52 "Where River Meets Sea," pp. 15–16
2 Arthropods pp. 54–61 ◆ Describe the major characteristics of arthropods. ◆ Identify the main groups of arthropods.	4 periods/ 2 blocks	**Discover** Will It Bend and Move? p. 54 **Try This** Pill Bugs—Wet or Dry? p. 58	TE TE TE TE	Including All Students, p. 55 Integrating Chemistry, p. 55 Building Inquiry Skills: Modeling, p. 56; Observing, p. 58; Making Generalizations, p. 60 Using the Visuals, pp. 56, 61
3 Insects pp. 62–69 ◆ Describe the characteristics of insects. ◆ Describe the overall impact of insects on humans. ◆ State and explain the life stages of insects.	4 periods/ 2 blocks	**Discover** What Kinds of Appendages Do Insects Have? p. 62 **Sharpen Your Skills** Graphing, p. 64 **Real-World Lab: You and Your Environment** What's Living in the Soil? pp. 68–69	TE TE TE	Building Inquiry Skills: Interpreting Diagrams, p. 63 Including All Students, p. 66 Integrating Environmental Science, p. 67
4 *INTEGRATING PHYSICS* **The Sounds of Insects** pp. 70–72 ◆ Explain how sound is produced. ◆ Identify one function that sound serves for many insects.	2 periods/ 1 block	**Discover** What Causes Sound? p. 70 **Try This** Tune In, p. 71 **Science at Home** p. 74	TE TE	Building Inquiry Skills: Observing, p.71 Building Inquiry Skills: Inferring, p. 72
5 Echinoderms pp. 73–76 ◆ Describe the typical echinoderm characteristics.	2–3 periods/ 1–2 blocks	**Discover** How Do Sea Stars Hold On? p. 73	TE TE TE ISLM	Including All Students, p. 74 Inquiry Challenge, p. 74 Building Inquiry Skills: Interpreting a Photograph, p. 75 B-2, "Characteristics of Sea Stars"
Study Guide/Chapter Review pp. 77–79	1 period/ $\frac{1}{2}$ block		ISAB	Provides teaching and review of all inquiry skills

For Standard or Block Schedule The Resource Pro® CD-ROM gives you maximum flexibility for planning your instruction with a standard or a block schedule. Resource Pro® contains Planning Express®, an advanced scheduling program, as well as the entire contents of the Teaching Resources and the Computer Test Bank.

CHAPTER PLANNING GUIDE

Program Resources	Assessment Strategies	Media and Technology
TR Chapter 2 Project Teacher Notes, pp. 38–39 **TR** Chapter 2 Project Student Materials, pp. 40–43 **TR** Chapter 2 Project Scoring Rubric, p. 44	**SE** Performance Assessment: Chapter 2 Project Wrap Up, p. 79 **TR** Chapter 2 Project: Scoring Rubric, p. 44 **TE** Check Your Progress, pp. 61, 67, 76	Science Explorer Internet Site
TR 2-1 Lesson Plan, p. 45 **TR** 2-1 Section Summary, p. 46 **TR** 2-1 Review and Reinforce, p. 47 **TR** 2-1 Enrich, p. 48 **TR** Skills Lab blackline masters, pp. 65–66 **SES** Book F, *Inside Earth,* Chapter 5 **SES** Book M, *Motion, Forces, and Energy,* Chapter 2	**SE** Section 1 Review, p. 52 **SE** Analyze and Conclude, p. 53 **TE** Ongoing Assessment, pp. 49, 51 **TE** Performance Assessment, p. 52 **TR** 2-1 Review and Reinforce, p. 47	Audiotapes: English-Spanish Summary 2-1 Exploring Physical Science Videodisc, Unit 3 Side 2, "Spineless" Transparency 5, "Exploring a Snail" Interactive Student Tutorial CD-ROM, B-2
TR 2-2 Lesson Plan, p. 49 **TR** 2-2 Section Summary, p. 50 **TR** 2-2 Review and Reinforce, p. 51 **TR** 2-2 Enrich, p. 52 **SES** Book L, *Chemical Interactions,* Chapter 4 **SES** Book C, *Cells and Heredity,* Chapter 5	**SE** Section 2 Review, p. 61 **TE** Ongoing Assessment, pp. 55, 57, 59 **TE** Performance Assessment, p. 61 **TR** 2-2 Review and Reinforce, p. 51	Audiotapes: English-Spanish Summary 2-2 Exploring Life Science Videodisc, Unit 3 Side 2, "Spineless" Transparency 6, "Exploring a Crayfish" Interactive Student Tutorial CD-ROM, B-2
TR 2-3 Lesson Plan, p. 53 **TR** 2-3 Section Summary, p. 54 **TR** 2-3 Review and Reinforce, p. 55 **TR** 2-3 Enrich, p. 56 **TR** Real-World Lab blackline masters, pp. 67–69 **SES** Book E, *Environmental Science,* Chapter 2	**SE** Section 3 Review, p. 67 **SE** Analyze and Conclude, p. 69 **TE** Ongoing Assessment, pp. 63, 65 **TE** Performance Assessment, p. 67 **TR** 2-3 Review and Reinforce, p. 55	Audiotapes: English-Spanish Summary 2-3 Exploring Life Science Videodisc, Unit 3 Side 2, "Insect Success Stories"; "The Good Bugs" Transparency 7, "Grasshopper Anatomy"; Transparency 8, "Exploring Insect Metamorphosis" Interactive Student Tutorial CD-ROM, B-2
TR 2-4 Lesson Plan, p. 57 **TR** 2-4 Section Summary, p. 58 **TR** 2-4 Review and Reinforce, p. 59 **TR** 2-4 Enrich, p. 60	**SE** Section 4 Review, p. 72 **TE** Ongoing Assessment, p. 71 **TE** Performance Assessment, p. 72 **TR** 2-4 Review and Reinforce, p. 59	Audiotapes: English-Spanish Summary 2-4 Exploring Physical Science Videodisc, Unit 6 Side 2, "Waves All Around Us" Interactive Student Tutorial CD-ROM, B-2
TR 2-5 Lesson Plan, p. 61 **TR** 2-5 Section Summary, p. 62 **TR** 2-5 Review and Reinforce, p. 63 **TR** 2-5 Enrich, p. 64 **SES** Book M, *Sound and Light,* Chapter 3	**SE** Section 5 Review, p. 76 **TE** Ongoing Assessment, p. 75 **TE** Performance Assessment, p. 76 **TR** 2-5 Review and Reinforce, p. 63	Exploring Life Science Videodisc, Unit 3 Side 2, "Spineless" Audiotapes: English-Spanish Summary 2-5 Transparency 9, "Exploring a Sea Star" Interactive Student Tutorial CD-ROM, B-2
TR Chapter 2 Performance Assessment, pp. 173–175 **TR** Chapter 2 Test, pp. 176–179 **ISAB** Provides teaching and review of all inquiry skills	**SE** Chapter Review, pp. 77–79 **TR** Chapter 2 Performance Assessment, pp. 173–175 **TR** Chapter 2 Test, pp. 176–179 **CTB** Chapter 2 Test	Interactive Student Tutorial CD-ROM, B-2 Computer Test Bank, Chapter 2 Test Got It! Video Quizzes

Key: **SE** Student Edition   **TE** Teacher's Edition   **TR** Teaching Resources
      CTB Computer Test Bank   **SES** Science Explorer Series Text   **ISLM** Integrated Science Laboratory Manual
      ISAB Inquiry Skills Activity Book   **PTA** Product Testing Activities by *Consumer Reports*   **IES** Interdisciplinary Explorations Series

Meeting the National Science Education Standards and AAAS Benchmarks

National Science Education Standards	Benchmarks for Science Literacy	Unifying Themes
Science as Inquiry (Content Standard A) ◆ **Ask questions that can be answered by scientific investigations** How do changes in environmental temperature affect the activity level of a snail? How do different conditions affect mealworm development? *(Skills Lab; Chapter Project)* ◆ **Design and conduct a scientific investigation** Students design a plan to investigate mealworm development. *(Chapter Project)* **Physical Science** (Content Standard B) ◆ **Motions and forces** All sound is produced by vibrations that create waves that move outward from the source. *(Section 4)* **Life Science** (Content Standard C) ◆ **Diversity and adaptations of organisms** Students learn the characteristics and adaptations of mollusks, arthropods, insects, and echinoderms. Many insects use sound to attract mates. *(Sections 1–5)* ◆ **Populations and ecosystems** The vast majority of insects are harmless or beneficial to humans. Students examine the animal life of a specific soil environment. *(Section 3; Real-World Lab)*	**1B Scientific Inquiry** Scientific investigations usually involve the collection of relevant evidence, the use of logical reasoning, and the application of imagination in devising hypotheses and explanations to make sense of the collected evidence. *(Skills Lab; Real-World Lab; Chapter Project)* **4F Motion** Vibrations in materials set up wavelike disturbances that spread away from the source. *(Section 4)* **5A Diversity of Life** Animals have a great variety of body plans and internal structures that contribute to their ability to make or find food and reproduce. In classifying organisms, biologists consider details of internal and external structures. *(Sections 1–5)* **5D Interdependence of Life** In any environment, the growth and survival of organisms depend on the physical conditions. Two organisms may interact with one another in several ways: producer/consumer, predator/prey, parasite/host, etc. *(Sections 1–3, 5; Real-World Lab; Chapter Project)* **12D Communication Skills** Organize information in simple graphs and identify relationships they reveal. *(Skills Lab; Chapter Project)*	◆ **Evolution** The natural history of mollusks is recorded by fossils that date as far back as 600 million years. Most of the fossils occur as shells in limestone rocks. *(Section 1)* ◆ **Unity and Diversity** Mollusks, arthropods, and echinoderms are grouped according to anatomical characteristics. Individual groups within these phyla are differentiated by specific characteristics. *(Sections 1–3, 5; Real-World Lab)* ◆ **Energy** Various feeding strategies of major groups of animals are explained. Specific feeding strategies are described and clarified with examples. The production of sound is briefly introduced. Compression waves and their relationship to sound are examined. *(Sections 1–5)* ◆ **Patterns of Change** Students learn about metamorphosis as a developmental pattern in arthropods. *(Sections 2, 3)*

Media and Technology

Exploring Life Science Videodiscs

◆ **Section 1** "Spineless" provides information for viewers to compare the digestion, circulation, and respiration of a variety of invertebrates.

◆ **Section 3** "Insect Success Stories" illustrates the characteristics that have allowed insects to become the most abundant creatures on Earth.

◆ **Section 3** "The Good Bugs" shows students how the use of "good" insects can help control populations of insect pests.

Exploring Physical Science Videodiscs

◆ **Section 4** "Waves All Around Us" identifies a variety of waves in viewers' everyday world.

◆ **Section 4** "A Wave Is a Wave Is a Wave" shows how waves of all types are similar in how they are formed and how they transfer energy.

Interactive Student Tutorial CD-ROM

◆ **Chapter Review** Interactive questions help students to self-assess their mastery of key chapter concepts.

Student Edition Connection Strategies

◆ **Section 1** Integrating Earth Science, p. 49
Integrating Physics, p. 52
◆ **Section 2** Integrating Chemistry, p. 55
◆ **Section 3** Social Studies Connection, p. 66
Integrating Environmental Science, p. 67
◆ **Section 4** Integrating Physics, p. 70

USING THE INTERNET

www.science-explorer.phschool.com

Visit the Science Explorer Internet site to find an up-to-date activity for Chapter 2 of *Animals*.

ACTIVITY	Time (minutes)	Materials Quantities for one work group	Skills
Section 1			
Discover, p. 48	20	**Nonconsumable** mollusk shells such as clams, mussels, oysters, land and marine snails, and nautiluses	Inferring
Sharpen Your Skills, p. 50	10	**Consumable** No special materials are required.	Classifying
Skills Lab, p. 53	60	**Consumable** spring water at three temperatures: cool (9–13ºC); medium (18–22ºC); warm (27–31ºC), graph paper **Nonconsumable** freshwater snail, plastic petri dish, thermometer, ruler, timer	Measuring
Section 2			
Discover, p. 54	15	**Consumable** sheets of heavy cardboard about 30 x 45 cm, tape	Inferring
Try This, p. 58	20	**Consumable** aluminum foil, paper towels, masking tape, water **Nonconsumable** shoe box, live pill bugs	Interpreting Data
Section 3			
Discover, p. 62	20	**Nonconsumable** insect collection, hand lenses	Observing
Sharpen Your Skills, p. 64	20	**Nonconsumable** protractor, compass, calculator	Graphing
Real World Lab, pp. 68–69	15; 45	**Consumable** 2-liter plastic bottle, coarse steel wool, cheesecloth, fresh sample of soil and leaf litter **Nonconsumable** gooseneck lamp; large, wide-mouthed jar; large scissors; trowel; large rubber band; hand lens; small jar	Observing, Classifying, Inferring
Section 4			
Discover, p. 70	5	**Nonconsumable** rubber bands	Inferring
Try This, p. 71	5	**Nonconsumable** tuning fork, pencil, glass of water	Predicting
Section 5			
Discover, p. 73	5	**Consumable** water **Nonconsumable** plastic dropper	Predicting

A list of all materials required for the Student Edition activities can be found on pages T14–T16. You can order Materials Kits by calling 1-800-828-7777 or by accessing the Science Explorer Internet site at **http://www.science-explorer.phschool.com.**

Going Through Changes

Many students may have heard about the metamorphosis of insects. In this project, they'll have the chance to observe that process.

Purpose In this project, students will observe metamorphosis while examining conditions (variables) that may affect the process.

Skills Focus Students will be able to
- observe how different conditions affect mealworm development;
- design experiments to test the effect of an environmental variable on metamorphosis;
- control the variable being tested;
- create data tables to record daily mealworm observations;
- draw conclusions regarding the affect of the environmental change on metamorphosis.

Project Time Line The larval stage of mealworms lasts for 10 weeks. However, mealworms obtained from a pet store are probably partly through the larval period. Larger larvae are generally older. Acquire mealworms in advance of the project. If necessary for scheduling purposes, keep the mealworms at a warm temperature to accelerate development or a cold temperature to delay development. Each day for the next few weeks, students count how many larvae, pupae, and adults they have in each container. Students may wish to continue collecting data until half the mealworms have become adults. Generally, pupae become adults in 2 to 3 weeks.

Before beginning the project, see Chapter 2 Project Teacher Notes on pages 38–39 in Teaching Resources for more details on carrying out the project. Also distribute the Students' Chapter 2 Project Student Materials and Scoring Rubric on pages 40–44 in Teaching Resources.

Possible Materials
- You can obtain mealworms from local pet stores that sell reptile and amphibian food. Make sure they are well fed and have a moisture source until the project launch day.
- Tell students to bring in plastic

containers with lids, such as empty margarine tubs. The slippery plastic makes it difficult for the mealworms to escape.
- Students can bring in dry cereal or uncooked oatmeal for mealworm food.
- Slices of apple, potato, carrot, or over-ripe banana can be used as moisture sources.
- Students can use plastic spoons, Popsicle sticks, or wooden splints to transfer the cereal to the containers and to count the mealworms.

WHAT'S AHEAD

SECTION 1 Mollusks
Discover **How Can You Classify Shells?**
Sharpen Your Skills **Classifying**
Skills Lab **A Snail's Pace**

SECTION 2 Arthropods
Discover **Will It Bend and Move?**
Try This **Pill Bugs—Wet or Dry?**

SECTION 3 Insects
Discover **What Kinds of Appendages Do Insects Have?**
Sharpen Your Skills **Graphing**
Real-World Lab **What's Living in the Soil?**

Launching the Project Obtain the mealworms in advance and have students begin to collect the materials. To introduce the project and to stimulate interest, ask: **Have any of you seen a caterpillar turn into a butterfly?** *(Answers may vary.)* **What are the major differences and similarities between caterpillars and butterflies?** *(Sample answer: differences—wings; similarities—legs)* Tell students the mealworms will turn into beetles. Reassure them that the beetles will not fly out when the lid of the container is removed.

Students can work in small groups as a cooperative learning task. To ensure that every student will have ample opportunity to participate in designing an experiment, you may wish to limit groups to three students.

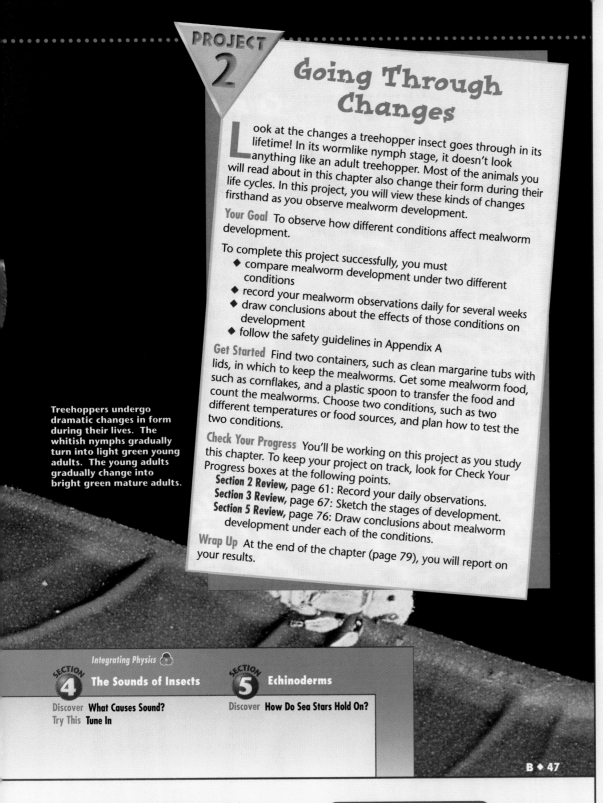

PROJECT 2

Going Through Changes

Look at the changes a treehopper insect goes through in its lifetime! In its wormlike nymph stage, it doesn't look anything like an adult treehopper. Most of the animals you will read about in this chapter also change their form during their life cycles. In this project, you will view these kinds of changes firsthand as you observe mealworm development.

Your Goal To observe how different conditions affect mealworm development.

To complete this project successfully, you must
◆ compare mealworm development under two different conditions
◆ record your mealworm observations daily for several weeks
◆ draw conclusions about the effects of those conditions on development
◆ follow the safety guidelines in Appendix A

Get Started Find two containers, such as clean margarine tubs with lids, in which to keep the mealworms. Get some mealworm food, such as cornflakes, and a plastic spoon to transfer the food and count the mealworms. Choose two conditions, such as two different temperatures or food sources, and plan how to test the two conditions.

Check Your Progress You'll be working on this project as you study this chapter. To keep your project on track, look for Check Your Progress boxes at the following points.
Section 2 Review, page 61: Record your daily observations.
Section 3 Review, page 67: Sketch the stages of development.
Section 5 Review, page 76: Draw conclusions about mealworm development under each of the conditions.

Wrap Up At the end of the chapter (page 79), you will report on your results.

Treehoppers undergo dramatic changes in form during their lives. The whitish nymphs gradually turn into light green young adults. The young adults gradually change into bright green mature adults.

SECTION **4** Integrating Physics
The Sounds of Insects
Discover **What Causes Sound?**
Try This **Tune In**

SECTION **5**
Echinoderms
Discover **How Do Sea Stars Hold On?**

B ◆ 47

Students can work in small groups as a cooperative learning task. To ensure that every student will have ample opportunity to participate in designing an experiment, you may wish to limit groups to three students.

On the launch day, have students prepare two containers. They will need to put food (such as cornflakes) and a moisture source (such as a piece of fruit or vegetable) in each container. Direct students to select and set up the two conditions they want to test. You may wish to have students write a hypothesis. Then distribute the mealworms.

Students can interpret their data on the number of larvae, pupae and adult mealworms in each container by drawing graphs to compare the different conditions. They can then use these graphs to evaluate their hypothesis.

Allow time for students to read the description of the project in their text and the Chapter Project Overview on pages 40–41 in Teaching Resources. Then encourage discussions on the environmental factors that might affect metamorphosis such as temperature, light, and type of food supplied. Also discuss materials that could be used, and any initial questions students may have. Pass out copies of the Chapter 2 Project Worksheets on pages 42–43 in Teaching Resources for students to review.

Program Resources

◆ **Teaching Resources** Chapter 2 Project Teacher's Notes, pp. 38-39; Chapter 2 Project Student Materials, pp. 40-43; Chapter 2 Project Scoring Rubric, p. 44

Performance Assessment

The Chapter 2 Project Scoring Rubric on page 44 of Teaching Resources will help you evaluate how well students complete the Chapter 2 Project. Students will be assessed on
◆ how well they describe the two conditions that they are comparing;
◆ how well they identify and observe the larval, pupal, and adult stages of mealworm development;
◆ how clearly the data sheets show the number of larvae, pupae, and adults in their samples;
◆ how correctly the graphs show the numbers of mealworm larvae, pupae, and adult beetles.
By sharing the Chapter 2 Project Scoring Rubric with students at the beginning of the project, you will make it clear to them what they are expected to do.

Objectives

After completing this lesson, students will be able to

◆ describe the main characteristics of mollusks and indicate evidence of early mollusks;

◆ identify the major groups of mollusks.

Key Terms mollusk, kidney, gill, radula, gastropod, bivalve, cephalopod

1 Engage/Explore

Activating Prior Knowledge

Ask students if they have ever eaten a mollusk. Students may not know what a mollusk is. Then, ask if any student has ever eaten clams, oysters, or squid. If students answer yes, inform them that all these animals are mollusks.

•••••• **DISCOVER** ••••••

Skills Focus inferring
Materials *mollusk shells such as those from clams, mussels, oysters, land and marine snails, and nautiluses*
Time 20 minutes
Tips Place the shells at stations around the room. Group students at each station. Help students develop a set of characteristics to use for grouping the shells. Remind students to handle specimens carefully as they may be fragile. Tell students to describe some features of the shells. Guide them to notice shiny and rough surfaces, the composition and color of shell material, and possible signs of growth, such as rings. Be sure that students write down the characteristics they used to group the shells. Let each group select a representative to describe the characteristics to the class.
Expected Outcome Students should become aware of the wide diversity of shells.
Think It Over It might help an animal to have a shell because the shell could protect it from predators and support its body.

SECTION 1 Mollusks

DISCOVER •••••••••••••••••••••••• *ACTIVITY*

How Can You Classify Shells?

1. Obtain an assortment of shells from your teacher. Examine each one carefully. Look at the shells and feel their surfaces.

2. Compare the outer surface of each shell to the inner surface.

3. Classify the shells into two or more groups based on the characteristics you observe.

Think It Over
Inferring How might it help an animal to have a shell?

GUIDE FOR READING

◆ What are the main characteristics of mollusks?

◆ What are the major groups of mollusks?

Reading Tip As you read, make a compare/contrast table to distinguish among the different mollusk groups.

▼ Wampum string and clamshell

From the shells of clams, Native Americans in the Northeast carved purple and white beads called wampum. They wove these beads into belts with complex designs that often had special, solemn significance. A wampum belt might record a group's history. When warring groups made peace, they exchanged weavings made of wampum. Iroquois women would honor a new chief with gifts of wampum strings.

The hard shells of clams provided the material for wampum, and the soft bodies within the shells were a major source of food for Native Americans who lived along the seacoast. Today, clams and similar animals, such as scallops and oysters, are still valuable sources of food for people in many parts of the world.

What Are Mollusks?

Clams, oysters, and scallops are all mollusks (phylum Mollusca). So are snails and octopuses. **Mollusks** are invertebrates with soft, unsegmented bodies that are often protected by hard outer shells. **In addition to soft bodies often covered with shells, mollusks have a thin layer of tissue called a mantle that covers their internal organs.** The mantle also produces the mollusk's shell. Most mollusks move with a muscular structure called a foot. The feet of different kinds of mollusks are adapted for various uses, such as crawling, digging, or catching prey.

Mollusks live nearly everywhere on Earth. Most live in water, from mountain streams to the deep ocean, but some live on land, usually in damp places.

READING STRATEGIES

Reading Tip Students' tables should include the three major mollusk groups—gastropods, bivalves, and cephalopods. Make sure students include number of shells, type of foot, and complexity of nervous system for each group of mollusks.

Vocabulary Tell students that *gastropod* means "stomach-footed," *cephalopod* means "head-footed," and *bivalve* means "two-shelled." Have students write down the name of each group of mollusks, what each name means, and a sentence describing why they think each group was given its name.

Like segmented worms, mollusks have bilateral symmetry. However, unlike segmented worms, the body parts of mollusks are not repeated. Instead, their internal organs, such as the stomach and reproductive organs, are all located together in one area. A mollusk's internal organs include a pair of **kidneys**, organs that remove the wastes produced by an animal's cells.

Most water-dwelling mollusks have **gills**, organs that remove oxygen from water. The gills are attached to the mantle and have a rich supply of blood vessels. Within these thin-walled blood vessels, oxygen from the surrounding water diffuses into the blood, while carbon dioxide diffuses out. The gills of most mollusks are covered by tiny, hairlike structures called cilia. The beating movement of these cilia makes water flow over the gills.

Many mollusks have an organ called a **radula** (RAJ oo luh) (plural *radulae*), which is a flexible ribbon of tiny teeth. Acting like sandpaper, the tiny teeth scrape food from a surface such as a leaf. A radula may have as many as 250,000 teeth. Biologists use the arrangement of teeth in the radula to help classify mollusks.

☑ *Checkpoint* *How is the body structure of a mollusk different from that of a segmented worm?*

Evidence of Early Mollusks

INTEGRATING EARTH SCIENCE Mollusks were living in Earth's oceans about 540 million years ago. Much evidence for this comes from fossil shells in limestone rocks. Some kinds of limestone are partially made from the shells of ancient, ocean-dwelling mollusks. After the mollusks died, their shells were broken into tiny pieces by waves and water currents. These shell pieces, along with the hard remains of other organisms, piled up on the ocean floor. These hard materials then underwent a chemical change in which they became cemented together to form limestone. During this process, some shells—or parts of shells—remained unbroken and eventually became fossils.

Figure 1 Some mollusks, like the chambered nautilus, left, are protected by shells. Other mollusks, like the nudibranch, right, do not have shells. *Classifying What characteristics do these two organisms share?*

Answers to Self-Assessment

Caption Question

Figure 1 Both the nautilus and the nudibranch are invertebrates with soft bodies and a mantle that covers their internal organs.

☑ *Checkpoint*

The bodies of mollusks are not segmented; their internal organs are all in one area.

---

2 Facilitate

What Are Mollusks?

Building Inquiry Skills: Classifying

Have students list the characteristics mollusks and segmented worms have in common and those that are unique to each organism. Then ask: **Based on this information, do you think mollusks and segmented worms are closely related? Why?** (*Answers will vary. Be sure students support their answer.*) **learning modality: logical/mathematical**

Evidence of Early Mollusks

 Integrating Earth Science

Materials *pieces of granite, limestone, marine snail or clam shells; 10% hydrochloric acid (HCl) solution; plastic dropper*
Time 15 minutes
Tips This demonstration shows students that limestone and marble both contain calcium carbonate.
CAUTION: *Hydrochloric acid can burn skin and clothing. Avoid direct contact. Neutralize spills and splashes with plenty of water. Wear safety goggles, gloves, and a lab apron. After the demonstration, dispose of the acid solution by diluting it with lots of water and pouring it down the sink.*
Inform students that materials that contain calcium carbonate fizz when hydrochloric acid is applied to them. Then apply a few drops of acid solution to the granite, then the limestone, and finally the shell. Students should watch for a reaction. The granite will not react; the limestone and shell should fizz. Thoroughly rinse each specimen. Students should infer that both limestone and the shells contain calcium carbonate. **learning modality: visual**

Ongoing Assessment

Writing Have students create a checklist of characteristics that identify an animal as a mollusk.

Snails and Their Relatives

Sharpen your Skills

Classifying

While wading in a stream, you step on a small animal with a hard external covering. When you examine the animal, you discover that it has a soft body inside its shell. It appears to be a mollusk. What characteristics would help you determine the major group of mollusks to which it belongs?

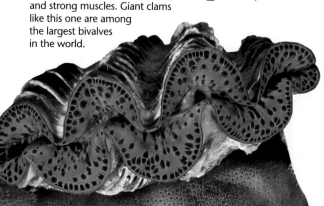

Figure 2 The two shells of a bivalve are held together by hinges and strong muscles. Giant clams like this one are among the largest bivalves in the world.

Snails and Their Relatives

Biologists classify mollusks into groups based on physical characteristics such as the presence of a shell, the type of shell, the type of foot, the arrangement of teeth in the radula, and the complexity of the nervous system. **The three major groups of mollusks are gastropods, bivalves, and cephalopods.**

The most numerous mollusks are the gastropods. **Gastropods**, which include snails and slugs, are mollusks that have a single shell or no shell at all. Most snails have a single, coiled shell, while many slugs have no shell. Gastropods usually creep along on a broad foot. Gastropods get their name, which means "stomach foot," from the fact that most of them have their foot on the same side of their body as their stomach. To learn more about the body of a gastropod, look at *Exploring a Snail*.

You can find gastropods nearly everywhere on Earth. They live in oceans, on rocky shores, in fresh water, and on dry land, too. Some snails even live in treetops.

Some gastropods are herbivores, while others are scavengers that feed on decaying material. Still others are carnivores. For example, the oyster drill is a snail that makes a hole in an oyster's shell by releasing acid and then boring a hole with its radula. The oyster drill then scrapes away the oyster's soft body.

Many snails have a tight-fitting plate or trapdoor on their foot that fits securely into the opening of their shell. When this kind of snail is threatened by a predator, it withdraws into its shell and tightly closes its trapdoor. Snails also pull back into their shells when conditions are dry and then come out when conditions are moist again. When they are sealed up in this way, gastropods can survive incredibly long times. In one museum the shells of two land snails, presumed to be dead, were glued to a piece of cardboard. Four years later, when someone put the cardboard in water, one of the snails crawled away!

☑ *Checkpoint* *How did gastropods get their name?*

Two-Shelled Mollusks

Clams, oysters, scallops, and mussels are **bivalves**, mollusks that have two shells held together by hinges and strong muscles. Unlike other mollusks, bivalves do not have radulae. Instead, most are filter feeders; they strain their food from water. Bivalves use their gills to capture food as they breathe. Food particles stick to mucus

EXPLORING a Snail

L like other gastropods, a snail has a head with sense organs, and it has a wide, muscular foot. The snails shown here live in a pond.

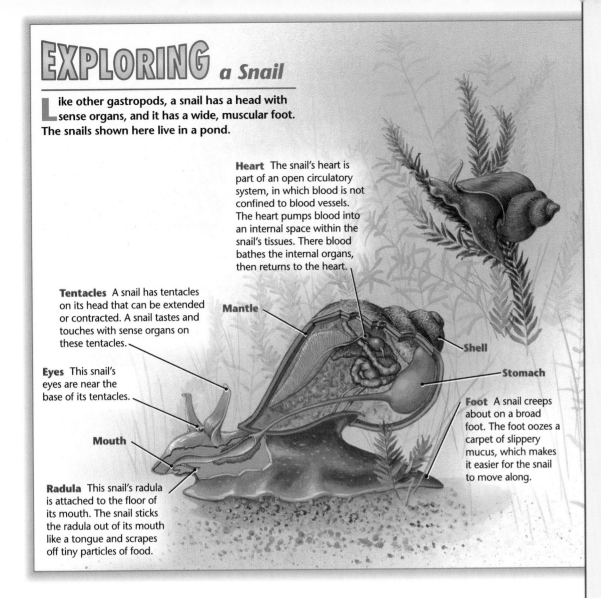

Heart The snail's heart is part of an open circulatory system, in which blood is not confined to blood vessels. The heart pumps blood into an internal space within the snail's tissues. There blood bathes the internal organs, then returns to the heart.

Tentacles A snail has tentacles on its head that can be extended or contracted. A snail tastes and touches with sense organs on these tentacles.

Eyes This snail's eyes are near the base of its tentacles.

Mouth

Radula This snail's radula is attached to the floor of its mouth. The snail sticks the radula out of its mouth like a tongue and scrapes off tiny particles of food.

Mantle

Shell

Stomach

Foot A snail creeps about on a broad foot. The foot oozes a carpet of slippery mucus, which makes it easier for the snail to move along.

that covers the gills. The cilia on the gills then move the food particles into the bivalve's mouth.

Bivalves are found in all kinds of watery environments. As adults, most bivalves stay in one place or move slowly. After their larval stage, for example, oysters and mussels attach themselves to an underwater surface. Clams, in contrast, are active; they use a thin foot to burrow down into the sand or mud. Scallops can also move from place to place. In fact, when startled, scallops clap their shells together and leap rapidly in the water over the sand.

Chapter 2 **B ◆ 51**

Answers to Self-Assessment

✓ Checkpoint

Gastropod means "stomach foot." Gastropods were given this name because their foot is on the same side of their body as their stomach.

EXPLORING a Snail

Materials *live snails in an aquarium, hand lens*

Time 20 minutes

Tips Reinforce the information presented in the visual essay by allowing students to observe live snails in an aquarium. Ask students to examine the snail in the visual essay and compare to the snails in the aquarium. Caution them not to touch the snails or tap on the sides of the aquarium. Have students look for the parts of the snail that are labeled in the visual essay. *(Students should be able to see the tentacles, mouth, foot, and shell. They may be able to see the eyes.)* **learning modality: visual**

Two-Shelled Mollusks

Building Inquiry Skills: Observing

Materials *a closed oyster, an opened oyster*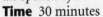

Time 30 minutes

Tips Obtain oysters from a seafood market, and request that half the oysters be opened. Refrigerate the oysters to avoid spoilage. Have students work in pairs. One student should examine the closed bivalve, identify each half of the shell, and explore the texture of the outer covering. The other student should examine the opened oyster and identify as many internal parts as possible. The two students should then compare observations. Students should wash their hands after handling the oysters. **cooperative learning**

Ongoing Assessment

Writing Ask students to write short paragraphs that compare gastropods and bivalves, and include an example of each. *(Gastropods, such as snails and slugs, have one shell or no shell, creep on a broad foot, and scrape food with their radulas. Bivalves, such as clams and oysters, have two shells and are filter feeders. Some use a foot to dig into the sand.)*

Mollusks with Tentacles

Integrating Physics

Materials *balloon, aquarium or sink, water*

Time 10 minutes

Tips To demonstrate how cephalopods move using jet propulsion, fill the balloon with water. Pinch the neck to keep water from squirting out. Immerse the balloon in an aquarium or sink and release the neck. Students will observe the balloon shooting through the water.

learning modality: visual

3 Assess

Section 1 Review Answers

1. Soft bodies, mantle, muscular foot; many have shells.
2. Gastropods have one shell or no shell; most creep on a broad foot. Bivalves have two shells, are filter feeders, and often have one foot adapted for digging. Cephalopods have a complex nervous system, swim using jet propulsion, and have tentacles around their mouths.
3. By straining food from water.
4. No. Gills must have many blood vessels to pick up enough oxygen.

Science at Home

Ask students which animals they expect to find. *(snails, oysters, clams, squid, canned clams, smoked oysters)* Suggest students visit a seafood store with a larger variety of seafood.

Performance Assessment

Drawing Have students draw one mollusk from each major group. Then they should list three characteristics all these animals have that make them mollusks. Finally, have them label one characteristic that distinguishes each group.

 Portfolio Students can save their drawings in their portfolios.

Figure 3 Octopuses live in coral reefs where they hide in holes when they are not hunting crabs and other small animals. *Observing What structures cover the octopus's tentacles?*

Sometimes sand or grit becomes lodged between a bivalve's mantle and its shell, irritating the soft mantle. Just as you might put smooth tape around rough bicycle handlebars to protect your hands, the bivalve's mantle produces a smooth, pearly coat to cover the irritating object. Eventually a pearl forms around the grit. Some oysters make pearls so beautiful that they are used in jewelry.

Mollusks with Tentacles

Octopuses, cuttlefish, nautiluses, and squids are **cephalopods**, mollusks whose feet are adapted to form tentacles around their mouths. Some octopuses have tentacles almost 5 meters long! While nautiluses have an external shell, squids and cuttlefish have a small shell within the body. Octopuses do not have shells.

Cephalopods capture food with their flexible, muscular tentacles. Sensitive suckers on the tentacles receive sensations of taste as well as touch. A cephalopod doesn't have to touch something to taste it; the suckers respond to chemicals in the water. For example, when an octopus feels beneath a rock, its tentacle may find a crab by taste before it touches it.

Cephalopods have large eyes and excellent vision. They also have the most complex nervous system, including a large brain, of any invertebrate. Cephalopods are highly intelligent animals that can remember things they have learned. In captivity, octopuses quickly learn when to expect deliveries of food and how to escape from their tanks.

Integrating Physics All cephalopods live in the ocean, where they swim by jet propulsion. They squeeze a current of water out of the mantle cavity through a tube, and like rockets, shoot off in the opposite direction. By turning the tube around, they can steer in any direction.

Section 1 Review

1. What characteristics do most mollusks have in common?
2. List the three main groups of mollusks. Describe the main characteristics of each group.
3. Explain how bivalves obtain food.
4. **Thinking Critically** **Predicting** Would gills function well if they had few blood vessels? Explain.

Science at Home

Visit a local supermarket with a family member and identify any mollusks that are being sold as food. Be sure to look in places other than the fish counter, such as the canned-foods section. Discuss the parts of the mollusks that are used for food and the parts that are not edible.

Background

Facts and Figures Bioluminescence is the ability of a animal to produce light. Many squids are bioluminescent. Squids who live deep in the ocean where there is little light are protected from predators by their bioluminescence. Some squids emit a burst of light that startles an approaching predator; others give off a continuous glow. Ocean predators may have difficulty seeing their prey against the ocean surface.

Answers to Self-Assessment

Caption Question

Figure 3 The tentacles of the octopus are covered with suckers.

A Snail's Pace

In this lab, you will use the skill of measuring to investigate how fast a snail moves in different water temperatures.

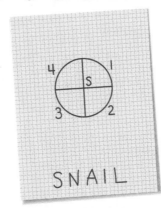

Problem

How do changes in environmental temperature affect the activity level of a snail?

Materials

freshwater snail	thermometer	ruler
plastic petri dish	graph paper	timer

spring water at three temperatures:
cool (9–13°C); medium (18–22°C);
warm (27–31°C)

Procedure

1. Create a data table for recording the water temperatures and the distance the snail travels at each temperature.
2. On one sheet of graph paper labeled *Snail*, trace a circle using the base of an empty petri dish. Divide and label the circle as shown in the illustration. On a second sheet of graph paper labeled *Data*, draw three more circles like the one in the illustration.
3. Place the petri dish over the circle on the Snail page, fill it with cool water, and record the water temperature. Then place the snail in the water just above the "S" in the circle. Be sure to handle the snail gently.
4. For five minutes, observe the snail. Record its movements by drawing a line that shows its path in the first circle on the Data page.
5. Find the distance the snail moved by measuring the line you drew. You may need to measure all the parts of the line and add them together. Record the distance in your data table.
6. Repeat Steps 3 through 5, first with medium-temperature water and then with warm water. Record the snail's paths in the second circle and third circle on the Data page.
7. Return the snail to your teacher when you are done. Wash your hands thoroughly.
8. For each temperature, compute the class average for distance traveled.

Analyze and Conclude

1. Make a bar graph showing the class average for each temperature. How does a snail's activity level change as temperature increases?
2. Do you think the pattern you found would continue at higher temperatures? Explain.
3. **Think About It** What factors in this lab were difficult to measure? How could you change the procedure to obtain more accurate measurements? Explain.

Design an Experiment

Design an experiment to measure the rate at which a snail moves in an aquarium with gravel on the bottom. Obtain your teacher's permission before trying your experiment.

Safety

Students should be very careful with the thermometers. Make sure they do not let them roll off a table top.
◆ Remind students to treat snails gently and disturb them as little as possible.
◆ Prepare the cool, medium, and warm water yourself.

Program Resources

Science Explorer Series *Motion, Forces, and Energy,* Chapter 2, discusses Newton's third law and cephalopod propulsion.
◆ **Teaching Resources** Skills Lab, blackline masters, pp. 65-66
◆ **Inquiry Skills Activity Book** Provides teaching and review of all inquiry skills

---

A Snail's Pace

Preparing for Inquiry

Key Concept The activity of some animals can be affected by the temperature of their environment.
Skills Objective Students will be able to
◆ measure activity using distance traveled in a specific time.
Time 45 minutes
Advance Planning Place the snails in a small aquarium of pond water. Aerate the aquarium if the snails will be kept more than a few days. For the lab, use the most active snails. For safety reasons, prepare the cool, medium, and warm water yourself.

Guiding Inquiry

Invitation Ask students to give examples of animals that seem to be more active on warm days (such as mosquitoes). Contrast these to animals whose activities seem less dependent on temperature (such as birds).

Introducing the Procedure
Remind students not to leave snails out of the water for very long.

Troubleshooting the Experiment
Do not allow students to tap the petri dish to get the snail moving.

Expected Outcome
Snails usually move more slowly in colder water than in warmer water.

Analyze and Conclude
1. Answers will vary. Plot temperature on *x*-axis and distance moved on *y*-axis.
2. Snails move more in warmer water, but hot water will kill them.
3. Sample: Distance; videotape snails and measure distance on the screen.

Extending Inquiry

Design an Experiment Sample: Tape rulers to the side and rear of the aquarium. Look from front of aquarium and record snail's position using rear ruler; look from side and record position using side ruler.

Objectives

After completing this lesson, students will be able to
◆ describe the major characteristics of arthropods;
◆ identify the main groups of arthropods.

Key Terms arthropod, exoskeleton, chitin, molting, antenna, crustacean, arachnid, abdomen

1 Engage/Explore

Activating Prior Knowledge

Ask students whether they have ever seen spiders, scorpions, insects, crabs, crayfish, or lobsters. Ask volunteers to describe these animals. Use leading questions to prompt students to mention the external shells and jointed limbs of these animals. Tell students that the features they described are characteristics of arthropods, which they will learn about in this section.

·········· DISCOVER ·········

Skills Focus inferring
Materials *sheets of heavy cardboard, about 30 × 45 cm; tape*
Time 15 minutes
Tips Use cardboard that is flexible enough to roll into a tube and tape that is strong enough to stay attached when students attempt to bend their elbows. Students whose partners already have an arm wrapped in cardboard will need assistance when putting on their own tubes.
Expected Outcome Students will find that restricting their joints makes it impossible for them to bend their elbows.
Think It Over Joints in skeletons allow movement.

DISCOVER ············

Will It Bend and Move?

1. Have a partner roll a piece of cardboard around your arm to form a tube that covers your elbow. Your partner should put three pieces of tape around the tube to hold it closed—one at each end and one in the middle.

2. With the tube in place, try to write your name on a piece of paper. Then try to scratch your head.

3. Keep the tube on your arm for 10 minutes. Observe how the tube affects your ability to do things.

Think It Over
Inferring Insects and many other animals have rigid skeletons on the outside of their bodies. Why do their skeletons need joints?

GUIDE FOR READING

◆ What are the major characteristics of arthropods?

◆ What are the main groups of arthropods?

Reading Tip Before you read, rewrite the headings in this section as questions. Answer the questions as you read.

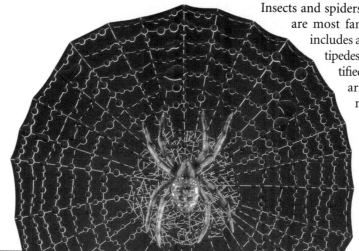

On a moonless night at the edge of a wooded area, a moth flits from flower to flower, drinking nectar. Nearby, a hungry spider waits in its web that stretches, nearly invisible, between bushes. Suddenly, the moth gets caught by the spider web. The sticky threads of the web trap one of the moth's wings. As the trapped moth struggles to free itself, the spider rushes toward it. At the last second, the moth gives a strong flap, breaks free, and flutters away—safe! Next time, the moth may not be so lucky.

The hungry spider and lucky moth are both arthropods. Insects and spiders are probably the arthropods you are most familiar with, but the phylum also includes animals such as crabs, lobsters, centipedes, and scorpions. Scientists have identified about 875,000 different species of arthropods, and there are probably many more that have not yet been discovered. Earth has more species of arthropods than of all other animals combined.

◀ Spider awaiting prey

READING STRATEGIES

Reading Tip Pair students after they have read the sections. Have them try to answer each other's questions without referring to the section. Then, have students compare answers and check them with the text.

Study and Comprehension Invite students to make up a mnemonic to help them remember the five main groups of

arthropods—crustaceans, arachnids, centipedes, millipedes, and insects. (*Sample: Crazy acrobats cause many injuries.*)

Vocabulary Point out that both *pod* in arthropod and *pede* in centipede come from roots meaning "foot." *Podos* is a Greek root, *ped* is Latin. Challenge students to think of more words containing these roots. (*Sample: tripod, pedal, pedestal*)

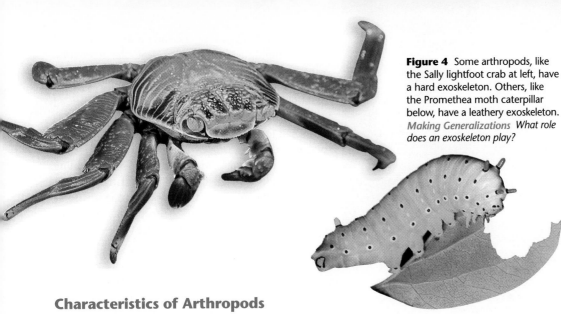

Figure 4 Some arthropods, like the Sally lightfoot crab at left, have a hard exoskeleton. Others, like the Promethea moth caterpillar below, have a leathery exoskeleton. *Making Generalizations What role does an exoskeleton play?*

Characteristics of Arthropods

Members of the **arthropod** phylum (phylum Arthropoda) share certain important characteristics. **An arthropod is an invertebrate that has an external skeleton, a segmented body, and jointed attachments called appendages.** Wings, mouthparts, and legs are all appendages. Jointed legs are such a distinctive characteristic that the arthropod phylum is named for it. *Arthros* means "joint" in Greek, and *podos* means "foot" or "leg."

Arthropods have additional characteristics in common, too. Arthropods have open circulatory systems—the blood leaves the blood vessels and bathes the internal organs. Most arthropods reproduce sexually. Unlike an earthworm, which has both male and female organs in its body, most arthropods are either male or female. Most arthropods have internal fertilization—sperm and egg unite inside the body of the female. This contrasts to external fertilization, which takes place outside an animal's body.

A Skeleton on the Outside If you were an arthropod, you would be completely covered by a waterproof shell. This waxy **exoskeleton,** or outer skeleton, protects the animal and helps prevent evaporation of water. Water animals are surrounded by water, but land animals need a way to keep from drying out. Arthropods were the first animals to move out of water and onto land, and their exoskeletons probably enabled them to do this. **INTEGRATING CHEMISTRY** Arthropod exoskeletons are made of a material called **chitin** (KY tin). Chitin is made of long molecules that are built from many smaller building blocks, like links in a chain. Long-chain molecules like chitin are called polymers. Cotton fibers and rubber are polymers, too. For any

---

2 Facilitate

Characteristics of Arthropods

Including All Students

Materials *fresh or frozen whole crab leg; whole shrimp with head from supermarket or seafood store*
Time 20 minutes
Tips Some students may need extra help to identify the features of an arthropod's exoskeleton. Allow them to handle and examine the two specimens. Help students see that both exoskeletons are jointed and made of chitin. Make sure students wash their hands after handling the specimens.
Extend Have students compare the exoskeleton of the shrimp to that of the crab. Ask students: **Which of the two animals has the more flexible exoskeleton?** *(shrimp)* **The stronger exoskeleton?** *(crab)* **learning modality: kinesthetic**

Integrating Chemistry

Materials *binocular microscope, fingernail clipper*
Time 10 minutes

Explain to students that humans produce a polymer similar to chitin called *keratin.* Tell them hair and fingernails are made of keratin. Have students examine a strand of hair and a fingernail clipping under the microscope. Ask them to describe the material that makes up the hair and fingernail nail. *(Strong and flexible)*
learning modality: visual

Answers to Self-Assessment

Caption Question

Figure 4 An exoskeleton prevents water loss and provides protection.

Ongoing Assessment

Writing Have students describe three characteristics of arthropods. *(Invertebrates; have jointed appendages, exoskeletons, segmented bodies, open circulatory systems; reproduce sexually.)*

Characteristics of Arthropods, continued

Building Inquiry Skills: Modeling

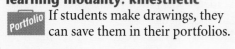

To reinforce the physical characteristics of arthropods, challenge students to invent their own arthropods and make models of them. Students may choose to build three-dimensional models out of clay, pipe cleaners, or other suitable materials. They may also draw detailed sketches. Designs must include the following characteristics: exoskeleton, segmented body, and jointed legs. Many will also include antennae. Ask students to use Figure 6 to classify their arthropods as insects, arachnids, or crustaceans.
learning modality: kinesthetic

Portfolio If students make drawings, they can save them in their portfolios.

Including All Students

To help students remember the meaning of *exoskeleton*, point out that *external* and *exoskeleton* both begin with *ex*. Explain that the prefixes *ex-* and *exo-* may mean "outside." Have students think of other words that begin with these prefixes. *(exit, expedition)* **limited English proficiency**

Using the Visuals: Figure 6

Divide the class into groups. Assign each group two of the arthropod groups in the table—for example, crustaceans and insects. Students in each group should then work together to create Venn diagrams comparing and contrasting the two arthropod groups. In addition to using the information in Figure 6, encourage students to look ahead to the parts of this section that describe those groups. **cooperative learning**

Figure 5 This rainforest cicada has just molted. You can see its old exoskeleton still hanging on the leaf just below it. *Applying Concepts Why must arthropods molt?*

Figure 6 Arthropod groups differ in the numbers of body sections, legs, and antennae, and in where they are found. *Interpreting Charts Which group of arthropods has no antennae?*

Insect praying mantis

Crustacean fiddler crab

Arachnid tarantula

polymer, the kinds, numbers, and the arrangement of its small building blocks determine its characteristics. Chitin's building blocks make it tough and flexible.

As an arthropod grows larger, its exoskeleton cannot expand. The growing arthropod is trapped within its exoskeleton, like a knight in armor that is too small for him. Arthropods solve this problem by occasionally shedding their exoskeletons and growing new ones that are larger. The process of shedding an outgrown exoskeleton is called **molting**. After an arthropod has molted, its new skeleton is soft for a time. During that time, the arthropod has less protection from danger than it does after its new skeleton has hardened.

Segmented Bodies Arthropods' bodies are segmented, something like an earthworm's. The segmented body plan is easiest to see in centipedes and millipedes, which have bodies made up of many identical-looking segments. You can also see segments on the tails of shrimp and lobsters.

In some groups of arthropods, several body segments become joined into distinct sections, with each section specialized to perform specific functions. Figure 6 shows the number of body sections and other physical characteristics that are typical of the three largest groups of arthropods.

Appendages Just as your fingers are appendages attached to your palms, many arthropods have jointed appendages attached to their bodies. The joints in the appendages give the animal flexibility and enable it to move. If you did the Discover activity, you saw how important joints are for allowing movement.

Arthropod appendages tend to be highly specialized tools. For example, the appendages attached to the head of a crayfish include mouthparts that it uses for crushing food. A crayfish also has two pairs of antennae. An

Comparisons of the Largest Arthropod Groups

Characteristic	Crustaceans	Arachnids	Insects
Number of body sections	2 or 3	2	3
Number of legs	5 or more pairs	4 pairs	3 pairs
Number of antennae	2 pairs	none	1 pair
Where found?	in water or damp places	mostly on land	mostly on land

56 ◆ B

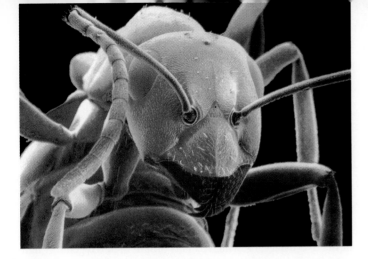

Figure 7 This wood ant's appendages include its antennae, legs, and mouthparts. It uses its mouthparts first to saw its food into small pieces and then to chew it.

antenna (plural *antennae*) is an appendage on the head that contains sense organs. A crayfish's antennae have organs for smelling, tasting, touching, and keeping balance. Legs are also appendages. Most of the crayfish's legs are adapted for walking, but the crayfish uses its first pair of legs, which have claws, for catching prey and defending against predators. The wings that most insects have are also appendages.

☑ *Checkpoint* **How do exoskeletons enable many arthropods to live on land?**

Origin of Arthropods

Since segmented worms and arthropods both have segmented bodies with appendages attached to some segments, many biologists have inferred that these two groups of animals have a common ancestor. However, DNA evidence indicates that arthropods and segmented worms may not be as closely related as previously thought.

Arthropods have been on Earth for about 540 million years. Like most other animal groups, arthropods first arose in the oceans. Today, however, they live almost everywhere. Some kinds of arthropods, like crayfish and crabs, are adapted to live in fresh or salt water. Very few insects, in contrast, live in salt water, but they live just about everywhere else.

Crustaceans

The major groups of arthropods are crustaceans, arachnids, centipedes, millipedes, and insects. If you've ever eaten shrimp cocktail or crab cakes, you've dined on crustaceans. A **crustacean** is an arthropod that has two or three body sections and usually

Program Resources

Science Explorer Series *Cells and Heredity,* Chapter 5, explores how long certain species have been on Earth.

Answers to Self-Assessment

Caption Questions

Figure 5 Because their exoskeletons cannot expand when the animals grow, arthropods must molt their outgrown exoskeletons.

Figure 6 Arachnids

☑ *Checkpoint*

An exoskeleton keeps water inside the arthropod, preventing it from drying out.

Including All Students

Some students may need extra help to understand how arthropod antennae work. Explain that antennae on arthropods are similar to the antennae on a radio or television set in that they detect information in the surroundings and transfer it to a central receiving point. Arthropod antennae detect the vibration of sound or movement. In addition, certain places on the antennae can sense chemicals in the air or water. The antennae help the arthropod "smell" and "taste" things in its environment. Antennae can also be sensitive to touch and therefore help the organism move around in its environment. **learning modality: logical/mathematical**

Origin of Arthropods

Building Inquiry Skills: Inferring

Tell students that the oldest rocks scientists have found which contain fossils of arthropods are about 540 million years old. Ask students to infer what characteristic the first arthropods had that enabled them to become fossils. *(A hard exoskeleton)* **learning modality: verbal**

Ongoing Assessment

Writing Ask students to write down the following arthropod characteristics: exoskeleton, segmented bodies, appendages. Have them write a sentence describing what they have learned about each characteristic. *(Sample answers: An exoskeleton is a hard covering made of chitin. An arthropod's body has segments that form body sections specialized to do different things. An arthropod's appendages are jointed.)*

Crustaceans

Building Inquiry Skills: Observing

Materials *crustacean; paper towels*

Time 15 minutes

Tips Allow students to observe the parts of a crustacean by examining a specimen. Have students place their crustaceans on paper towels. Sketch and label the body, tail, antennae, and legs. Ask: **What parts of the body help the crustacean protect itself?** *(Hard exoskeleton, claws or pincers)* Be sure students wash their hands after they have handled the crustacean.

learning modality: kinesthetic

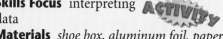

Skills Focus interpreting data

Materials *shoe box, aluminum foil, paper towels, masking tape, live pill bugs, water*

Time 20 minutes

Tips Group students. During the first trial, have them design their data table. During the second and third trials, have students reread the text information on crustaceans.

Interpreting Data The pill bugs will prefer the moist environment.

Extend Challenge students to design and carry out an experiment which tests whether pill bugs prefer a warm or cool environment. Check students' plans to ensure that they are logical and safe.

learning modality: logical/ mathematical

Spiders and Their Relatives

Addressing Naive Conceptions

Clear up some misconceptions about spiders by asking students to decide if the following statements are true or false.

◆ **All spiders catch their prey in webs.** *(False. Some spiders use webs, but others chase or trap their prey.)*
◆ **Spiders' bites are extremely dangerous to people.** *(False. Spiders rarely bite people, and most spider bites are uncomfortable but not dangerous.)*

learning modality: verbal

Pill Bugs—Wet or Dry?

Pill bugs are crustaceans that roll up in a ball when they're disturbed. In this activity, you will find out whether they prefer a moist or dry environment.

1. Line a shoe box with aluminum foil. Tape down two paper towels side by side in the box. Tape a strip of masking tape between the two towels. Carefully moisten one of the paper towels. Keep the other towel dry.

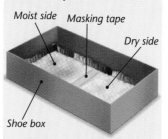

Moist side Masking tape

Dry side

Shoe box

2. Put ten pill bugs on the masking tape. Then put a lid on the box.

3. After 5 minutes, lift the lid and quickly count the pill bugs on the dry towel, the moist towel, and the masking tape. Record your results in a data table.

4. Repeat Steps 2 and 3 two more times. Then average the results of the three trials. Wash your hands after handling the pill bugs.

Interpreting Data Do pill bugs prefer a moist or dry environment?

---

has three pairs of appendages for chewing. In addition, crustaceans always have five or more pairs of legs; each body segment has a pair of legs or modified legs attached to it. Crustaceans are the only arthropods that have two pairs of antennae. *Exploring a Crayfish* shows a typical crustacean.

Life Cycle Most crustaceans, such as crabs, barnacles, and shrimp, begin their lives as microscopic, swimming larvae. The bodies of these larvae do not resemble those of adults. Crustacean larvae develop into adults by **metamorphosis** (met uh MAWR fuh sis), a process in which an animal's body undergoes dramatic changes in form during its life cycle.

Environments Nearly every kind of watery environment is home to crustaceans, which usually obtain their oxygen through gills. Crustaceans thrive in freshwater lakes and rivers, and even in puddles that last a long time. You can find crustaceans in the deepest parts of oceans, floating in ocean currents, and crawling along coastlines. A few crustaceans live in damp areas on land, too. Some huge crabs even live in the tops of palm trees!

Feeding Crustaceans obtain food in many ways. Many eat dead plants and animals. Others are predators, eating animals they have killed. The pistol shrimp is a predator with an appendage that moves with such force that it stuns its prey. Krill, which are shrimplike crustaceans found in huge swarms in cold ocean waters, are herbivores that eat plantlike microorganisms. In turn, krill are eaten by predators such as fishes, penguins, seals, sea birds, and even by great blue whales, the world's largest animals.

☑ *Checkpoint* *An animal has an exoskeleton, two body sections, and eight legs. Is it a crustacean? Why or why not?*

Spiders and Their Relatives

Spiders, mites, and ticks are the arachnids that people most often encounter. To qualify as an **arachnid** (uh RAK nid), an arthropod must have only two body sections. The first section is a combined head and chest. The hind section, called the **abdomen**, contains the arachnid's reproductive organs and part of its digestive tract. Arachnids have eight legs, but no antennae. They breathe with organs called book lungs or with a network of tiny tubes that lead to openings on the exoskeleton.

Spiders Spiders are the most familiar, most feared, and most fascinating kind of arachnid. All spiders are predators, and most of them eat insects. Some spiders, such as tarantulas and wolf spiders, run down their prey, while others, such as golden garden spiders, spin webs and wait for their prey to become entangled.

Background

Facts and Figures Horseshoe crabs are not crabs or crustaceans. They are actually more closely related to arachnids because they have feeding pincers like scorpions and lack antennae. Because its basic body design has remained almost unchanged for millions of years, the horseshoe crab is often called a "living fossil." Their fossil relatives are recognized as far back as 505 million years ago, and forms similar to modern-day horseshoe crabs as far back as 208 million years ago.

Horseshoe crabs have been used in eye research because of their large eyes and large optic nerve (the nerve that sends signals from the eye to the brain). In addition, a substance in the crabs' blood, which they use to kill invading bacteria, is now used to test drugs to make sure they are bacteria-free before they are given to people.

EXPLORING *a Crayfish*

Crayfish are crustaceans that live in ponds, streams, or rivers, where they hide beneath rocks and burrow in the mud. Some build a tall mud "chimney" around their burrow entrance. Crayfish will eat nearly any animal or plant, dead or alive, including other crayfish.

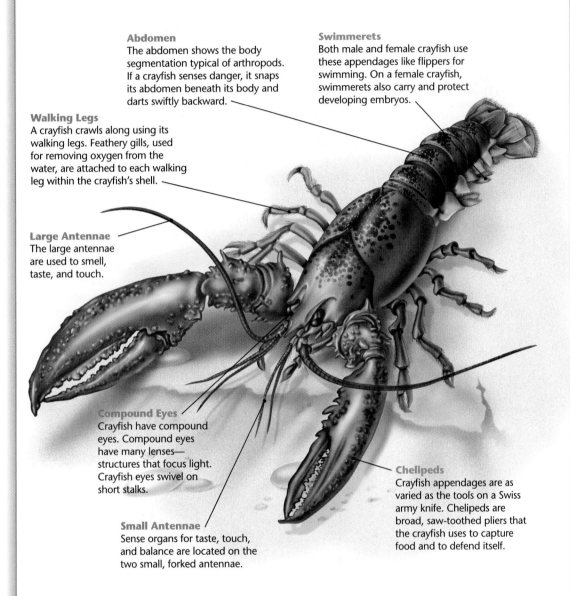

Abdomen
The abdomen shows the body segmentation typical of arthropods. If a crayfish senses danger, it snaps its abdomen beneath its body and darts swiftly backward.

Swimmerets
Both male and female crayfish use these appendages like flippers for swimming. On a female crayfish, swimmerets also carry and protect developing embryos.

Walking Legs
A crayfish crawls along using its walking legs. Feathery gills, used for removing oxygen from the water, are attached to each walking leg within the crayfish's shell.

Large Antennae
The large antennae are used to smell, taste, and touch.

Compound Eyes
Crayfish have compound eyes. Compound eyes have many lenses—structures that focus light. Crayfish eyes swivel on short stalks.

Small Antennae
Sense organs for taste, touch, and balance are located on the two small, forked antennae.

Chelipeds
Crayfish appendages are as varied as the tools on a Swiss army knife. Chelipeds are broad, saw-toothed pliers that the crayfish uses to capture food and to defend itself.

Begin by asking students to observe the segmentation in the crayfish's abdomen. Make certain that students distinguish between the locations and functions of the small and large antennae. Ask: **How are the chelipeds different from the walking legs?** (*The chelipeds are much larger and have pincers.*)

Extend After students study the visual essay, have them write paragraphs describing a typical day in the life of a crayfish. In their paragraphs, they should infer how a crayfish uses the body parts listed in the visual essay. Paragraphs should also include where crayfish live and hide, and what they eat. (*Students' paragraphs might include the following: large antennae, walking legs, swimmerets—to move around; small antennae, compound eyes—to find food; chelipeds—to eat; chelipeds, tail, swimmerets, walking legs—to escape predators. Crayfish live in ponds, streams, or rivers; hide beneath rocks and burrow in the mud. They eat nearly any animal or plant.*)

Students can save their paragraphs in their portfolios. **learning modality: logical/mathematical**

Media and Technology

 Transparencies "Exploring a Crayfish," Transparency 6

 Exploring Life Science Videodisc Unit 3, Side 2, "Spineless"

Chapter 2

Answers to Self-Assessment

☑ *Checkpoint*

The animal is not a crustacean. Although crustaceans have exoskeletons and sometimes have only two body sections, they always have at least ten legs. The animal described in the question is an arachnid.

Ongoing Assessment

Oral Presentation Provide each student with a photograph or drawing of an unfamiliar crustacean or arachnid. Ask students to decide to which group their animals belong, and to label all major appendages. Then randomly choose students to present their animals to the class and explain why they classified them as crustaceans or arachnids.

B ◆ 59

Spiders and Their Relatives, continued

Figure 8 Arachnids are arthropods with two body sections, eight legs, and no antennae. **A.** A tick is a parasite that attaches itself to its prey to feed upon its blood. **B.** A scorpion is a carnivore that injects venom from a stinger at the end of its abdomen. **C.** The Honduran tarantula, a spider, uses its fangs to inject venom into a racer snake.

Spiders have hollow fangs, which are organs that inject venom into prey. Spider venom turns the tissues of the prey into mush. Later the spider uses its fangs like drinking straws, sucking in the mush. In spite of what some people might think, spiders rarely bite people. When they do, most spider bites are painful but not life-threatening. However, the bites of the brown recluse or the black widow may require hospital care.

Mites If chiggers have ever given you an itchy rash, you've had an unpleasant encounter with tiny arachnids called mites. Chiggers and many other mites are parasites. Ear mites, for example, give dogs and cats itchy ears. Mites are everywhere. Even the cleanest houses have microscopic dust mites. If you are allergic to dust, you may actually be allergic to the exoskeletons of dust mites. Mites also live in fresh water and in the ocean.

Ticks Ticks are parasites that live on the outside of a host animal's body. Nearly every kind of land animal has a species of tick that sucks its blood. Some ticks that attack humans can carry diseases. Lyme disease, for example, is spread by the bite of an infected deer tick.

Scorpions Scorpions, which live mainly in hot climates, are also arachnids. Usually active at night, scorpions hide in cool places during the day—under rocks and logs, or in holes in the ground, for example.

At the end of its abdomen, a scorpion has a spinelike stinger. The scorpion uses the stinger to inject venom into its prey, which is usually a spider or insect. Sometimes scorpions sting people. These stings, while painful, usually do not cause serious harm.

☑ *Checkpoint* *How do spiders obtain and digest their food?*

Centipedes and Millipedes

Centipedes and millipedes have highly segmented bodies, as you can see in Figure 9. Centipedes have one pair of legs attached to each segment, and some centipedes have over 100 segments. In fact, the word *centipede* means "hundred feet." Centipedes are swift predators with sharp jaws. They inject venom into the smaller animals that they catch for food.

Millipedes, which may have more than 80 segments, have two pairs of legs on each segment—more legs than any other arthropod. Though *millipede* means "thousand feet," they don't have quite that many legs. Most millipedes are herbivores that graze on partly decayed leaves. When they are disturbed, millipedes can curl up into an armored ball and squirt an awful-smelling liquid at a potential predator.

Figure 9 Centipedes and millipedes are arthropods with many body segments. Centipedes, left, are carnivores, while millipedes, right, are herbivores. *Comparing and Contrasting How can you tell the difference between these two organisms?*

Section 2 Review

1. Identify four characteristics that all arthropods share.
2. List the major groups of arthropods.
3. What characteristic distinguishes crustaceans from all other arthropods?
4. What are the main characteristics of arachnids?
5. **Thinking Critically** **Applying Concepts** Some seafood restaurants serve a dish called soft-shelled crab. What do you think happened to the crab just before it was caught? Why is that process important?

Check Your Progress
CHAPTER PROJECT 2
Construct a data table in your notebook. Each day, observe both groups of mealworms. Record how many mealworms in each group are still wormlike larvae, how many have formed motionless pupae, and how many, if any, have become adult insects. (*Hint:* You will learn about the stages of insect metamorphosis in Section 3. You may find it helpful to refer to *Exploring Insect Metamorphosis* on page 65 as you fill in your data table.)

Answers to Self-Assessment

Caption Question

Figure 9 The centipede has one pair of legs on each segment; the millipede has two.

✓ *Checkpoint*

Spiders inject venom into their prey by using hollow fangs. The venom liquefies the tissues of the prey, which are then sucked up by the spider.

Centipedes and Millipedes

Using the Visuals: Figure 9

To help students compare **ACTIVITY** and contrast the millipede and centipede, have them draw each organism. Instruct them to label characteristics specific to centipedes and to millipedes. (*Centipedes—one pair of legs on each segment, sharp jaws; on millipedes—two pairs of legs on each segment.*)

Portfolio Students can save their drawings in their portfolios.
learning modality: visual

3 Assess

Section 2 Review Answers

1. External skeleton, segmented bodies, jointed appendages, and an open circulatory system.
2. Crustaceans, arachnids, insects, centipedes, millipedes
3. Two pairs of antennae
4. Two body sections, eight legs, no antennae
5. It had just molted. Molting is important because it allows arthropods to shed exoskeletons they have outgrown.

Check Your Progress
CHAPTER PROJECT 2
Ensure each mealworm container has food and a source of moisture. Ask students to record their observations along with counts of the larvae, pupae, and adults.

Performance Assessment

Writing Have students describe one distinguishing characteristic of each of the following groups: crustaceans, arachnids, centipedes, and millipedes. (*Crustaceans—two pairs of antennae; arachnids—two body sections; centipedes—two pair of legs per body segment; millipedes—one pair of legs per body segment*)

Objectives

After completing this lesson, students will be able to

◆ describe the characteristics of insects;
◆ describe the overall impact of insects on humans;
◆ state and explain the life stages of insects.

Key Terms insect, thorax, complete metamorphosis, pupa, gradual metamorphosis, nymph, camouflage

1 Engage/Explore

Activating Prior Knowledge

Ask students to name as many insects as they can. *(Samples: ant, mosquito, fly, grasshopper, butterfly, bee)* Ask: **Can you think of something all these animals have in common?** *(Sample: antennae)* Students may not be able to think of a shared characteristic. Tell them that they will learn the characteristics insects share in this section.

•••••••• **DISCOVER** ••••••••

Skills Focus observing
Materials *insect collection, hand lenses*
Time 20 minutes
Tips Facilitate careful observation of the specimens by asking students to describe one or two insects that they find particularly interesting. Ask students to point out several characteristics that the insects have in common.
Expected Outcome Students should observe that all the insects have the same number of legs (six) and body sections (three).
Think It Over Encourage students to compare insects that are very different. Consider grouping similar insects and asking students to choose insects from different groups to compare. *(Answers may vary. Sample: A grasshopper and a dragonfly both have six jointed legs and two pairs of wings. The grasshopper has large hind legs that it uses to jump. The dragonfly has large flat wings that it uses to fly.)*

DISCOVER •••••••••••••••••••••••••••••••••••••• **ACTIVITY**

What Kinds of Appendages Do Insects Have?

1. Your teacher will give you a collection of insects. Examine the insects carefully.

2. Note the physical characteristics of each insect's body covering.

3. Count the legs, wings, body sections, and antennae on each insect.

4. Carefully observe the appendages—antennae, mouthparts, wings, and legs. Contrast the appendages on different insects. Then return the insects to your teacher and wash your hands.

Think It Over
Observing Compare the legs and wings of two different species of insect. What kind of movements is each insect adapted to perform?

GUIDE FOR READING

◆ What are the characteristics of insects?

◆ What is the overall impact of insects on humans?

Reading Tip As you read, make an outline of this section using the headings as the main topics.

Monarch butterflies, with their beautiful orange and black wings, may seem delicate, but they are champion travelers. Every autumn, about 100 million of these butterflies fly south from southeastern Canada and the eastern United States, heading for the mountains of central Mexico. Some monarch butterflies fly thousands of kilometers before they reach their destination.

The monarch butterflies who make this long journey have never been to Mexico before. But somehow they find their way to the same trees where their ancestors, now dead, spent the previous winter. No one is certain how they are able to do this.

In the spring, the butterflies fly northward. After flying a few hundred miles, they stop, mate, lay eggs, and die. But their children—and later, their grandchildren and great-grandchildren—continue the northward journey. Eventually, monarch butterflies reach the area their ancestors left the previous fall.

Wintering monarch butterflies ▼

READING STRATEGIES

Reading Tip Remind students that the major headings in the text should be the major topics in the outline. If students have trouble recognizing subtopics, suggest that they write a subhead for each paragraph. These can be the subtopics in their outlines. For example:

I. The Insect Body
   A. Body regions and appendages
      1. Three body regions
      2. Six legs
      3. One pair of antennae
      4. One or two pairs of wings
   B. Compound and simple eyes
   C. Oxygen tubes

Study and Comprehension As students complete the chapter, have them create an illustration to accompany each subheading. Illustrations should contain relevant information covered in the paragraphs.

The Insect Body

The monarch butterfly is an **insect**, as is a dragonfly, cockroach, or bee. You can identify insects, like other arthropods, by counting their body sections and legs. **Insects are arthropods with three body sections, six legs, one pair of antennae, and usually one or two pairs of wings.** The three body regions are the head, thorax, and abdomen. An insect's **thorax,** or mid-section, is the section to which wings and legs are attached. Sense organs, such as the eyes and antennae, are located on an insect's head. The abdomen contains many of the insect's internal organs. You can see all three body sections on the grasshopper in Figure 11.

Like most crustaceans, insects usually have two large compound eyes, which contain many lenses. Compound eyes are especially keen at seeing movement. Most insects also have small simple eyes, which can distinguish between light and darkness.

Insects obtain oxygen through a system of tubes. These tubes lead to openings on the insect's exoskeleton. Air, which contains oxygen, enters the insect's body through these tubes and travels directly to the insect's body cells.

☑ *Checkpoint* *How are an insect's compound eyes different from its simple eyes?*

From Egg to Adult

Insects begin life as tiny, hard-shelled, fertilized eggs. After they hatch, insects begin a process of metamorphosis that eventually produces an adult insect. Each insect species undergoes one of two different types of metamorphosis.

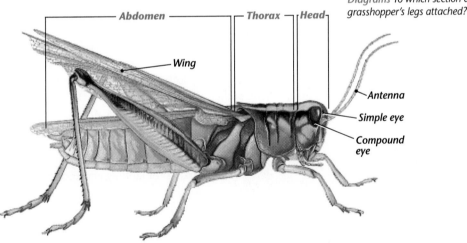

Figure 10 Most insects, like this black fly, have compound eyes with many lenses. Because compound eyes are very effective at seeing movement, insects can quickly escape from potential predators.

Figure 11 A grasshopper's body, like that of every insect, consists of three sections. *Interpreting Diagrams To which section are the grasshopper's legs attached?*

Abdomen — Thorax — Head

Wing

Antenna

Simple eye

Compound eye

Program Resources

◆ **Teaching Resources** 2-3 Lesson Plan, p. 53; 2-3 Section Summary, p. 54

Media and Technology

 Audiotapes English-Spanish Summary 2-3

 Transparencies "Grasshopper Anatomy," Transparency 7

Answers to Self-Assessment

Caption Question

Figure 11 The grasshopper's legs are attached to its thorax.

☑ *Checkpoint*

An insect's compound eyes are made up of many individual lenses and are adapted for sensing motion. Simple eyes are adapted for distinguishing between light and darkness.

---

2 *Facilitate*

The Insect Body

Building Inquiry Skills: Interpreting Diagrams

Obtain intact dead grasshoppers from a pet or bait shop. Have students review each external feature from Figure 11 and work together to identify that feature on their specimens. Students should wash hands after finishing. **cooperative learning**

Addressing Naive Conceptions

Students may think spiders are insects. Ask: **How can you identify an animal as an insect by looking at its body?** *(If it is an insect, it has three body sections.)* Show students pictures of spiders and have them try to identify the head, thorax, and abdomen. Ask: **Are these animals insects?** *(no)* **How do you know?** *(They have only two body sections.)* *(Sample: ticks, scorpions)* **learning modality: visual**

From Egg to Adult

Building Inquiry Skills: Comparing and Contrasting

Have students make Venn diagrams to compare and contrast gradual and complete metamorphosis. **learning modality: logical/mathematical**

Ongoing Assessment

Skills Check Ask students: **If you saw an animal in the woods, how would you decide whether it could be classified as an insect?** *(Accept answers which describe major characteristics of insects. Sample: If the animal had an exoskeleton, three main body parts, six jointed legs, a pair of antennae, and wings, it is probably an insect.)*

From Egg to Adult, continued

Sharpen your Skills

Graphing ACTIVITY

Approximately 760,000 species of insects have been identified so far. The table gives an approximate species count for the major groups. Use the data to construct a circle graph that shows the percentage of total insect species in each group. (See the Skills Handbook.)

Insect Groups	
Group	**Number of Species**
Ants, bees, and wasps	100,000
Beetles and weevils	300,000
Butterflies and moths	110,000
Flies and mosquitoes	100,000
Other insect groups	150,000

The two types of insect metamorphosis are shown in *Exploring Insect Metamorphosis.* The first type, which is called **complete metamorphosis**, has four dramatically different stages: egg, larva, pupa, and adult. As you learned in Chapter 1, a larva is an immature form of an animal that looks significantly different from the adult. Insect larvae, such as the caterpillars of butterflies and moths, usually look something like worms. Larvae are specialized for eating and growing. After a time, the larva goes into the second stage of complete metamorphosis and becomes a **pupa** (plural *pupae*). During the pupal stage, the insect is enclosed in a protective covering and gradually changes from a larva to an adult. A butterfly in a chrysalis and a moth in a cocoon are examples of insect pupae. When it has completed its development, an adult insect emerges from the protective pupa. Beetles, butterflies, houseflies, and ants all undergo complete metamorphosis.

In contrast, the second type of metamorphosis, called **gradual metamorphosis**, has no distinctly different larval stage—an egg hatches into a stage called a **nymph**, which often resembles the adult insect. A nymph may molt several times before becoming an adult. Grasshoppers, termites, cockroaches, and dragonflies go through gradual metamorphosis.

✓ *Checkpoint* *List the stages of complete metamorphosis.*

How Insects Feed

The rule seems to be this: If it is living, or if it once was living, some kind of insect will eat it. Everyone knows that insects eat plants and parts of plants, such as leaves and nectar. But insects also eat products that are made from plants, such as paper. The next time you open a very old book, watch for book lice. These very small insects live in old books, chewing tiny crooked tunnels through the pages.

Insects feed on animals, too. Some, like fleas and mosquitoes, feed on the blood of living animals. Others, like dung beetles, feed on animal droppings. Still others, like burying beetles, feed on the decaying bodies of dead animals.

Insect mouthparts are adapted for a highly specific way of getting food. For example, a bee has a bristly tongue that laps nectar from flowers, and a mosquito has sharp mouthparts for jabbing and sucking blood.

Figure 12 This caterpillar feeds almost continuously. As a larva, it must store all the energy it will need for its pupal stage.

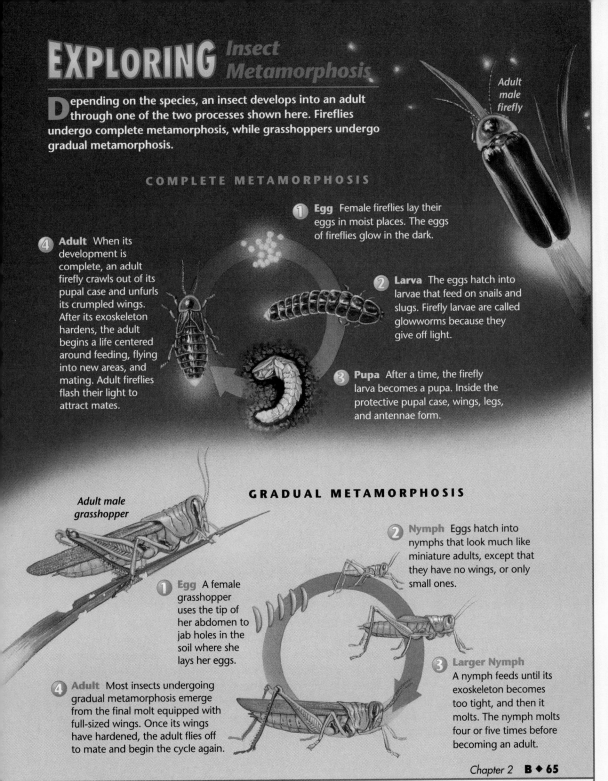

EXPLORING Insect Metamorphosis

Depending on the species, an insect develops into an adult through one of the two processes shown here. Fireflies undergo complete metamorphosis, while grasshoppers undergo gradual metamorphosis.

Adult male firefly

COMPLETE METAMORPHOSIS

1 Egg Female fireflies lay their eggs in moist places. The eggs of fireflies glow in the dark.

2 Larva The eggs hatch into larvae that feed on snails and slugs. Firefly larvae are called glowworms because they give off light.

3 Pupa After a time, the firefly larva becomes a pupa. Inside the protective pupal case, wings, legs, and antennae form.

4 Adult When its development is complete, an adult firefly crawls out of its pupal case and unfurls its crumpled wings. After its exoskeleton hardens, the adult begins a life centered around feeding, flying into new areas, and mating. Adult fireflies flash their light to attract mates.

GRADUAL METAMORPHOSIS

Adult male grasshopper

1 Egg A female grasshopper uses the tip of her abdomen to jab holes in the soil where she lays her eggs.

2 Nymph Eggs hatch into nymphs that look much like miniature adults, except that they have no wings, or only small ones.

3 Larger Nymph A nymph feeds until its exoskeleton becomes too tight, and then it molts. The nymph molts four or five times before becoming an adult.

4 Adult Most insects undergoing gradual metamorphosis emerge from the final molt equipped with full-sized wings. Once its wings have hardened, the adult flies off to mate and begin the cycle again.

Chapter 2 **B ◆ 65**

Answers to Self-Assessment

✓ Checkpoint

The stages of complete metamorphosis are egg, larva, pupa, and adult.

EXPLORING

Insect Metamorphosis

Point out that the visual essay contrasts the metamorphoses of a firefly and a grasshopper. The insects are similar in that they lay eggs. However, once the eggs hatch, the insects develop quite differently. Ask: **How is a firefly's metamorphosis different from a grasshopper's?** *(A firefly goes through four distinct stages while a grasshopper changes its form gradually.)* **When does the grasshopper acquire wings?** *(After the final molt)* **What do adults do that larvae and nymphs do not?** *(Reproduce)* **Extend** Have students who are cultivating mealworms for the chapter project describe the kind of metamorphosis the mealworm undergoes. *(Complete)* Challenge them to compare the different stages of mealworm development with the different stages of firefly development. **learning modality: visual**

Ongoing Assessment

Skills Check Have students list stages of gradual and complete metamorphosis. *(Gradual metamorphosis—egg, nymph, adult; complete metamorphosis—egg, larva, pupa, adult)*

Figure 13 The well-camouflaged thorn insect, left, and leaf insect, right, have very effective built-in defenses against predators. *Observing Why do you think the insect on the left is called a thorn insect?*

Defending Themselves

Including All Students

In this activity, students who have difficulty hearing will be able to access information about camouflage by viewing pictures and discriminating between various classes of defense. Bring to class several color pictures of interesting insects with different types of defenses. Camouflage is the most obvious. Walking sticks are great subjects. Many moths blend in with the bark of trees. Other types of pictures can be of wasp stingers or large eyelike spots on the open wings of butterflies. Wings or large jumping legs help insects avoid predators. Number the pictures, then pass them around. Each student can write a numbered list of the types of defenses employed by each insect. When students have finished making their lists, review the pictures with the entire class.
learning modality: visual

Insects and Humans

Social Studies CONNECTION

In the fall of 1347, a ship sailed from a port on the Black Sea to the European island of Sicily. That ship carried insects that helped change the course of history. The insects were fleas, and their bite passed a deadly disease known as bubonic plague, or the Black Death, on to humans.

People who caught the plague usually died quickly. The Frenchman Jean de Venette wrote, "He who was well one day was dead the next." The Black Death rapidly spread all over Europe, killing about a third of the people. Because so many died, the plague caused serious economic problems and led to great social unrest.

In Your Journal

Imagine that the year is 1380. You lived through the plague epidemic and are now 45 years old. Write about how the plague epidemic has changed your village.

Defending Themselves

Insects have many defenses against predators, including a hard exoskeleton that helps protect them. Many insects can run quickly or fly away from danger, as you know if you've ever tried to swat a fly. Some insects, such as stinkbugs, smell or taste bad to predators. Other insects, such as bees and wasps, defend themselves with painful stings.

One of the most common defenses is **camouflage,** or protective coloration, in which the insect blends with its surroundings so perfectly that it is nearly invisible to a predator. Test yourself by trying to find the camouflaged insects in Figure 13. Walking sticks, many caterpillars, and grasshoppers are just a few insects that use camouflage as a defense.

Other insects are protected by their resemblance to different animals. The spots on the wings of certain moths, for example, resemble large eyes; predators who see these spots often avoid the moths, mistaking them for much larger animals.

☑ *Checkpoint* **What are four ways in which insects protect themselves?**

Insects and Humans

For every person alive today, scientists estimate that there are at least 200 million living insects. Many of those insects have an impact on people's lives. Some species of insects do major damage to crops. In addition, insects such as flies, fleas, and mosquitoes can carry microorganisms that cause diseases in humans. For example, when they bite humans, some mosquito species can transmit the microorganism that causes malaria.

The vast majority of insects, however, are harmless or beneficial to humans. Bees make honey, and the larvae of the silkworm moth spin the fibers used to make silk cloth. Some insects prey on harmful insects, helping to reduce those insect populations. And while some insects destroy food crops, many more insects, such as butterflies and flies, enable food crops and other plants to reproduce by carrying pollen from one plant to another. If insects were to disappear from Earth, you would never get a mosquito bite. But you wouldn't have much food to eat, either.

Controlling Insect Pests

 **INTEGRATING ENVIRONMENTAL SCIENCE** People have tried to eliminate harmful insects by applying chemicals, called pesticides, to plants. However, pesticides also kill helpful insects, such as bees, and can harm other animals, including some birds. And after a time, insect populations become resistant to the pesticides—the pesticides no longer kill the insects.

Scientists are searching for other ways to deal with harmful insects. One method is the use of biological controls. Biological controls introduce natural predators or diseases into insect populations. For example, ladybug beetles can be added to fields where crops are grown. Ladybugs prey on aphids, which are insects that destroy peaches, potatoes, and other crop plants. Soil also can be treated with bacteria that are harmless to humans but cause diseases in the larvae of pest insects such as Japanese beetles. These biological controls kill only one or a few pest species. Because biological controls kill only specific pests, they are less damaging to the environment than insecticides.

Figure 14 Bees and other pollinators are among the most beneficial of all insects. As a bee drinks nectar from a flower, pollen sticks to its body. When the insect carries that pollen to the next plant it eats from, it helps that plant to reproduce.

 **Section 3 Review**

1. List the characteristics that insects share.
2. Identify two ways in which insects benefit humans.
3. Compare and contrast complete and gradual metamorphosis.
4. **Thinking Critically Inferring** Honeybees sting predators that try to attack them. Hover flies, which do not sting, resemble honeybees. How might this resemblance be an advantage to the hover fly?

Check Your Progress CHAPTER PROJECT 2

Continue observing the mealworms every day. Update the data table with your observations. As you observe the mealworms at different stages of development, make a sketch of a larva, a pupa, and an adult.

Chapter 2 **B ◆ 67**

Answers to Self-Assessment

Caption Question

Figure 13 The insect is called a thorn insect because it looks like a thorn.

☑ *Checkpoint*

Some insects flee from danger, some defend themselves with painful stings, some smell or taste bad to predators, some use camouflage to blend into their surroundings.

Controlling Insect Pests

Integrating Environmental Science

Bring a Japanese beetle trap, an aphid trap, or an apple maggot trap to class. Ask students to infer how these traps work. Many traps are designed to look like food to the insects. When the insects land on a trap, they are caught in a sticky substance, as on the aphid traps, or lured into a bag they cannot escape from, as in the Japanese beetle trap. Do not allow students to handle the traps, since they may get chemical attractants on their hands. **learning modality: visual**

 ACTIVITY

3 Assess

Section 3 Review Answers

1. Three body sections; six legs; one pair of antennae; usually wings
2. Accept any two: insects pollinate crops; make products such as silk and honey; prey on pests.
3. Complete metamorphosis—four distinct stages: egg; wormlike larva; nonmoving pupa enclosed in a case; adult. Gradual metamorphosis—the newly hatched insect, called a nymph, changes gradually as it goes through a series of molts.
4. Predators mistake the hover fly for a honeybee and avoid it, fearing to be stung.

Check Your Progress CHAPTER PROJECT 2

Verify that students' data are being collected on time and appear reasonable. Check students' sketches. Tell students they must be able to identify the stages of mealworm development from their sketches.

Performance Assessment

Drawing Have students sketch an insect and label three major characteristics that classify it as an insect. (*Three body sections, one pair of antennae, and wings*)

B ◆ 67

What's Living in the Soil?

Preparing for Inquiry

Key Concept Soil and leaf litter make up a miniature environment that contains a variety of organisms.

Skills Objectives Students will be able to

◆ observe soil, leaf litter, and the organisms they contain;

◆ classify organisms into phyla based on key distinguishing characteristics;

◆ infer the quantity and types of organisms living in the soil.

Time 15 minutes on the first day, 45 minutes on the second day

Advance Planning Try the lab in advance to ensure that there are enough organisms present. Three or four days before the lab, go to two different sites. Try to select sites that are moist but not too wet. Collect leaf litter and the first inch or so of soil in buckets. Keep the buckets covered to keep contents moist. Set up the lamp and jars, and test a soil sample from each site. If you do not obtain enough organisms, collect more material from another site.

Alternative Materials Two weeks before the lab, ask students to bring their own wide mouth jars such as mayonnaise jars. Baby food jars work well as the small inside jars.

Guiding Inquiry

Invitation Have students think about how many animals might be present in soil. Ask: **What advantage do you think living in the soil gives some animals?** *(Moist environment, decaying organic matter for food, protection from predators)* Invite students to write predictions about the number and kind of organisms they will see in a few scoops of soil.

Introducing the Procedure

◆ Tell students not to disturb the funnel once they have placed soil and leaf litter in it. If they do, soil may run into the collection jar.

What's Living in the Soil?

The soil beneath a tree, in a garden, or under a rock is home to many organisms, including a variety of arthropods. Each of these patches of soil can be thought of as a miniature environment with its own group of living residents. In this lab, you will examine one specific soil environment.

Problem

What kinds of animals live in soil and leaf litter?

Skills Focus

observing, classifying, inferring

Materials

2-liter plastic bottle
coarse steel wool
cheesecloth
gooseneck lamp
large, wide-mouthed jar
fresh sample of soil and leaf litter
large scissors
trowel
large rubber band
hand lens
small jar

Procedure

1. Select a location where your equipment can be set up and remain undisturbed for about 24 hours. At that location, place the small jar inside the center of the large jar as shown in the photograph.

2. Use scissors to cut a large plastic bottle in half. **CAUTION:** *Cut in a direction away from yourself and others.* Turn the top half of the bottle upside down to serve as a funnel.

3. Insert a small amount of coarse steel wool into the mouth of the funnel to keep the soil from falling out. Do not pack the steel wool too tightly. Leave spaces for small organisms to crawl through. Place the funnel into the large jar as shown in the photograph.

4. Using the trowel, fill the funnel with soil and surface leaf litter. When you finish handling the leaves and soil, wash your hands thoroughly.

5. Look closely to see whether the soil and litter are dry or wet. Record your observation.

6. Make a cover for your sample by placing a piece of cheesecloth over the top of the funnel. Hold the cheesecloth in place with a large rubber band. Immediately position a lamp about 15 cm above the funnel, and turn on the light. Allow this set-up to remain undisturbed for about 24 hours. **CAUTION:** *Hot light bulbs can cause burns. Do not touch the bulb.*

7. When you are ready to make your observations, turn off the lamp. Leave the funnel and jar in place while making your observations. Use a hand lens to examine each organism in the jar. **CAUTION:** *Do not touch any of the organisms.*

8. Use a data table like the one on the next page to sketch each type of organism and to record other observations. Be sure to include evidence that will help you classify the organisms. (*Hint:* Remember that some animals may be at different stages of metamorphosis.)

◆ Warn students only to observe the animals, not to handle them, since some might bite or sting.

◆ Students should find that millipedes and other small animals (to include worms) are best viewed with a hand lens.

◆ The types and numbers of soil organisms found will vary in different regions of the country. Help students familiarize themselves with the animals they might find.

Sample Data Table

Name of Animal	Sketch of Animal	Number Found	Size (mm)	Important Characteristics	Probable Phylum
Round-worm		2	2.5	no legs, moves by wriggling	Roundworms
Earth-worm		1	100	no legs, bristles on sides	Segmented Worms
Spider		1	20	4 pairs of legs, exoskeleton	Arthropods
Millipede		2	30	many legs, exoskeleton	Arthropods
Beetle		1	25	3 pairs of legs, hard outer wings	Arthropods

DATA TABLE

Sketch of Organism	Number Found	Size	Important Characteristics	Probable Phylum

9. Examine the soil and leaf litter, and record whether this material is dry or wet.
10. When you are finished, follow your teacher's directions about returning the organisms to the soil.

Analyze and Conclude

1. Describe the conditions of the soil environment at the beginning and end of the lab. What caused the change?
2. What types of animals did you collect in the small jar? What characteristics did you use to identify each type of animal? Which types of animals were the most common?
3. Why do you think the animals moved down the funnel away from the soil?
4. **Apply** Using what you have learned about arthropods and other animals, make an inference about the role that each animal you collected plays in the environment.

More to Explore

What kinds of organisms might live in other soil types—for example, soil at the edge of a pond, dry sandy soil, or commercially prepared potting soil? Propose one or more ways to answer this question.

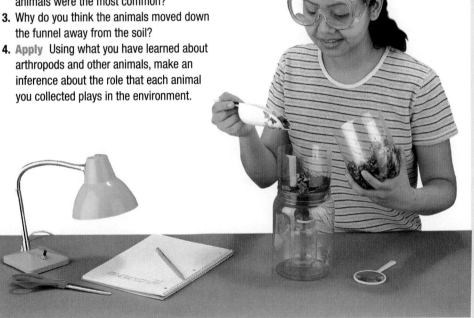

Program Resources

◆ **Teaching Resources** Real-World Lab blackline masters, pp. 67-69

Media and Technology

 Exploring Life Science Videodisc Unit 3, Side 2, "The Good Bugs"

Chapter 6

Safety

Emphasize to students that no organisms should be handled, since animals such as centipedes and ants may sting or bite. Students should always wash their hands carefully with antibacterial soap after handling soil or leaf litter. Explain that there may be pathogens in organic matter collected outdoors. To avoid danger of fire, keep the light bulb at a safe distance from the leaf litter.

Troubleshooting the Experiment

◆ If students have trouble classifying the organisms, have them list the features of worms and arthropods. Features include the presence or absence of an exoskeleton, the presence or absence of legs and wings, and the number of pairs of legs.
◆ Certain times of the year are better than others for finding a greater variety and abundance of organisms. If students find only a few organisms, tell them not to be discouraged. The scarcity of organisms may be the result of seasonal conditions.
◆ Make sure students return the leaf litter and organisms to the bucket after use.

Expected Outcome

◆ Several kinds of organisms may be present, and distinguishing among them may be difficult. Have students count the number of pairs of legs, number of body segments and, if possible, observe how the organism moves. See the table for some animals likely to be encountered.

Analyze and Conclude

1. At first the soil was damp and clumped together. At the end of the lab, it was dry and loose. The heat from the lamp dried out the soil.
2. Answers will vary. Students should refer to the animals listed in their data tables. These will most likely be worms and arthropods.
3. The animals moved away from the heat and drying soil.
4. Answers will vary. Sample: Some animals are important as decomposers (for example, worms and some insects). Some are predators (for example, pseudoscorpions and spiders).

Extending Inquiry

More to Explore To find out which types of organisms live in other types of soil, students can repeat the lab with those other soil types.

SECTION 4 The Sounds of Insects

Objectives

After completing this lesson, students will be able to
◆ explain how sound is produced;
◆ identify one function that sound serves for many insects.

1 Engage/Explore

Activating Prior Knowledge

Ask students: **What sounds do insects make?** (Sample: They buzz, chirp, and hum.) **What insects can you think of that make sounds?** (Sample: mosquitoes, crickets, bees) Explain that in this section, students learn how some insects make sounds.

········· **DISCOVER** ·········

Skills Focus inferring
Materials *rubber bands*
Time 5 minutes
Tips Make sure the rubber bands are heavy enough so that they are not likely to break. Collect the rubber bands immediately after the activity.
Expected Outcome Students should notice that vibrations cause sound.
Extend Have students pluck rubber bands stretched to different lengths. Ask: **What changes did you observe in the speed of vibration and the sound produced when you plucked a rubber band that was stretched more?** (*The speed of vibration increased, and the sound had a higher pitch.*)

Including All Students

Some students may have difficulty understanding the word *compressed*. Students can draw a group of spread-out particles and a group of compressed particles to help them learn the definitions. **limited English proficiency**

SECTION 4 The Sounds of Insects

DISCOVER ····················· ACTIVITY····

What Causes Sound?

1. Form a letter C with the index finger and thumb of one hand. Stretch a rubber band over the tips of your finger and thumb, as shown in the picture. Predict what will happen when you pluck the rubber band.

2. Pluck the rubber band so that it makes a sound. Observe the rubber band as it is making a sound. Note how the rubber band moves.

3. Repeat Step 2, but as soon as you pluck the rubber band, touch it so that it stops moving. Note what happens to the sound.

Think It Over
Inferring What is the relationship between sound and vibration?

> #### GUIDE FOR READING
>
> ◆ How is sound produced?
> ◆ What function does sound serve for many insects?
>
> *Reading Tip* As you read about the way in which sound is produced, refer to Figure 16.

Somewhere in your neighborhood, on this warm spring evening, a cricket is singing. With a flashlight in your hand, you quietly move toward the chirpy sound. When you're right on top of the sound, you turn on your light and see a black insect on the ground. Its wings are slightly raised, and are scraping against one another so fast that they look blurry. You have found a male cricket who is using sound to attract a mate. A female cricket may soon respond to his call.

How is Sound Produced?

The wings of the cricket vibrate—they move back and forth, faster than the eye can follow. When the cricket's wings stop moving, the chirping stops and all becomes quiet. Why is this so?

Figure 15 This male Borneo cricket can rub his wings together very quickly to make a chirping sound. He uses this chirping sound to call potential mates.

READING STRATEGIES

Reading Tip Help students understand that the two wedge-shaped insets in Figure 16 show waves of sound traveling out from the vibrating string. The particles are air molecules. Point out the alternating areas in which the molecules are compressed and spread out.

Study and Comprehension Before students read, ask them to write down what they know about sound. Then write what they want to know. After students read the section, ask them to write what they learned about sound. Tell them this reading strategy is called KWL, which stands for Know, Want to know, and Learned.

Figure 16 The vibration of a guitar string produces waves that consist of alternate areas in which air molecules are compressed and spread out. *Applying Concepts* *How does the sound of the guitar reach your ear?*

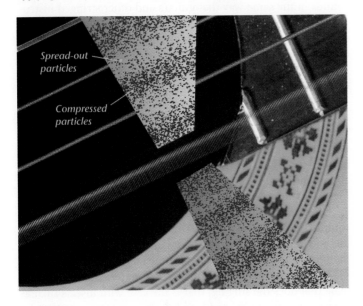

Spread-out particles

Compressed particles

All sound is produced by vibrations that create waves that move outward from the source. Figure 16 shows how the vibrations of a guitar string create sound. After you pull the string to the left and release it, the moving string bumps into air particles in its path. It shoves these particles together, compressing them, and pushes the compressed particles outward. This compressed area is followed by an area in which the air particles are spread out.

Since the guitar string keeps moving back and forth, over and over, it creates many alternating regions of compressed particles and spread-out particles. Together, the compressions and spread-out areas move outward in waves from the guitar string, as Figure 16 shows. The rapidly moving wings of a cricket produce sound in much the same way as a vibrating guitar string.

Sound waves must travel through a medium—a solid, a liquid, or a gas. The sound waves made by both the guitar strings and cricket wings travel through air, which is a gas. Sound can also travel through liquids, such as water, and through solids, such as wood. If you tap on your desk and lower your ear to the desk at the same time, you can hear sound vibrations traveling through solid material.

 Checkpoint *Through what medium does the sound of thunder travel?*

TRY THIS

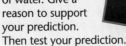

Tune In

You can use a tuning fork to see how sound is caused by vibrations.

1. Hit the prongs of a tuning fork with a pencil and listen to the sound it makes. At the same time, look closely at the fork's prongs. What do you see?

2. Lightly touch the prongs of the fork. What do you feel?

Predicting Predict what will happen when you strike the prongs of the tuning fork and then plunge the prong tips into a glass of water. Give a reason to support your prediction. Then test your prediction.

How Is Sound Produced?

Building Inquiry Skills: Observing

Point out that sound waves and water waves  are different in many ways, but they are similar in the way they move outward from a source. Have students work in pairs to investigate the outward motion of water waves. Give each pair a stone and a clear plastic bowl half full of water. Have one student drop the stone into the water and the other student observe what happens to the water. Ask: **In what direction did the waves move?** (*They moved outward from the place the pebble hit the water.*) Explain that these water waves model how sound waves move away from their source. **cooperative learning**

TRY THIS

Skills Focus predicting
Materials *tuning fork,*  *pencil, glass of water*
Time 5 minutes
Tips If you have a limited number of tuning forks, you can make this activity a demonstration or a group activity.
Predicting Because the prongs are vibrating rapidly, they will cause movement in the water. Accept reasonable predictions.
Extend Have students predict what will happen if a tuning fork is struck and then plunged into talcum powder. Allow students to test their predictions.
learning modality: kinesthetic

Program Resources

◆ **Teaching Resources** 2-4 Lesson Plan, p. 57; 2-4 Section Summary, p. 58

Media and Technology

 Exploring Physical Science Videodisc Unit 6, Side 2, "Waves All Around Us"

Chapter 1

Answers to Self-Assessment

Caption Question

Figure 16 The vibrations of the guitar string produce sound waves that travel through the air until the sound wave reaches the ear.

☑ *Checkpoint*

The sound of thunder travels through a gas—the air.

Ongoing Assessment

Oral Presentation Invite students to choose something that makes a sound and ask them to describe how the sound is produced. Students' answers should reflect that sound is caused by vibrations that create waves in a liquid, a gas, or a solid.

B ◆ 71

Communicating by Sound

Building Inquiry Skills: Inferring

Ask: **Why would most insects that produce sounds also be able to sense and interpret sounds?** *(Since many sounds are used to attract mates or warn of predators, insects must be able to hear the sounds so that they can respond.)*
learning modality: verbal

3 Assess

Section 4 Review Answers

1. The drumstick causes the drumhead to vibrate. The vibration causes air molecules to compress and then spread out. Alternate areas of compressed and spread-out molecules then travel through the air in waves.
2. Male grasshoppers and cicadas use sound to attract mates.
3. Sample: Katydids and crickets produce sound by rubbing rough areas of their wings. Cicadas vibrate a membrane on their abdomens like a drum skin.
4. The spaceship does not make a sound, since there is no medium (air) through which the sound waves can move.

Science at Home

Make certain students understand that the instructions are to create waves similar to sound waves. Moving the spring from side to side also creates waves, but this motion is different from the motion of sound waves.

Performance Assessment

Drawing Strike a tuning fork and hold it in the air. Ask students to draw a diagram illustrating how the sound reaches your ear.
 Students can save their sketches in their portfolios.

Communicating by Sound

Insects make sound in a variety of ways. Many insects make sounds in the same way that guitars and other stringed instruments do. They rub a roughened part of their body against a sharp-edged part. The rough part is something like a guitar pick, and the sharp part is like the instrument's strings. Crickets chirp and katydids make their sandpapery songs with a rough patch on each wing.

Different species of insects use different parts of their bodies to produce sound. Large black beetles rub their hind wings against rough patches on their abdomen, making a faint screeching sound. Deathwatch beetles tap on the ground with their heads. Cicadas have thin sheets of tissue called tymbals on their abdomens. Tymbals produce sound by vibrating like the covering of a drum.

Hissing cockroaches are among the few insects that make sounds by forcing air out of their bodies. This is the same method that is used by humans and other vertebrates to produce the sounds with which they communicate.

Many insects use sound to attract mates. Usually it is the male that does the singing; that is the case with insects such as crickets, grasshoppers, and katydids. However, in some species the female makes the sound. For example, female mosquitoes attract males by using their wings to make distinctive, high-pitched vibrations.

 Section 4 Review

1. Explain how beating a drum produces a sound.
2. What is communicated by the song of a grasshopper or cicada?
3. Describe two different ways in which insects produce sounds.
4. **Thinking Critically** **Applying Concepts** You are traveling in a spaceship in outer space, where there is no air. Another spaceship speeds past you. Does the spaceship make a sound? Why or why not?

Science at Home

You can use a spring toy like the one above to show your family how sound waves travel. Have a family member hold one end of the spring. Hold the other end in your hand. Gently stretch the spring so that it is fully extended and parallel to the floor. Start a wave moving by pushing on one end. Point out how the wave of compressed coils travels along the spring. Explain to your family how the wave is similar to a sound wave traveling through the air.

72 ◆ B

Background

Facts and Figures Many flying insects survive by using their ability to hear sounds. For example, bats hunt flying insects by producing high-pitched squeaks and listening for the echoes. Some moths have structures that can hear the bat squeaks. The squeaks tell moths they are being hunted, and they will dive or fly in erratic patterns to avoid being eaten.

Program Resources

◆ **Teaching Resources** 2-4 Review and Reinforce, p. 59; 2-4 Enrich, p. 60

Media and Technology

 Interactive Student Tutorial CD-ROM B-2

 Audiotapes English-Spanish Summary 2-4

SECTION 5 Echinoderms

DISCOVER **ACTIVITY**

How Do Sea Stars Hold On?

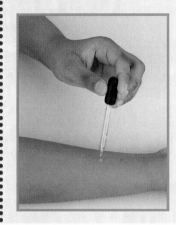

1. Sea stars use hundreds of tiny structures on their arms to cling to rocks and move across underwater surfaces. Use a plastic dropper to see how these structures work. Fill the dropper with water, and then squeeze out most of the water.

2. Squeeze one last drop of water onto the inside of your arm. Then, while squeezing the bulb, touch the tip of the dropper into the water drop. With the dropper tip against your skin, release the bulb.

3. Hold the dropper by the tube and lift it slowly, paying attention to what happens to your skin.

Think It Over
Predicting Besides moving and clinging to surfaces, what might sea stars use their suction structures for?

They look like stars, pincushions, coins, and cucumbers— are these creatures really animals? Sea stars, brittle stars, and basket stars have star-shaped bodies. Sea urchins look like living pincushions, while sand dollars are flat, round discs. Sea cucumbers, with green algae growing within their tissues, look like dill pickles—until they slowly start to crawl along the sand. All of these odd little animals belong to the same phylum.

GUIDE FOR READING

◆ What characteristics are typical of echinoderms?

Reading Tip Before you read, look at *Exploring a Sea Star* on page 75 to note some echinoderm characteristics.

The "Spiny Skinned" Animals

Biologists classify sea stars, sea urchins, sand dollars, and sea cucumbers as echinoderms (phylum Echinodermata). An **echinoderm** (ee KY noh durm) is a radially symmetrical invertebrate that lives on the ocean floor. *Echinoderm* means "spiny skinned." This name is appropriate because the skin of most of these animals is supported by a spiny internal skeleton, or **endoskeleton**, made of plates that contain calcium.

Adult echinoderms have a unique kind of radial symmetry in which body parts, usually in multiples of five, are arranged like spokes on a wheel. If you count the legs on a sea star or the body sections of a sea urchin, you will almost always get five or a multiple of five.

▼ Magnificent sea urchin

Chapter 2 **B ◆ 73**

Objectives

After completing this lesson, students will be able to
◆ describe the typical echinoderm characteristics.

Key Terms echinoderm, endoskeleton, water vascular system, regeneration

1 Engage/Explore

Activating Prior Knowledge

Ask students to name and describe the two kinds of symmetry. *(Bilateral: one line of symmetry; radial: many lines of symmetry through a central point)* Have students examine the figures in this section. Ask: **Which kind of symmetry do the animals in these figures display?** *(Radial symmetry)* Have students name an animal with radial symmetry they learned about in the symmetry section of Chapter 1. *(Sample: Sea anemone)*

········· **DISCOVER** ·········

Skills Focus predicting
Materials *plastic dropper, water*

Time 5 minutes
Tips If students have trouble creating suction against their arm, have them practice the activity without using water. Tell them to squeeze the bulb, press the dropper tip against their skin, and then release the bulb. After a few tries, have them try the activity again with a drop of water.
Expected Outcome The droppers will briefly attach to the students' skins.
Think It Over Sea stars might use their suction structures to pry open mollusk shells.

The "Spiny Skinned" Animals

Including All Students

In this section, students 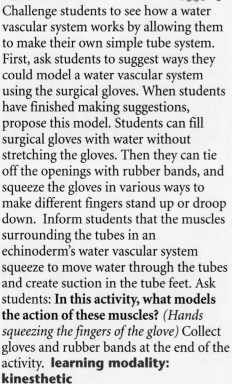 encounter terms that are difficult to pronounce and understand. Guide students whose native language is not English in the pronunciation of words such as *vascular* and *echinoderm*. Allow them to practice saying the words with a partner until they master the pronunciation. **limited English proficiency**

Inquiry Challenge

Materials *surgical gloves*
Time 20 minutes

Challenge students to see how a water vascular system works by allowing them to make their own simple tube system. First, ask students to suggest ways they could model a water vascular system using the surgical gloves. When students have finished making suggestions, propose this model. Students can fill surgical gloves with water without stretching the gloves. Then they can tie off the openings with rubber bands, and squeeze the gloves in various ways to make different fingers stand up or droop down. Inform students that the muscles surrounding the tubes in an echinoderm's water vascular system squeeze to move water through the tubes and create suction in the tube feet. Ask students: **In this activity, what models the action of these muscles?** (*Hands squeezing the fingers of the glove*) Collect gloves and rubber bands at the end of the activity. **learning modality: kinesthetic**

In addition to five-part radial symmetry and an endoskeleton, echinoderms also have an internal fluid system called a water vascular system. The **water vascular system** consists of fluid-filled tubes within the echinoderm's body. Portions of the tubes can contract, squeezing water into structures called tube feet, which are external parts of the water vascular system. The ends of tube feet are sticky and, when filled with water, they act like small, sticky suction cups. The stickiness and suction enable the tube feet to grip the surface beneath the echinoderm. Most echinoderms also use their tube feet to move along slowly and to capture food. If you turn a sea star upside down, you will see rows of moving tube feet.

Echinoderms crawl about on the bottom of the ocean, seeking food, shelter, and mates. Like other radially symmetrical animals, echinoderms do not have a head end where sense organs and nerve tissue are found. Instead, they are adapted to respond to food, mates, or predators coming from any direction.

Most echinoderms are either male or female. Eggs are usually fertilized right in the seawater, after the female releases her eggs and the male releases his sperm. The fertilized eggs develop into tiny, swimming larvae that eventually undergo metamorphosis and become adult echinoderms.

Figure 17 This red sea star is in the process of regenerating two of its arms, possibly lost in a struggle with a predator.

☑ *Checkpoint* *What is the function of an echinoderm's tube feet?*

Sea Stars

Sea stars are predators that eat mollusks, crabs, and even other echinoderms. A sea star uses its arms and tube feet, shown in *Exploring a Sea Star,* to capture prey. The sea star grasps a clam with all five arms. Then it pulls on the tightly closed shells with its tube feet. When the shells open, the sea star forces its stomach out through its mouth and into the opening between the clam's shells. Digestive chemicals break down the clam's tissues, and the sea star sucks in the partially digested body of its prey. Sea star behavior is quite impressive for an animal that doesn't have a brain.

If a sea star loses an arm, it can grow a replacement. The process by which an animal grows a new part to replace a lost one is called regeneration. Figure 17 shows a sea star with two partially regenerated arms. A few species of sea stars can even grow a whole animal from a single arm. Some sea stars reproduce by splitting into many parts. The arms pull the sea star apart in five different directions and five new sea stars regenerate!

Background

Facts and Figures Fossil records show that echinoderms have existed for hundreds of millions of years. During the age before the dinosaurs lived, crinoids, or sea lilies, were common. Crinoids still exist today. These enchinoderms live in deeper regions on the ocean floor. Crinoids are filter-feeding animals with five or more long, feathery arms. They are usually attached to the sea floor by a long stem. Many people once thought they were plants because they resemble beautiful flowers.

EXPLORING a Sea Star

Sea stars, which are also called starfishes, usually have five arms. However, some have as many as fifty arms.

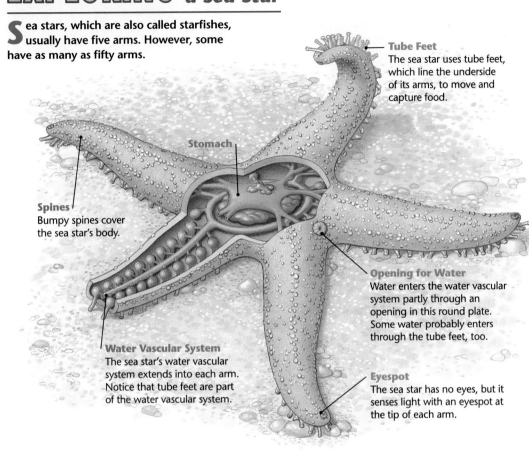

Tube Feet
The sea star uses tube feet, which line the underside of its arms, to move and capture food.

Stomach

Spines
Bumpy spines cover the sea star's body.

Water Vascular System
The sea star's water vascular system extends into each arm. Notice that tube feet are part of the water vascular system.

Opening for Water
Water enters the water vascular system partly through an opening in this round plate. Some water probably enters through the tube feet, too.

Eyespot
The sea star has no eyes, but it senses light with an eyespot at the tip of each arm.

Other Echinoderms

Brittle stars are close relatives of sea stars. Like sea stars, brittle stars have five arms, but their arms are long and slender, with flexible joints. Like sea stars, brittle stars can regenerate lost arms. Brittle stars' tube feet, which have no suction cups, are used for catching food but not for moving. Instead, brittle stars propel themselves along the ocean bottom by moving their giant arms against the ground. They are among the most mobile of all the echinoderms.

Unlike sea stars and brittle stars, sand dollars and sea urchins have no arms. Sand dollars look like large coins. Their flat bodies are covered with very short spines that help them burrow into sand.

Chapter 2 **B ◆ 75**

Answers to Self-Assessment

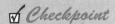 *Checkpoint*
Tube feet allow echinoderms to grip a surface, move along the sea floor, and capture prey.

EXPLORING
a Sea Star

Direct students' attention to the labeled parts of the sea star. Point out that the parts labeled Tube Feet, Opening for Water, and Water Vascular system are *all* parts of the water vascular system. Have students work in pairs. One student should trace a finger along a pathway water might travel through the sea star and describe the pathway to a partner. The partner should listen for accuracy and clarity. *(The water goes into the opening for water, through the water vascular tubes, into tube feet, back into the tubes, into other tube feet, and eventually exits from the opening.)* **cooperative learning**

Other Echinoderms

Building Inquiry Skills: Interpreting a Photograph

The five-part symmetry of echinoderms, especially sea urchins and sea cucumbers, is sometimes difficult to see if the animal is viewed from certain angles. Invite students to imagine what the sea cucumber in Figure 18 looks like when viewed from the top. Tell students that the five-part radial symmetry would be evident from this angle. Have them draw a sketch showing what they think the sea cucumber looks like from the top. **learning modality: visual**

 Students can save their paragraphs in their portfolios.

Ongoing Assessment

Writing Give each student a piece of paper labeled Sea Star, Brittle Star, Sand Dollar, Sea Urchin, or Sea Cucumber. Have students write a paragraph describing the animal. Students' paragraphs should mention the general characteristics of echinoderms and the specific characteristics of their animal.

 Students can save their paragraphs in their portfolios.

3 Assess

Section 5 Review Answers

1. Echinoderms are radially symmetrical invertebrates with an endoskeleton. They have five-part symmetry and a water vascular system. Most are spiny.

2. Regeneration is the process by which an animal grows a new part to replace a lost one. When a sea star loses an arm, it can regenerate a new one.

3. Both sea stars and sea urchins have five-part radial symmetry. Both move with tube feet. Sea stars have five arms. Sea urchins have no arms; they are covered with spines and resemble pin-cushions.

4. Tube feet operate by suction. Each time the animal moves, it must pull its feet up by releasing the suction, and then put them down again. Because this process is slow, tube feet are adapted to slow movement.

Check Your Progress

CHAPTER PROJECT 2

When one-half of a student's mealworms have reached the adult stage, have the student write a simple summary of his or her observations. To draw conclusions, students can make a bar graph comparing the numbers of mealworms in different stages of development under the two conditions. Tell students their conclusions must be based on data they have collected. Have follow-up discussions with students who made inappropriate conclusions. When the project is finished, collect the insects from students.

Figure 18 The blue-and-red sea cucumber **(A)**, spiny brittle stars **(B)**, and sand dollar **(C)** are all echinoderms. *Observing What type of symmetry do these organisms exhibit?*

Movable spines cover and protect the bodies of sea urchins, making them look like pincushions or round brushes. The spines cover a central shell that is made of plates joined together. Sea urchins move by using bands of tube feet that extend out between the spines. With the five strong teeth that can be projected from their mouths, sea urchins can scrape algae, chew sea-weed, and crush pieces of coral and the shells of small mollusks. Some sea urchins use their teeth and spines to dig themselves into rock crevices to hide from predators.

As you might expect from their name, sea cucumbers look a little bit like leathery-skinned cucumbers—but you won't see one in a tossed salad. These strange animals, which live on the sandy or rocky ocean floor, can be red, brown, blue, or green. Their bodies are soft, flexible, and muscular. Sea cucumbers have rows of tube feet on their underside, enabling them to crawl slowly along the ocean bottom. At one end of a sea cucumber is a mouth sur-rounded by tentacles. The sea cucumber, which is a filter feeder, can lengthen its tentacles to sweep food toward its mouth, and then pull the tentacles back into its tough skin.

Section 5 Review

1. Identify the main characteristics of echinoderms.
2. Define *regeneration* and explain how it applies to sea stars.
3. Compare and contrast sea urchins and sea stars.
4. **Thinking Critically** **Inferring** How are tube feet adapted to slow, rather than rapid, movement?

Check Your Progress

CHAPTER PROJECT 2

Continue to examine the mealworm containers every day and record your data. In your notebook, record any differences between the two groups of mealworms. Begin to draw conclusions about how the different conditions affected metamorphosis. When you have finished working with the insects, return them to your teacher.

Performance Assessment

Drawing Have students sketch a hypothetical echinoderm. Be sure students' sketches include the major characteristics of echinoderms. *(Students' sketches should include five-part radial symmetry, a water vascular system, and an endoskeleton.)*

Media and Technology

Exploring Life Science Videodisc
Unit 3, Side 2, "Spineless"

Chapter 2

Program Resources

◆ **Teaching Resources** 2-5 Review and Reinforce, p. 63; 2-5 Enrich, p. 64
◆ **Integrated Science Laboratory Manual** B-2, "Characteristics of Sea Stars"

Answers to Self-Assessment

Caption Question

Figure 18 These organisms exhibit five-part radial symmetry.

SECTION 1 Mollusks

Key Ideas

◆ Most mollusks have shells, soft bodies, a mantle covering internal organs, and a muscular foot.

◆ Mollusks are classified based on the presence of a shell, the type of shell, the type of foot, the arrangement of teeth in the radula, and the complexity of the nervous system.

◆ Major groups of mollusks include gastropods, bivalves, and cephalopods.

Key Terms

mollusk   kidney
gill   radula
gastropod   bivalve
cephalopod

SECTION 2 Arthropods

Key Ideas

◆ Arthropods have an exoskeleton, jointed appendages, and a segmented body.

◆ Major groups of arthropods include crustaceans, arachnids, centipedes, millipedes, and insects.

◆ Crustaceans are the only arthropods with two pairs of antennae.

◆ Arachnids have two body sections, eight legs, and no antennae.

Key Terms

arthropod   exoskeleton   chitin
molting   antenna   crustacean
metamorphosis   arachnid   abdomen

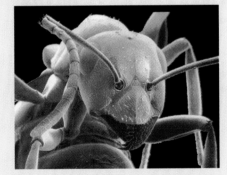

SECTION 3 Insects

Key Ideas

◆ Insects are arthropods with three body sections, six legs, one pair of antennae, and usually one or two pairs of wings.

◆ An insect undergoing complete metamorphosis goes through four distinct stages— egg, larva, pupa, and adult. An insect undergoing gradual metamorphosis hatches from an egg to a nymph; the nymph may molt several times before becoming an adult.

◆ While some insects are harmful to humans, the vast majority are harmless or beneficial.

Key Terms

insect   thorax
complete metamorphosis   pupa
gradual metamorphosis   nymph
camouflage

SECTION 4 The Sounds of Insects

INTEGRATING PHYSICS

Key Ideas

◆ Sound is generated by something that vibrates. Sound travels in waves through solids, liquids, and gases.

◆ Many insects use sound to attract mates.

SECTION 5 Echinoderms

Key Ideas

◆ Echinoderms are characterized by an endoskeleton, five-part radial symmetry, and a water vascular system.

◆ Echinoderms include sea stars, sea urchins, brittle stars, and sea cucumbers.

Key Terms

echinoderm   endoskeleton
water vascular system

USING THE INTERNET   ACTIVITY

www.science-explorer.phschool.com

Chapter 2 **B ◆ 77**

Program Resources

◆ **Teaching Resources** Chapter 2 Project Scoring Rubric, p. 44; Chapter 2 Performance Assessment Teacher Notes, pp. 173–174; Chapter 2 Performance Assessment Student Worksheet p. 175; Chapter 2 Test, pp. 176–177

◆ **Inquiry Skills Handbook** Provides teaching and review of all inquiry skills

Media and Technology

 Interactive Student Tutorial CD-ROM B-2

 Computer Test Bank Chapter 2 Test

Reviewing Content:
Multiple Choice
1. a **2.** d **3.** c **4.** d **5.** c

True or False
6. true **7.** crustaceans **8.** thorax **9.** true
10. true

Checking Concepts

11. A snail uses its radula like a tongue to scrape up tiny particles of food.

12. A cephalopod swims by using jet propulsion. It does not move by using a foot like most mollusks do.

13. Accept any five: antennae smell, taste, touch, and balance; legs walk; swimmerets function in swimming; swimmerets of female hold eggs; plierlike appendages catch food and defend crayfish.

14. Both digest the food outside their bodies and then suck the digested food inside.

15. Centipedes are carnivores and have one pair of legs per body segment. Most millipedes are herbivores; all millipedes have two pairs of legs per body segment.

16. Insects damage crops and carry diseases such as malaria.

17. Unlike other arthropods, all insects have six legs and one pair of antennae. In addition, most have wings.

18. Sound travels from its source in waves of alternating compressed and spread-out areas of particles.

19. An echinoderm's radial symmetry is a 5-part symmetry, while a jellyfish's symmetry is not 5-part.

20. Answers will vary. Students should focus on the new, soft exoskeleton of the animal that is exposed to fish or other predators before it hardens.

Thinking Visually

21. a. crustaceans **b.** insects **c.** eight legs, two body segments **d.** highly segmented body, one or two pairs of legs on each segment

---

Reviewing Content

 For more review of key concepts, see the Interactive Student Tutorial CD-ROM.

Multiple Choice
Choose the letter of the best answer.

1. Mollusks with tentacles are known as
   a. cephalopods.
   b. gastropods.
   c. bivalves.
   d. sea stars.

2. Which of these is true of the legs of arthropods?
   a. They always number six.
   b. They are always attached to the abdomen.
   c. They are rigid.
   d. They are jointed.

3. At which stage of its development is a moth enclosed in a cocoon?
   a. egg
   b. larva
   c. pupa
   d. adult

4. Sound can travel through
   a. solids only.
   b. liquids only.
   c. gases only.
   d. solids, liquids, and gases.

5. A sea star is a(n)
   a. mollusk.
   b. arthropod.
   c. echinoderm.
   d. sponge.

True or False
If the statement is true, write true. If it is false, change the underlined word or words to make the statement true.

6. All <u>arthropods</u> have an exoskeleton.

7. All <u>sea urchins</u> have two pairs of antennae.

8. An insect's midsection is called an <u>abdomen</u>.

9. Many insects use <u>sound</u> to attract mates.

10. All echinoderms have an <u>endoskeleton</u>.

Checking Concepts

11. Explain how a snail uses its radula.

12. How is a cephalopod's way of moving different from that of most mollusks?

13. Describe five things that a crayfish can do with its appendages.

14. How is the process by which a spider digests its food similar to that of a sea star?

15. How are centipedes different from millipedes?

16. Identify some ways in which insects harm people.

17. How are insects different from other arthropods?

18. How does sound travel from its source?

19. How is an echinoderm's radial symmetry different from that of a jellyfish?

20. Writing to Learn Imagine that you are a lobster that has just molted. Using vivid, precise words, describe a dangerous situation that you might encounter before your new exoskeleton has hardened.

Thinking Visually

21. Concept Map The concept map below shows the classification of arthropods. Copy the map and complete it. (For more on concept maps, see the Skills Handbook.)

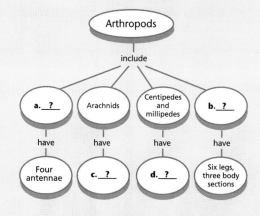

Applying Skills

22.

Insect	Wing-Beat Rate (times/sec)	Flight Speed (kph)
Hummingbird Moth	85	17.8
Bumblebee	250	10.3
Housefly	190	7.1

23.

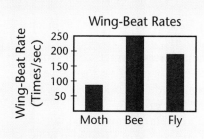

Applying Skills

The following information appeared in a book on insects. Use it to answer Questions 22–25.

"A hummingbird moth beats its wings an average of 85 times per second, and it flies at a speed of about 17.8 kilometers per hour (kph). A bumblebee's wings beat about 250 times per second, and it flies about 10.3 kph. A housefly's wings beat about 190 times per second, and it flies about 7.1 kph."

22. **Creating Data Tables** Make a data table to organize the wing-beat rate and flight speed information above.

23. **Graphing** Construct two bar graphs: one showing the three insect wing-beat rates and another showing the flight speeds.

24. **Interpreting Data** Which of the three insects has the highest wing-beat rate? Which insect flies the fastest?

25. **Drawing Conclusions** On the basis of the data, do you see any relationship between the rate at which an insect beats its wings and the speed at which it flies? Explain. What factors besides wing-beat rate might affect an insect's flight speed?

Thinking Critically

26. **Applying Concepts** Explain why the development of a lion, which grows larger as it changes from a tiny cub to a 200-pound adult, is not metamorphosis.

27. **Comparing and Contrasting** Compare and contrast bivalves and cephalopods.

28. **Making Judgments** Do you think that pesticides should be used to kill harmful insects? Support your ideas with facts.

29. **Relating Cause and Effect** Sea stars sometimes get caught in fishing nets. At one time, in an attempt to protect clams from their natural predators, workers on fishing boats cut the sea stars into pieces and threw the pieces back in the water. What do you think happened to the sea star population? Explain.

30. **Classifying** Your friend said he found a dead insect that had two pairs of antennae and eight legs. Is this possible? Why or why not?

shell; cephalopod feet are adapted to form tentacles; cephalopods move by jet propulsion, while bivalves move slowly with feet; cephalopods have complex nervous systems, but bivalves do not.

28. Any argument presented by students is acceptable as long as it is supported by facts.

29. The sea star population increased because new sea stars could regenerate from the pieces thrown into the water.

30. No. All insects have six legs and one pair of antennae.

Performance Assessment

Wrap Up
Presenting Your Project
Remind students to include illustrations of their setup, data, graph, and results. They must also include diagrams of the larvae, pupae, and adults, with arrows between these diagrams to illustrate the sequence of complete metamorphosis.

Students can evaluate their displays by showing them to a friend or family member who is unfamiliar with the project. Suggest that students update their displays using this feedback before showing them to the class.

Consider grouping students according to the variable they tested. Direct each group to discuss their results. Have them combine their data, create a graph to display the data, and then summarize their results. Instruct each group to present its graph and results to the rest of the class.

Reflect and Record Ask students to discuss their conclusions. Encourage discussion of why metamorphosis was or was not affected by the variables they tested.

Performance Assessment

Wrap Up

Presenting Your Project Prepare a display with diagrams to show how you set up your experiment and what your results were. Construct and display graphs to show the data you collected. Include pictures of the mealworms in each stage of development.

Reflect and Record In your journal, write your conclusion of how the experimental conditions affected the growth and development of the mealworms. Also suggest some possible explanations for your results.

Getting Involved

In Your Community Contact your local Board of Health or other appropriate community office to learn what, if any, measures your community takes to deal with insect pests. For example, does your community spray pesticides to kill mosquitoes? If your community does spray pesticides, ask what pesticides are used and what measures are taken to protect people and wildlife.

Chapter 2 **B ◆ 79**

Getting Involved

In addition to their local Board of Health, students can contact their county Agricultural Extension Service or the United States Department of Agriculture. Licensed local exterminators can provide additional information.

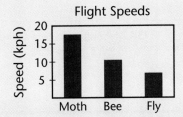

Flight Speeds

24. The bumblebee has the highest wing-beat rate. The hummingbird moth flies the fastest.
25. There is no trend in the data to support any relationship between wing-beat rate and speed of flight. Other factors might include mass and shape of the insect and shape of the insect's wings.

Thinking Critically

26. The cub looks similar to the adult lion from the time it is born. It grows larger, but it does not change its form.
27. Alike: Bivalves and cephalopods have mantle covering internal organs; have soft bodies; live in water. Different: Bivalves have two shells, but many cephalopods have no

Fishes, Amphibians, and Reptiles

Sections	Time	Student Edition Activities	Other Activities	
CHAPTER PROJECT 3 **Adaptations** p. 81	Ongoing (3 weeks)	Check Your Progress, pp. 93, 100, 110 Wrap Up, p. 117	TE	Chapter 3 Project Notes, pp. 80–81
1 **What Is a Vertebrate?** pp. 82–86 ◆ Describe the main characteristic that is shared by all vertebrates and how vertebrates evolved. ◆ Describe how vertebrates differ in the way they control body temperature.	3 periods/ 1½ blocks	**Discover** How Is an Umbrella like a Skeleton?, p. 82 **Try This** Bead-y Bones, p. 84 **Science at Home** p. 86	TE	Building Inquiry Skills: Relating Cause and Effect, p. 84
2 **Fishes** pp. 87–94 ◆ Explain how fish use their gills. ◆ Name the three major groups of fish. ◆ Explain how fish provide food for people.	4 periods/ 2 blocks	**Discover** How Does Water Flow over a Fish's Gills?, p. 87 **Sharpen your Skills** Communicating, p. 88 **Real-World Lab: How It Works** Home Sweet Home, p. 94	TE TE IES ISLM	Building Inquiry Skills: Observation, p. 90 Integrating Physics, p. 91 "Where River Meets Sea," pp. 13–14, 22–23 B-3, "Adaptations of Fish"
3 **Amphibians** pp. 95–100 ◆ Describe amphibian characteristics, life cycles, and groups. ◆ Describe how amphibians are adapted for movement on land and threats to their survival.	3 periods/ 1–2 blocks	**Discover** What's the Advantage of Being Green?, p. 95 **Try This** Webbing Through Water, p. 98	TE IES	Including All Students, p. 96 "Fate of the Rain Forest," p. 11
4 **Reptiles** pp. 101–110 ◆ Describe some adaptations that allow reptiles to live on dry land. ◆ State how a reptile's egg is different from an amphibian's egg.	5 periods/ 2–3 blocks	**Discover** How Do Snakes Feed?, p. 101 **Skills Lab: Interpreting Data** Soaking Up Those Rays, pp. 106–107 **Sharpen your Skills** Drawing Conclusions, p. 109	TE TE IES	Building Inquiry Skills: Inferring, p.102 Including All Students Demonstration, p. 108 "Sleuth's Supper," p. 20
5 **INTEGRATING EARTH SCIENCE** **Vertebrate History in Rocks** pp. 111–114 ◆ Describe what scientists can learn from studying fossils.	2 periods/ 1 block	**Discover** What Can You Tell From an Imprint?, p. 111 **Science at Home** p. 114	TE	Including All Students, p. 112
Study Guide/Chapter Review pp. 115–117	1 period/ ½ block		ISAB	Provides teaching and review of all inquiry skills

For Standard or Block Schedule The Resource Pro® CD-ROM gives you maximum flexibility for planning your instruction for any type of schedule. Resource Pro® contains Planning Express®, an advanced scheduling program, as well as the entire contents of the Teaching Resources and the Computer Test Bank.

CHAPTER PLANNING GUIDE

Program Resources	Assessment Strategies	Media and Technology
TR Chapter 3 Project Teacher Notes, pp. 70–71 **TR** Chapter 3 Project Overview and Worksheet, pp. 72–75 **TR** Chapter 3 Project Scoring Rubric, p. 76	**SE** Performance Assessment: Wrap Up, p. 117 **TE** Check Your Progress, pp. 93, 100, 110 **TR** Chapter 3 Project Scoring Rubric, p. 76	Interactive Student Tutorial CD-ROM, B-3
TR 3-1 Lesson Plan, p. 77 **TR** 3-1 Section Summary, p. 78 **TR** 3-1 Review and Reinforce, p. 79 **TR** 3-1 Enrich, p. 80	**SE** Section 1 Review, p. 86 **TE** Ongoing Assessment, pp. 83, 85 **TE** Performance Assessment, p. 86 **TR** 3-1 Review and Reinforce, p. 79	Exploring Life Science Videodisc, Unit 3 Side 2, "Backbones"; "How Does Everything Fit?" Audiotapes: English-Spanish Summary 3-1 Transparency 10, "Vertebrate Evolution" Interactive Student Tutorial CD-ROM, B-3
TR 3-2 Lesson Plan, p. 81 **TR** 3-2 Section Summary, p. 82 **TR** 3-2 Review and Reinforce, p. 83 **TR** 3-2 Enrich, p. 84 **TR** Chapter 3 Real-World Lab, pp. 99–101 **SES** Book M, *Motion, Forces, and Energy,* Chapter 3 **SES** Book E, *Environmental Science,* Chapter 5	**SE** Section 2 Review, p. 93 **SE** Analyze and Conclude, p. 94 **TE** Ongoing Assessment, pp. 89, 91 **TE** Performance Assessment, p. 93 **TR** 3-2 Review and Reinforce, p. 83	Audiotapes: English-Spanish Summary 3-2 Transparency 11, "Exploring a Bony Fish" Interactive Student Tutorial CD-ROM, B-3
TR 3-3 Lesson Plan, p. 85 **TR** 3-3 Section Summary, p. 86 **TR** 3-3 Review and Reinforce, p. 87 **TR** 3-3 Enrich, p. 88 **SES** Book E, *Environmental Science,* Chapter 2	**SE** Section 3 Review, p. 100 **TE** Ongoing Assessment, pp. 97, 99 **TE** Performance Assessment, p. 100 **TR** 3-3 Review and Reinforce, p. 87	Audiotapes: English-Spanish Summary 3-3 Transparencies 12, "Frog Metamorphosis"; 13, "Exploring a Frog" Interactive Student Tutorial CD-ROM, B-3
TR 3-4 Lesson Plan, p. 89 **TR** 3-4 Section Summary, p. 90 **TR** 3-4 Review and Reinforce, p. 91 **TR** 3-4 Enrich, p. 92 **TR** Chapter 3 Skills Lab, pp. 97–98	**SE** Section 4 Review, p. 110 **SE** Analyze and Conclude, p. 106 **TE** Ongoing Assessment, pp. 103, 105, 109 **TE** Performance Assessment, p. 110 **TR** 3-4 Review and Reinforce, p. 91	Exploring Life Science Videodisc, Unit 3 Side 2, "Travelin' Along" Audiotapes: English-Spanish Summary 3-4 Transparencies 14, "A Reptile Egg"; 15, "Exploring a Lizard" Interactive Student Tutorial CD-ROM, B-3
TR 3-5 Lesson Plan, p. 93 **TR** 3-5 Section Summary, p. 94 **TR** 3-5 Review and Reinforce, p. 95 **TR** 3-5 Enrich, p. 96	**SE** Section 5 Review, p. 114 **TE** Ongoing Assessment, p. 113 **TE** Performance Assessment, p. 114 **TR** 3-5 Review and Reinforce, p. 95	Exploring Life Science Videodisc, Unit 5 Side 2, "Fossils"; "The Earth Library" Audiotapes: English-Spanish Summary 3-5 Interactive Student Tutorial CD-ROM, B-3
TR Chapter 3 Performance Assessment, pp. 180–182 **TR** Chapter 3 Test, pp. 183–186 **ISAB** Provides teaching and review of all inquiry skills	**SE** Chapter Review, pp. 116–117 **TR** Chapter 3 Performance Assessment, pp. 180–182 **TR** Chapter 3 Test, pp. 183–186 **CTB** Chapter 3 Test	Computer Test Bank, Test B-3 Science Explorer Internet Site Got It! Video Quizzes

Key: **SE** Student Edition   **TE** Teacher's Edition   **TR** Teaching Resources
CTB Computer Test Bank   **SES** Science Explorer Series Text   **ISLM** Integrated Science Laboratory Manual
ISAB Inquiry Skills Activity Book   **PTA** Product Testing Activities by *Consumer Reports*   **IES** Interdisciplinary Explorations Series

Meeting the National Science Education Standards and AAAS Benchmarks

National Science Education Standards	Benchmarks for Science Literacy	Unifying Themes
Science as Inquiry (Content Standard A) ◆ **Communicate scientific procedures and explanations** Students report on how successfully they were able to create an artificial environment for organisms (snails and guppies) and determine how the environment meets the needs of the organisms. *(Real-World Lab)* ◆ **Design and conduct a scientific investigation** Students create an artificial environment for two organisms and monitor the organisms' behavior. They also design an extension to the activity allowing more organisms to be added. *(Real-World Lab)* **Earth and Space Science** (Content Standard D) ◆ **Earth's history** The fossils found in sedimentary rocks reveal the history of vertebrate evolution through time. *(Section 5)* **Life Science** (Content Standard C) ◆ **Diversity and adaptations of organisms** The specialized characteristics of vertebrates reveal great diversity of form. Adaptations allow vertebrates to occupy many different habitats. *(Sections 1–4)* ◆ **Structure and function of living systems** Vertebrates have similar structures to perform similar functions. Different vertebrate groups have specialized structures, such as a two-loop circulatory system and three-chambered heart. *(Sections 1–4)*	**5A Diversity of Life** Fishes, amphibians, and reptiles show great diversity of form but share common characteristics allowing them to be grouped together as vertebrates. Within each group, there are many variations on the vertebrate theme ranging from the tiniest salamander to the largest dinosaur. Specialized adaptations allowed vertebrates to move from the oceans and become land dwellers. *(Sections 1–4; Real-World Lab; Skills Lab; Chapter Project)* **5D Interdependence of Life** Predators and prey are interconnected through complex relationships. Organisms depend on their environment to supply needs. *(Sections 2, 3; Real-World Lab)* **5F Evolution of Life** Vertebrates evolved from the first chordates. Vertebrate evolution shows over time an increasing variety of specialized adaptations allowing exploitation of many different habitats. This history of change is revealed in the fossil record. *(Section 5)* **11B Models** Students create models showing a particular adaptation in fishes, amphibians, and reptiles. Students use clay and objects to model how certain fossils are formed. *(Section 5; Chapter Project)* **12D Communication Skills** Students interpret pictures of lizard behavior and transfer the information to data tables. *(Skills Lab)*	◆ **Modeling** Students construct models of reptiles, amphibians, and fishes, in order to understand how adaptations aid survival. *(Chapter Project)* ◆ **Patterns of Change** The fossil record shows how changes in reproduction, the skeletal system, respiration, and the circulatory system have allowed animals to move out of the water and populate dry land. *(Sections 1–5)* ◆ **Evolution** Populations of organisms have successfully adapted to many different environments. In vertebrate evolution, this includes a set of adaptations, such as a stronger skeleton and lungs, that have allowed species to become land dwellers. *(Sections 1, 5)* ◆ **Structure** Fish, reptiles, and amphibians possess many similar structures. Specialization in the skeletal system and the respiratory system has allowed some animals to adapt to life on dry land. *(Sections 1–5; Chapter Project)* ◆ **Unity and Diversity** Fish, reptiles, and amphibians are all vertebrates, because they all possess a backbone. Each group is distinguished from the others by specialized features. Within each group there is great diversity of size and other variations. *(Sections 1–5; Chapter Project)* ◆ **Systems and Interactions** Organisms interact as part of the environment. Artificial environments must supply all of an animal's needs. *(Real-World Lab)*

Media and Technology

Exploring Life Science Videodisc

◆ **Section 1** "Backbones" compares the systems and functions of vertebrates as they have evolved over time.

◆ **Section 1** "How Does Everything Fit?" demonstrates the important interactions among all types of animals and the humans on Earth.

◆ **Section 4** "Travelin' Along" allows viewers to travel with sea turtles from birth to death.

◆ **Section 5** "Fossils" illustrates the conditions needed for fossils to form and demonstrates the challenges of recovering them.

◆ **Section 5** "The Earth Library" illustrates geologic processes, superposition, and index fossils to describe the history of Earth.

Interactive Student Tutorial CD-ROM

◆ **Chapter Review** Interactive questions help students to self-assess their mastery of key chapter concepts.

Student Edition Connection Strategies

◆ **Section 2** Integrating Physics, p. 91
Integrating Environmental Science, p. 92

◆ **Section 3** Language Arts Connection, p. 97
Integrating Environmental Science, p. 100

◆ **Section 5** Integrating Earth Science, p. 111
Science and History, pp. 112–113

USING THE INTERNET

ACTIVITY

www.science-explorer.phschool.com

Visit the Science Explorer Internet site to find an up-to-date activity for Chapter 3 of *Animals*.

ACTIVITY	Time (minutes)	Materials Quantities for one work group	Skills
Section 1			
Discover, p. 82	15	**Nonconsumable** umbrella	Inferring
Try This, p. 84	10	**Consumable** short lengths of string **Nonconsumable** enough beads (in two different sizes) to cover the length of the string	Making Models
Section 2			
Discover, p. 87	10	**Nonconsumable** several live fish, each one in an aquarium or fishbowl	Observing
Sharpen Your Skills, p. 88	50	**Consumable** preserved fish, rubber gloves **Nonconsumable** goggles, dissecting tray, blunt probe, hand lens	Communicating
Real-World Lab, p. 94	30 min set up; 10 min per day for 2 wk	**Consumable** gravel, snails, tap water, guppy food, guppies, water plants **Nonconsumable** aquarium filter, rectangular aquarium tank (15 to 20 liters) with cover, metric ruler, thermometer, aquarium heater, dip net	Making Models, Posing Questions
Section 3			
Discover, p. 95	10	**Nonconsumable** dried yellow and green peas; paper cup; green construction paper, approximately 1 m x 1 m; clock or watch with second hand	Inferring
Try This, p. 98	15	**Consumable** plastic bags **Nonconsumable** heavy rubber bands, pail of water or sink	Making Models
Section 4			
Discover, p. 101	10	**Nonconsumable** sock with ribbed cuff, grapefruit, strong rubber band	Inferring
Skills Lab, pp. 106–107	30	**Consumable** paper **Nonconsumable** pencil	Interpreting Data, Interpreting Diagram, Drawing Conclusions
Sharpen your Skills, p. 109	15	**Consumable** No special materials are required.	Drawing Conclusions
Section 5			
Discover, p. 111	15	**Consumable** paper **Nonconsumable** modeling clay, small objects of various textures and degrees of rigidity	Observing

A list of all materials required for the Student Edition activities can be found on pages T14–T16. You can order Materials Kits by calling 1-800-828-7777 or by accessing the Science Explorer Internet site at **www.science-explorer.phschool.com.**

Adaptations have evolved over time in species because the adaptations allow individual organisms to be more successful at acquiring food, escaping predators, or reproducing. In this project, students will select one adaptation to model in three different animals, a reptile, an amphibian, and a fish.

Purpose In this project, students will investigate and model how adaptations enable animals to survive in their environments.

Skills Focus Students will be able to
♦ make models of adaptations that perform similar functions in three different kinds of organisms;
♦ compare and contrast the adaptations of the three organisms;
♦ communicate their findings about the adaptations that they model to their classmates.

Project Time Line Before beginning the project, see Chapter 3 Project Teacher Notes on pages 70–71 in Teaching Resources for more details on carrying out the project. Distribute to students Chapter 3 Project Overview and Worksheets and Scoring Rubric on pages 72–76 in Teaching Resources. This project should progress in several stages and will take 4–5 weeks to complete. During the first week, students get together with a partner or in small groups and skim the chapter and any other sources of relevant information such as books and magazines. By the beginning of the second week, students should have selected an adaptation to model. As students complete each chapter section, they should begin to construct a model of one type of organism they studied in the section. To save time and keep students on track, have them work on their projects at home as well as in the classroom. Students should be given about one week to build the model for each organism and then a few days to prepare their class presentation.

Possible Materials Provide a wide variety of materials from which students can choose. Have students bring extra

This three-horned chameleon has just invited a cricket to lunch.

WHAT'S AHEAD

80 ♦ B

materials that they might have at home for others in the class to use. Some possibilities are listed below. Encourage students to suggest and use other materials as well.
♦ For model building, include toothpicks, pipe cleaners, Styrofoam, cardboard, construction paper, chicken wire, balsa wood, balloons, modeling clay, papier mâché, glue, tape, scissors, paints, markers, and other decorating materials.
♦ For information about organisms, students can consult magazines and picture books.

Launching the Project Allow time for students to read the description of the project in their texts and the Chapter 3 Project Overview on pages 72–73 in Teaching Resources. To begin the project, allow students to work with others and think about various adaptations. Suggest that they skim through the chapter, picture books, and magazines to help them think about the ways fishes, amphibians, and reptiles are different. Students can discuss the characteristics of fishes, amphibians, and reptiles that allow them to move, feed, and

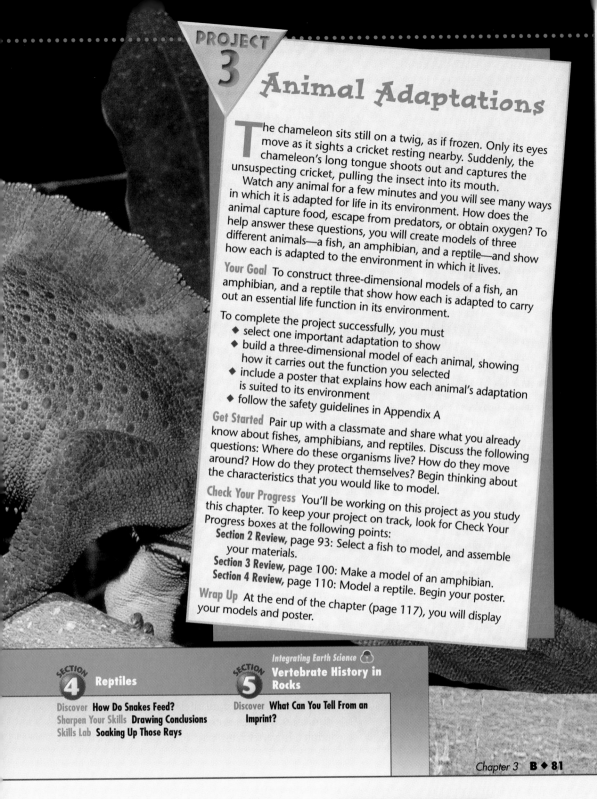

Animal Adaptations

The chameleon sits still on a twig, as if frozen. Only its eyes move as it sights a cricket resting nearby. Suddenly, the chameleon's long tongue shoots out and captures the unsuspecting cricket, pulling the insect into its mouth.

Watch any animal for a few minutes and you will see many ways in which it is adapted for life in its environment. How does the animal capture food, escape from predators, or obtain oxygen? To help answer these questions, you will create models of three different animals—a fish, an amphibian, and a reptile—and show how each is adapted to the environment in which it lives.

Your Goal To construct three-dimensional models of a fish, an amphibian, and a reptile that show how each is adapted to carry out an essential life function in its environment.

To complete the project successfully, you must
◆ select one important adaptation to show
◆ build a three-dimensional model of each animal, showing how it carries out the function you selected
◆ include a poster that explains how each animal's adaptation is suited to its environment
◆ follow the safety guidelines in Appendix A

Get Started Pair up with a classmate and share what you already know about fishes, amphibians, and reptiles. Discuss the following questions: Where do these organisms live? How do they move around? How do they protect themselves? Begin thinking about the characteristics that you would like to model.

Check Your Progress You'll be working on this project as you study this chapter. To keep your project on track, look for Check Your Progress boxes at the following points:
Section 2 Review, page 93: Select a fish to model, and assemble your materials.
Section 3 Review, page 100: Make a model of an amphibian.
Section 4 Review, page 110: Model a reptile. Begin your poster.

Wrap Up At the end of the chapter (page 117), you will display your models and poster.

protect themselves. Suggest that students choose adaptations that are quite different in at least two of the three organisms. To make sure everyone is on track and understands the project, you may wish to hold a class discussion after this brainstorming period. As students complete each section, they should begin to construct models of the type of organisms they just studied. Before they construct their models, students should sketch the design and think about the materials they will need to complete the model. Where

appropriate, suggest that students model only a part of the organisms. For example, if they are modeling feeding behaviors, they could model the mouths. Pass out copies of the Chapter 3 Project Worksheets on pages 74–75 in Teaching Resources for students to review.

You could have students work in small groups as a cooperative learning task. To ensure that every student will have ample opportunity to participate in model planning and building, each group should consist of three to four students.

Program Resources

◆ **Teaching Resources** Chapter 3 Project Teacher's Notes, pp. 70–71; Chapter 3 Project Overview and Worksheets, pp. 72–75; Chapter 3 Project Scoring Rubric, p. 76

Performance Assessment

The Chapter 3 Project Scoring Rubric on page 76 of Teaching Resources will help you evaluate how well students complete the Chapter 3 Project. You may wish to share the scoring rubric with your students so they are clear about what is expected of them. Students will be assessed on
◆ the thoroughness of their research into the adaptation that they model; and the appropriateness and accuracy of their sketches;
◆ the size, proportion, and accuracy of their models;
◆ the clarity and thoroughness of their posters;
◆ the thoroughness and organization of their presentations.

What Is a Vertebrate?

Objectives

After completing this lesson, students will be able to

◆ describe the main characteristics shared by all vertebrates and how vertebrates evolved;

◆ explain how vertebrates differ in the way they control body temperature.

Key Terms chordates, notochord, cartilage, vertebrae, ectotherm, endotherm

1 Engage/Explore

Activating Prior Knowledge

Ask students to recall what they learned about vertebrates and invertebrates in Chapter 1. Then ask a volunteer to list on the board all the kinds of vertebrates and invertebrates the students see in a single day. Once the lists are completed, have them compare and contrast several obvious ways vertebrates and invertebrates are similar and ways they are different.

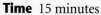

DISCOVER

Skills Focus inferring
Materials *umbrella*
Time 15 minutes
Tips To avoid injuries, make sure students are standing in an open area away from others when they open the umbrellas.
Expected Outcome Students should understand that, without its ribs, an umbrella loses its support and cannot function.
Think It Over The umbrella's ribs provide support to the umbrella and give it shape, just as human bones support and give shape to the body. The ribs of an umbrella are different from human bones in that they are near the surface, rather than deep within the body and covered by soft tissue. **learning modality: kinesthetic**

What Is a Vertebrate?

DISCOVER •••••••••••••••••••••••••• ACTIVITY••••

How Is an Umbrella Like a Skeleton?

1. Open an umbrella. Turn it upside down and examine how it is made.

2. Now fold the umbrella, and watch how the braces and ribs collapse against the central pole.

3. Think of what would happen if you removed the ribs from the umbrella and then tried to use it during a rainstorm.

Think It Over

Inferring What is the function of the ribs of an umbrella? How are the ribs of the umbrella similar to the bones in your skeleton? How are they different?

GUIDE FOR READING

◆ What main characteristic is shared by all vertebrates?

◆ How do vertebrates differ in the way in which they control body temperature?

Reading Tip As you read, write a definition, in your own words, of each boldfaced science term.

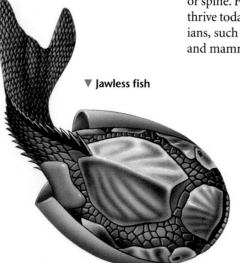

▼ Jawless fish

L ook backward in time, into an ocean 530 million years ago. There you see a strange-looking creature, about as long as your middle finger. The creature is swimming with a side-to-side motion, like a flag flapping in an invisible wind. Its tail-fin is broad and flat. Tiny armorlike plates cover its small body. Its eyes are set wide apart. If you could see inside the animal, you would notice that it has a backbone. You are looking at one of the earliest vertebrates, at home in an ancient sea.

Recall from Chapter 1 that vertebrates are animals with a backbone, which is also called a vertebral column, spinal column, or spine. Fishes were the first vertebrates to appear, and they still thrive today in Earth's waters. Other vertebrates include amphibians, such as frogs, and reptiles, such as snakes, as well as birds and mammals.

The Chordate Phylum

Vertebrates are a subgroup in the phylum Chordata. Members of this phylum, called **chordates** (KAWR daytz), share these characteristics: at some point in their lives, they have a notochord, a nerve cord, and slits in their throat area. The phylum name comes from the **notochord,** a flexible rod that supports the animal's back. Some chordates, like the lancelet in Figure 1, keep the notochord all their lives. Others, such as tunicates, have a notochord as larvae, but not as adults. In vertebrates, part or all of the notochord is

---

READING STRATEGIES

Vocabulary Tell students that in ancient Greek, *ektos* meant "outside," *endon* meant "within," and *thermos* meant "hot." Ask students for examples of other words containing these Greek roots. (Answers may vary. Sample: *endotherm, ectotherm, thermos, thermometer*)

Program Resources

◆ **Teaching Resources** 3-1 Lesson Plan, p. 77; 3-1 Section Summary, p. 78

Media and Technology

 Audiotapes English-Spanish Summary 3-1

replaced by a backbone. A few vertebrates have backbones made of **cartilage,** a connective tissue that is softer than bone, but flexible and strong. Most vertebrates have backbones made of hard bone.

Besides a notochord, all chordates have a nerve cord that runs down their back—your spinal cord is such a nerve cord. The nerve cord is the connection between the brain and the nerves, on which messages travel back and forth. Many other groups of animals—crustaceans and worms, for example—have nerve cords, but their nerve cords do not run down their backs.

In addition, chordates have slits in their throat area called pharyngeal (fayr uhn JEE uhl) slits. Fishes keep these slits as part of their gills for their entire lives, but in many vertebrates, including humans, pharyngeal slits disappear before birth.

Figure 1 This lancelet exhibits all the typical characteristics of a chordate. It has a notochord that helps support its body, pharyngeal slits that help it to breathe, and a nerve cord.

✓ *Checkpoint* *What characteristics do all chordates share?*

The Backbone and Endoskeleton

A vertebrate's backbone runs down the center of its back. The backbone is formed by many similar bones, called **vertebrae** (singular *vertebra*), lined up in a row, like beads on a string. Joints between the vertebrae give the vertebral column flexibility. You are able to bend over and tie your sneakers partly because your backbone is flexible. Each vertebra has a hole in it that allows the spinal cord to pass through it. The spinal cord fits into the vertebrae like fingers fit into rings.

A vertebrate's backbone is part of an endoskeleton, or internal skeleton. The endoskeleton supports and protects the body, helps give it shape, and gives muscles a place to attach. In addition to the backbone, the vertebrate's endoskeleton includes

Figure 2 The bodies of all vertebrates are supported by an endoskeleton with a backbone. *Comparing and Contrasting What are two ways in which the cow and chicken skeletons are similar? What are two ways in which they are different?*

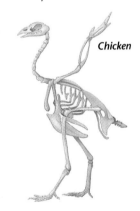

Cow

Chicken

Answers to Self-Assessment

Caption Question

Figure 2 Both skeletons have backbones, ribs, legs. A chicken skeleton is small and built for standing on two legs, while a cow skeleton is large and stands on four legs.

✓ *Checkpoint*

All chordates have a notochord, a nerve cord, and pharyngeal slits.

---

2 *Facilitate*

The Chordate Phylum

Demonstration

ACTIVITY

To help students visualize the notochord, give them semirigid plastic rulers. Allow students to manipulate the rulers to see that they have some flexibility, but not a lot. Explain that notochords, too, have some flexibility. **learning modality: kinesthetic**

The Backbone and Endoskeleton

Using the Visuals: Figure 2

Students whose comprehension of English is poor may not understand the text explanation of the relationship between the backbone and the endoskeleton. Instruct students to place a finger where the neck starts on the cow skeleton and trace along the vertebrae until they come to where the tail begins. Help them trace the backbone on the chicken skeleton. **limited English proficiency**

Ongoing Assessment

Drawing Provide students with unlabeled diagrams of vertebrate skeletons. Ask them to label the skull, backbone, and ribs.

The Backbone and Endoskeleton, continued

TRY THIS

Skills Focus making models

Materials *short lengths of string, enough beads to cover the length of the string*

Time 10 minutes

Tips Direct students to pack the beads tightly along the string. Ask: **What gives the beads and string flexibility?** (*The spaces between the beads*)

Making Models The string represents the spinal cord, and the beads represent the vertebrae.

Extend Have students tape or glue three consecutive beads together. Ask how this affects the flexibility of the model. (*The model is less flexible.*) Then ask students what might happen if three vertebrae in a person's backbone were fused. (*The person's back would be less flexible.*)

learning modality: kinesthetic

Maintaining Body Temperature

Building Inquiry Skills: Relating Cause and Effect

Materials *thermometer, two small cans, small bag of down feathers, string, 150-W light bulb and fixture*

Time 15 minutes

🔥 ⚡ CAUTION: *Make sure students do not touch the light bulb.* Divide students into small groups. Give each group a thermometer, a cloth bag filled with down feathers, some string, and two small cans. Have students put the thermometer into one of the cans and place it under the light bulb. After about 5 minutes, record the temperature. Instruct students to tie the down-filled bag around the other can, put the thermometer in it, and place this can under the same source of heat for about 5 minutes. Record the temperature. Invite students to discuss why the two temperature readings were different. (*The feathers acted as insulation.*)

learning modality: logical/mathematical

Bead-y Bones

You can use a string and beads to model the structure of a vertebrate's backbone.

1. Tie a large knot at one end of a piece of string.
2. Slide beads onto the string one by one. Stop when there is just enough string left to tie another large knot.
3. Tie a large knot in the unknotted end of the string.
4. Try to bend the string of beads at different places.

Making Models What does the string represent in your model? What do the beads represent?

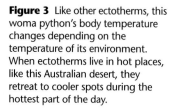

Figure 3 Like other ectotherms, this woma python's body temperature changes depending on the temperature of its environment. When ectotherms live in hot places, like this Australian desert, they retreat to cooler spots during the hottest part of the day.

the skull and ribs. The skull protects the brain and sense organs. The ribs attach to the vertebrae and protect the heart, lungs, and other internal organs. Many vertebrates also have arm and leg bones adapted for a variety of movements.

A vertebrate's endoskeleton has several important characteristics. For one thing, unlike an arthropod's exoskeleton, it grows as the animal grows. It also forms an internal frame that supports the body against the downward pull of gravity, while allowing easy movement. Because of these endoskeleton characteristics, vertebrates can grow bigger than animals with exoskeletons or no skeletons at all.

☑ *Checkpoint* *What functions does a vertebrate's skeleton perform?*

Maintaining Body Temperature

One characteristic that distinguishes the major groups of vertebrates from each other is the way in which they control their body temperature. **Most fishes, amphibians, and reptiles have a body temperature that is close to the temperature of their environment. In contrast, birds and mammals have a stable body temperature that is typically much warmer than their environment.** Fishes, amphibians, and reptiles are ectotherms. An **ectotherm** is an animal whose body does not produce much internal heat—its body temperature changes depending on the temperature of its environment. For example, when a turtle is lying in the sun on a riverbank, it has a higher body temperature than when it is swimming in a cool river. Ectotherms are sometimes called "coldblooded," but this term is misleading because the blood of ectotherms is often quite warm.

In contrast to a turtle, a beaver would have the same body temperature whether it was in cool water or on warm land. The beaver is a mammal, and mammals and birds are endotherms. An **endotherm** is an animal whose body controls and regulates its temperature by controlling the internal heat it produces. An endotherm's body temperature usually does not change much, even when the temperature of its environment changes.

Endotherms also have other adaptations, such as fur or feathers and sweat glands, for maintaining their body temperature. Fur and feathers keep endotherms warm on cool days. On hot days, on the other hand, some endotherms sweat. As the sweat evaporates, the animal is cooled. Because endotherms can keep their body temperatures stable, they can live in a greater variety of environments than ectotherms can.

Evolution of Vertebrates

The first tiny chordates swam in Earth's waters long before vertebrates appeared. If you look at Figure 5 on the next page, you will see that the pattern of vertebrate evolution looks something like a branching tree. Fossil evidence indicates that the earliest vertebrates were fishes, which first appeared about 530 million years ago. Amphibians, which appeared on Earth about 380 million years ago, are descended from fishes. Then, about 320 million years ago, amphibians gave rise to reptiles. Both mammals and birds, which you will learn about in Chapter 4, are descended from reptiles. Mammals appeared about 220 million years ago. Birds, which were the latest group of vertebrates to arise, appeared about 150 million years ago.

Figure 4 Emperor penguins are the only animals that spend the winter in Antarctica. Though Antarctic winter temperatures can fall to −50°C, a dense coat keeps the adult birds warm. A thick, fluffy baby coat keeps a penguin chick warm until it gets its adult coat. *Inferring Do you think the emperor penguin is an ectotherm or an endotherm?*

Program Resources

◆ **Teaching Resources** 3-1 Review and Reinforce, p. 79; 3-1 Enrich, p. 80

Media and Technology

 Interactive Student Tutorial CD-ROM B-3

 Transparencies "Vertebrate Evolution," Transparency 10

Answers to Self-Assessment

Caption Question

Figure 4 The penguin is an endotherm.

☑ *Checkpoint*

The vertebrate skeleton supports and protects the body, gives the body shape, and provides the muscles with places for attachment.

Addressing Naive Conceptions

Students may think that "coldblooded" animals are always cold. In fact, the body temperature of an ectotherm can be greater than that of the typical endotherm. The body temperature of an ectotherm reflects the temperature of its environment and whether it has been in the sun, shade, or underground. Point out that land-dwelling, "coldblooded" animals are rare in cold regions, but common in the tropics and other warm zones. Invite the class to speculate on why this might be so. Remind students that for ectotherms to keep their body temperatures high, they must have external sources of warmth. Lead students to understand that in winter in colder climates, the body temperature of an ectotherm would rarely reach a height sufficient for basic life processes.
learning modality: verbal

Evolution of Vertebrates

Building Inquiry Skills: Inferring

Remind students that chordates have a notochord, a rod that extends down the back of the animal. In most true vertebrates, the notochord is replaced by a backbone as the animal grows. There are very few surviving chordate species with only a notochord, but thousands of species of vertebrates. Ask students to think of why vertebrates may be better adapted to survive in many environments than invertebrates chordates. (*Vertebrae provide more support for the body and protect the nerve chord.*)

Ongoing Assessment

Drawing Have each student draw a picture of an ectotherm (except the turtle mentioned in the text) in an environment that would cause its body temperature to be high and that same animal in an environment that would lower its body temperature. These should be environments where the chosen animal might actually live.
 Students can save their drawings in their portfolios.

Evolution of Vertebrates, continued

Using the Visuals: Figure 5

To help students understand the visual, ask: **Which evolved first, amphibians or reptiles?** *(amphibians)* **When did mammals first evolve?** *(About 220 million years ago)* **learning modality: visual**

3 Assess

Section 1 Review

1. The backbone supports the body, gives the body flexibility, and protects the spinal cord.

2. The body temperature of ectotherms (e.g., goldfish and frogs) changes depending on the temperature of the environment. Endotherms (e.g., robins and mice) have bodies that control internal body heat and therefore maintain nearly constant body temperatures.

3. Birds and mammals

4. Endotherms would probably be more active at night because they would not be slowed down by the drop in environmental temperature as much as ectotherms would be.

Science at Home

If a student's family has a whole fish for dinner, encourage the student to examine the fish skeleton after dinner with the family, pointing out the backbone. Have the student observe how the skeleton gives the fish its distinctive shape and how it also forms the frame that protects the internal organs.

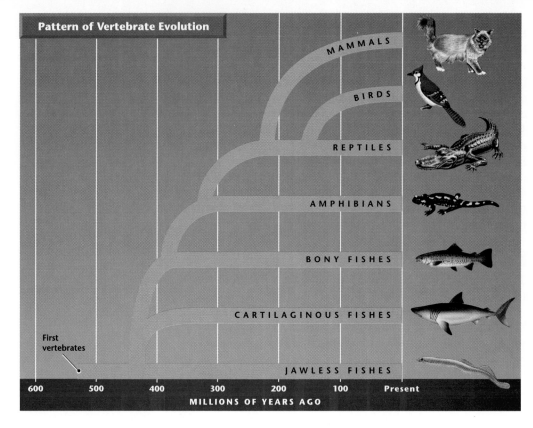

Figure 5 The diagram shows the branching pattern of vertebrate evolution. The first vertebrates, the jawless fishes, arose about 530 million years ago.
Interpreting Diagrams About how much time passed between the time when fishes first appeared and the time that birds arose?

Section 1 Review

1. What are three functions of a backbone?
2. Explain how ectotherms and endotherms differ in the way they control their body temperature. Give two examples of each.
3. What two groups of present-day vertebrates are the descendants of reptiles?
4. **Thinking Critically Making Generalizations** Would you expect ectotherms or endotherms to be more active at night? Explain your answer.

Science at Home

Have members of your family feel the tops of the vertebrae running down the center of their backs. Then have them feel the hard skull beneath the skin on their foreheads. In addition, if you have fish with bones for dinner, examine the fish skeleton with your family after dinner, pointing out the backbone. Show where the spinal cord runs through the vertebrae. Discuss the functions of the backbone and skull.

Performance Assessment

Drawing Have students sketch simple human skeletons and label the skull, ribs, backbone, vertebrae, and spinal cord. Then ask them to title their sketches "An Endotherm" or "An Ectotherm."

 Students can save their sketches in their portfolios.

Background

Facts and Figures One of the oldest known fossil chordates is called *Pikaia* (pee KY uh). It comes from the Burgess Shale of British Columbia and is about 530 million years old. Fossils of primitive chordates are very rare because these animals had no hard parts. (Hard parts are more easily preserved.) Much of our understanding of early chordates comes from the study of such important fossils as *Pikaia*.

Answers to Self-Assessment

Caption Question

Figure 5 About 280 million years passed between the time when the fishes first appeared and the time that birds arose.

DISCOVER ••••••••••••••••••••••••••••••••••• ACTIVITY

How Does Water Flow Over a Fish's Gills?

1. Closely observe a fish in an aquarium for a few minutes. Note how frequently the fish opens its mouth. Water moves through the fish's mouth across its gills.

2. Notice the flaps on each side of the fish's head behind its eyes. Observe how the flaps open and close.

3. Observe the movements of the mouth and the flaps at the same time. Note any relationship between the movements of these two structures.

Think It Over

Observing What do the flaps on the sides of the fish do when the fish opens its mouth? What role do you think these two structures play in a fish's life?

I n the warm waters of a coral reef, a fish called a moray eel hovers in the water, barely moving. A smaller fish, a wrasse, swims up to the moray and begins to eat tiny parasites that are attached to the moray's skin. Like a vacuum cleaner on a rug, the wrasse moves slowly over the moray eel, eating dead skin and bacteria as well as parasites. The wrasse even cleans inside the moray's mouth and gills. Both fishes benefit from this cleaning. The moray gets rid of parasites and other unwanted materials, and the wrasse gets a meal.

Both the wrasse and the moray it cleans belong to the vertebrate group known as fishes. A **fish** is an ectothermic vertebrate that lives in the water and has fins, which are structures used for moving. In addition, most fishes obtain oxygen through gills and have scales. Scales are thin, overlapping plates that cover the skin of a fish. They are made of a hard substance similar to that of your fingernails.

Fishes make up the largest group of vertebrates—nearly half of all vertebrate species are fishes. In addition, fishes have been swimming in Earth's waters for more than 500 million years—longer than any other kind of vertebrate.

GUIDE FOR READING

◆ How do fish use their gills?

◆ What are the three groups of fishes?

Reading Tip As you read about the different groups of fishes, make a table that compares and contrasts the characteristics of the groups.

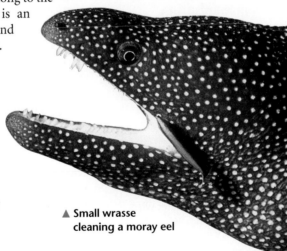

▲ Small wrasse cleaning a moray eel

READING STRATEGIES

Reading Tip Students' tables must include jawless, cartilaginous, and bony fishes. Have students look over the section. Possible heads for the table include: Type of skeleton; Are jaws present?; Other characteristics; Examples.

Study and Comprehension Help students understand what they read by preparing a short lesson to teach other students. Allow students to choose jawless fishes, cartilaginous fishes, or bony fishes as topics for their lessons. Tell them they must use the information from the text.

Objectives

After completing this lesson, students will be able to
◆ explain how fish use their gills;
◆ name the three major groups of fishes;
◆ explain how fish provide food for people.

Key Terms fish, swim bladder, buoyant force

1 Engage/Explore

Activating Prior Knowledge

Encourage students to describe characteristics of fish they have observed either directly or indirectly. Ask questions such as: **What did the skin look like? What did the scales feel like? Where are the fins located?**

•••••••• DISCOVER ••••••••

Skills Focus observing
Materials *several live fish, each one in an aquarium or fishbowl*
Time 10 minutes
Tips Use a larger fish, such as a goldfish, with gill movements that can be easily observed. Once the fish is calm, it will breathe with a regular rhythm. After observing the breathing for a while, students should be able to tell that the mouth and flaps open at the same time.
Expected Outcome Students should observe that when the fish opens its mouth, its gill flaps also open.
Extend Ask students to count the number of times the gill flaps open per minute. Direct them to work in pairs and compare their results with those of the other groups.
Think It Over The mouth and the gill flaps open at the same time. The mouth enables water to enter the fish and pass over the gills, which take in oxygen from the water. The flaps open to enable the water to leave.

2 Facilitate

Obtaining Oxygen

Addressing Naive Conceptions

Some students may not realize that gases such as oxygen and carbon dioxide can dissolve in liquids like water. To reinforce this concept, use the example of a carbonated beverage. Ask: **What happens when you pop the top on a soft drink?** *(Bubbles form.)* **learning modality: verbal**

Sharpen your Skills

Skills Focus
communicating
Materials *preserved fish, goggles, dissecting tray, blunt probe, hand lens, rubber gloves*
Time 50 minutes
Tips Provide gloves to all students. Help students see the connection between the mouth and gill slits by letting them pass the end of the probe into the fish's mouth and out through the gill openings. Students should wash their hands after handling the fish.
Extend Have students closely examine the feathery structure of the gills. Ask: **How is the structure of the gills related to their functions?** *(The feathery structure provides more surface area for absorbing oxygen.)* **learning modality: kinesthetic**

Moving and Feeding

Real-Life Learning

Encourage students who have fished before to tell the class about strategies they use to catch various types of fish. Ask: **What do you think people need to know about the feeding and hunting strategies of fish?** *(Sample answer: They must know about the feeding habits and habitats of the fish.)* **learning modality: verbal**

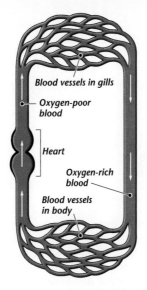

Figure 6 Trace the path of blood through a fish's one-loop circulatory system. *Interpreting Diagrams* *Where does the blood pick up oxygen?*

Sharpen your Skills

Communicating

Put on your goggles.
Observe a preserved fish. Note its size, shape, and the number and locations of its fins. Lift the gill cover and observe the gill with a hand lens. Make a diagram of your observations, and include a written description. Wash your hands.

Ask a classmate to check your work to make sure it clearly communicates what you observed. Then make any necessary improvements.

Obtaining Oxygen

Fishes get their oxygen from water. As a fish cruises along, it automatically opens its mouth, as you observed in the Discover activity, and takes a gulp of water. The water, which contains oxygen, moves through openings in the fish's throat region that lead to the gills. Gills, which look like tiny feathers, are red because of the many blood vessels within them. **As water flows over the gills, oxygen moves from the water into the fish's blood, while carbon dioxide, a waste product, moves out of the blood and into the water.** After flowing over the gills, water leaves the fish by flowing out through slits beneath the gill covers.

From the gills, the blood travels throughout the fish's body, supplying the body cells with oxygen. Like all vertebrates, fishes have a closed circulatory system, in which blood flows through blood vessels to all regions of the body. The heart of a fish pumps blood in one continuous loop—from the heart to the gills, from the gills to the rest of the body, and back to the heart. Trace this path in Figure 6.

Moving and Feeding

Fins help fish swim. A typical fin, such as those on the angelfish in Figure 7, consists of a thin membrane stretched across bony supports. Like a wide canoe paddle, a fin provides a large surface to push against the water. If you've ever swum wearing a pair of swim fins and noticed how much faster you move through the water, you understand the great advantage of the large surface of a fin.

Because fishes spend most of their time hunting for food or feeding, most of their movements are related to eating. The bodies of most fishes are adapted for efficient feeding. Some carnivores, such as barracuda, have sharp and pointed teeth—good for stabbing smaller fishes. Insect-eating fish, such as trout, have short, blunt teeth with which they grip and crush their prey. Filter feeders, such as basking sharks, use comblike structures on their gills to filter tiny animals and plants from the water.

A fish's highly developed nervous system and sense organs help it find food and avoid predators. Fishes can see much better in water than you can. Keen senses of touch, smell, and taste also help fishes capture food. A shark can smell and taste even a tiny amount of blood—as little as one drop in 115 liters of water! Some fishes have taste organs in unusual places; a catfish, for example, tastes with its whiskers.

☑ *Checkpoint* *How does having fins help a fish?*

Background

Facts and Figures Many different types of fish are able to blend into their environment for protection. One example is the coloration of many of the fishes that swim in schools, such as tuna and sardines. Light penetrates only a short distance down in the water in the ocean. Past the point where the light penetrates, the water appears dark. So when predators look down at a school of fishes, the dark color of all the fishes grouped together helps them blend in with the darkness. When predators deep in the ocean look up, they see the light of the sun, and they cannot distinguish the silvery bellies of the fishes from the glare of the sun. The two-toned coloration of schooling fishes helps protect them from danger above and below.

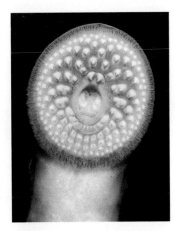

Figure 7 A fish's fins act as paddles to propel it through the water. You can clearly see the bone structure of a fin on the skeleton of an angelfish.

How Fishes Reproduce

Most fishes have external fertilization. Recall from Chapter 2 that in external fertilization, the eggs are fertilized outside of the female's body. The male hovers close to the female and spreads a cloud of sperm over the eggs as she releases them. Sharks and guppies, in contrast, have internal fertilization, in which the eggs are fertilized inside the female's body. The young fish then develop inside her body. When they are mature enough to live on their own, she gives birth to them.

Fishes Without Jaws

Biologists classify fishes into three major groups: jawless fishes, cartilaginous fishes, and bony fishes. They are distinguished from one another by the structure of their mouths and the types of skeletons they have. Jawless fishes were the earliest vertebrates. Today there are only about 60 species. Modern jawless fishes are unlike other fishes in that they have no scales. Their skeletons are made of cartilage, and they do not have pairs of fins. Most remarkably, they cannot bite like other fishes because their mouths do not have jaws! How can a fish without a jaw eat? The mouths of jawless fishes have structures for scraping, stabbing, and sucking.

Hagfishes and lampreys are the only kinds of jawless fishes. Hagfishes look like large, slimy worms. They crawl into the bodies of dead or dying fishes and use their sandpapery tongue to consume their decaying tissues. Many lampreys are parasites of other fishes. They attach their mouths to healthy fishes and then suck in the tissues and blood of their victims. If you look at the lamprey's mouth in Figure 8, you can probably imagine the damage it can do.

Figure 8 Lampreys are fish with eel-shaped bodies. They use their sharp teeth and suction-cup mouth to feed on other fish. *Classifying To what group of fishes do lampreys belong?*

Chapter 3 **B ◆ 89**

Answers to Self-Assessment

Caption Questions

Figure 6 The blood picks up oxygen in the gills.

Figure 8 Lampreys are jawless fishes.

☑ *Checkpoint*

Fins work like paddles with a large surface. They push against the water and propel the fish.

How Fishes Reproduce

Building Inquiry Skills: Applying Concepts

Challenge students to make inferences about the advantages and disadvantages of external and internal fertilization in fishes. Ask volunteers to list on the board the advantages and disadvantages of each kind of fertilization. (*External fertilization: advantage—more offspring produced; disadvantage—lower survival rate. Internal fertilization: advantage— higher survival rate; disadvantage—fewer offspring produced*) **learning modality: verbal**

Fishes Without Jaws

Using the Visuals: Figure 8

Direct students to locate the mouth of the jawless fish in the figure. Have them describe the mouth. Ask them whether the lamprey's mouth looks like the mouths of fishes they are familiar with. (*Students will probably say no.*) Invite students to infer how the lamprey's specialized mouth helps it feed. Inform students that the lamprey feeds by attaching to a living fish, boring a hole in the fish's side, and eating the fluids that leak out. Its teethlike structures help the lamprey stay attached to its host. **learning modality: verbal**

Ongoing Assessment

Writing Ask students to write several paragraphs that describe an hour in a fish's life. Students' paragraphs should include how the fish hunts for food and eludes predators. Encourage students to focus on how their fish uses its highly developed sense organs. Ask students to think about this question as they write: **How does a fish view the world through its senses?**

 Students can save their paragraphs in their portfolios.

B ◆ 89

Cartilaginous Fishes

Building Inquiry Skills: Observation

Materials *partial skeleton from a whole, cooked chicken breast*

Time 15 minutes

Allow students to work in small groups, to reduce the number of chicken breasts required. Before removing the skeleton from the breast, cut the cartilage away from the meat to ensure the cartilage stays with the bone when removed. Give a skeleton to each group, and direct students to distinguish between the bones and the cartilage. Tell them that the cartilage in the chicken breast is bluish-white; the bone is brown. Urge students to attempt to bend and twist both cartilage and bone. Circulate among groups to verify that students can distinguish between the two. Then have students write brief answers to the following questions.

◆ **Which is more flexible, bone or cartilage?** *(cartilage)*
◆ **Which is more difficult to twist out of shape?** *(bone)*
◆ **Which is more likely to break than to bend?** *(bone)*

Extend Ask students to discuss how having a skeleton made of both bone and cartilage benefits the chicken. *(Bone is stronger than cartilage and so it provides stronger support. Cartilage gives flexibility to some parts of the body.)* **cooperative learning**

Cultural Diversity

Cartilaginous is an adjective formed from the noun *cartilage*. English has many words like this. Have students find other examples in the text of an adjective and noun sharing the same root. *(oxygen—oxygenated; nerve—nervous; sense—sensory)* Invite nonnative English speakers to give examples from their own languages. **limited English proficiency**

Cartilaginous Fishes

Sharks, rays, and skates are cartilaginous (cahrt uhl AJ uh nuhs) fishes. As the group's name suggests, the skeletons of these fishes are made of cartilage, just like the skeletons of jawless fishes. However, unlike lampreys and hagfishes, cartilaginous fishes have jaws and pairs of fins. Pointed, toothlike scales cover their bodies, giving them a texture that is rougher than sandpaper. Cartilaginous fishes are all carnivores. Rays and skates live on the ocean floor, where they filter feed or hunt mollusks, crustaceans, and small fishes.

Figure 9 This blue-spotted ray is a cartilaginous fish that lives on the ocean floor. *Comparing and Contrasting How do cartilaginous fishes differ from jawless fishes?*

A Shark's Body Most shark bodies are streamlined so they can move quickly through the water. A shark's mouth is usually on the bottom part of its head. It contains jagged teeth arranged in rows. Most sharks use only the first couple of rows for feeding—the remaining rows are replacements. If a shark loses a front-row tooth, a tooth behind it moves up to replace it.

Always on the Move Most sharks cannot pump water over their gills. Instead they rely on swimming or currents to keep water moving across their gills. When sharks sleep, they position themselves in currents that send water over their gills.

Sharks spend most of their time hunting for food. They will attack and eat nearly anything that smells like food. Because they see poorly, sometimes they swallow strange objects. For example, one shark was found to have a raincoat, three overcoats, and an automobile license plate in its stomach.

☑ *Checkpoint* *Why must sharks always keep water moving over their gills?*

Figure 10 This sand tiger shark exhibits a very familiar shark trait—many sharp teeth. Despite this shark's ferocious appearance, however, sand tiger sharks do not typically attack humans.

Background

Facts and Figures One part of a fish's sensory system consists of a canal called the lateral line that runs along the sides of the fish's body. This important groove can easily be seen in most bony fishes. The lateral line is covered with sensory hairs similar to the sensory hairs found in the inner ears of other vertebrates, including humans.

These hairs respond to the slight pressure changes caused by vibrations in the water. This enables a fish to detect changes in currents or water pressure. Predatory fishes can detect the slightest movement of prey with these sensitive organs. Their lateral lines allow them to hunt for food even if the water is murky.

Bony Fishes

Most familiar kinds of fishes, such as trout, tuna, and goldfish, have skeletons made of hard bone. Their bodies are covered with scales, and a pocket on each side of the head holds the fish's gills. Each gill pocket is covered by a flexible flap that opens to release water. To learn more about the major characteristics of bony fishes, look closely at the perch in *Exploring a Bony Fish*.

Swim Bladders and Buoyancy If you drop a brick into water, it sinks to the bottom. A wooden block, in contrast, floats on the surface. Unlike the brick or the block, fishes neither sink nor float on the surface.

INTEGRATING PHYSICS

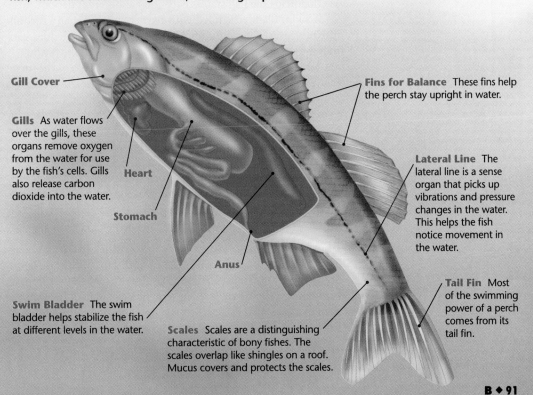

EXPLORING *a Bony Fish*

In a quiet, shady area near the bank of a stream or pond, you might find some yellow perch swimming along. These freshwater fish, which like slow-moving water, travel in groups called schools.

Gill Cover

Gills As water flows over the gills, these organs remove oxygen from the water for use by the fish's cells. Gills also release carbon dioxide into the water.

Heart

Stomach

Anus

Swim Bladder The swim bladder helps stabilize the fish at different levels in the water.

Scales Scales are a distinguishing characteristic of bony fishes. The scales overlap like shingles on a roof. Mucus covers and protects the scales.

Fins for Balance These fins help the perch stay upright in water.

Lateral Line The lateral line is a sense organ that picks up vibrations and pressure changes in the water. This helps the fish notice movement in the water.

Tail Fin Most of the swimming power of a perch comes from its tail fin.

B ◆ 91

Program Resources

- **Science Explorer Series** *Motion, Forces, and Energy,* Chapter 3
- ◆ **Interdisciplinary Exploration Series** "Where River Meets Sea," pp. 13–14, 22–23

Media and Technology

Transparencies "Exploring a Bony Fish," Transparency 11

Answers to Self-Assessment

Caption Question

Figure 9 Cartilaginous fishes have jaws and paired fins. Jawless fishes do not.

✓ *Checkpoint*

Since sharks cannot pump water over their gills, they must move through the water or rest in moving water in order to obtain oxygen.

Bony Fishes

EXPLORING

a Bony Fish

Direct students to explain the function of each structure shown in the visual. Then ask them to think of how the structures described in the visual accomplish that function. For example, ask: **How does the tail fin help the perch move through the water?** (*The tail fin provides a large surface to push against the water, propelling the fish.*) Choose pairs of students, and have them describe how they think each structure works. **learning modality: visual**

Integrating Physics

ACTIVITY

Materials *small balloon, fishing weight, string, sink or bucket filled with water, ruler, watch or timer*
Time 30 minutes

Explore the concept of neutral buoyancy by challenging students to construct model swim bladders using the given materials. Students should work in pairs. One option is for pairs to partially inflate the balloon, tie it to the weight with a short piece of string, and immerse the model in a sink or aquarium. The goal is to have the balloon/weight combination hang motionless underwater—neither rising nor sinking. While one student immerses the model, the partner can measure the amount of time it takes for the model to either sink to the bottom or float to the top. If it does neither, the model has achieved neutral buoyancy. Even with a fairly heavy weight, students will find that the balloon will have to be inflated only slightly to achieve neutral buoyancy. **learning modality: kinesthetic**

Ongoing Assessment

Skills Check Have students infer what would happen to a shark in still water if the shark could not move. (*The shark would die, because it could not obtain oxygen.*)

B ◆ 91

Bony Fishes, continued

Building Inquiry Skills: Observing

Locate an aquarium or fishpond where students can conduct a scientific study of the behavior of fishes. Students should spend at least 10 minutes, or more if possible, observing and recording interesting behavior. Suggest that students choose one species of fish to observe. Give them these questions to direct their observations:

◆ Is this a bony fish, a jawless fish, or a cartilaginous fish?
◆ How does the fish interact with its surroundings?
◆ What does it eat?
◆ How does it find food?
◆ How does it react to stimuli, such as sound?
◆ How does it interact with other fishes?
◆ What habitat does it seem to prefer?

Students will probably not be able to answer all the questions within the allotted time, but they may be able to devise strategies for answering them.

learning modality: visual

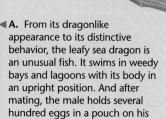

Figure 11 The photographs show just a few species of bony fishes. *Making Generalizations What characteristics do all of these fish have in common?*

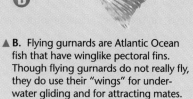

◄**A.** From its dragonlike appearance to its distinctive behavior, the leafy sea dragon is an unusual fish. It swims in weedy bays and lagoons with its body in an upright position. And after mating, the male holds several hundred eggs in a pouch on his belly until they are ready to hatch.

▲**B.** Flying gurnards are Atlantic Ocean fish that have winglike pectoral fins. Though flying gurnards do not really fly, they do use their "wings" for underwater gliding and for attracting mates.

Instead, they swim at different depths in the water. Most bony fishes have an organ called a **swim bladder**, an internal gas-filled sac that helps the fish stabilize its body at different depths.

A swim bladder is filled with oxygen, nitrogen, and carbon dioxide gases. The volume of gases in the swim bladder can become larger or smaller. This change in volume affects the buoyant force on the fish. **Buoyant force** (BOI uhnt force) is the force that water exerts upward on any underwater object. If the buoyant force on an object is greater than the weight of the object, then the object floats. If the buoyant force is less than the weight of the object, the object sinks. A brick sinks because it weighs more than the buoyant force pushing upward against it; a wooden block floats because it weighs less than the buoyant force.

A fish has greater buoyancy when the volume of gases in its swim bladder is large than when the gas volume is small. By adjusting its buoyancy as it moves in the water, a fish can float at different depths without using a large amount of energy.

Diversity of Bony Fishes Bony fishes, which make up about 95 percent of all fish species, live in both salt and fresh water. Some live in the lightless depths of the oceans, and seldom, if ever, come near the surface. Others thrive in light-filled waters, such as those of coral reefs or shallow ponds. Figure 11 shows some of the great variety of bony fishes.

☑ *Checkpoint* If a pencil floats, how does the buoyant force on the pencil compare to the pencil's weight?

Background

Facts and Figures Some fishes use their swim bladders to communicate. Special muscles located around the bladder tense and vibrate the membrane of the bladder. This membrane acts like the skin of a drum, producing very loud sounds. The sounds produced by the vibrating of the swim bladder can be carried over long distances through water. The sounds can be heard as a kind of drumming or thumping sound. One of the best "drummers" is the croaker, which is named for the sound it makes. It communicates with other croakers and uses its song to find mates. The sounds of many fishes can be heard in the ocean.

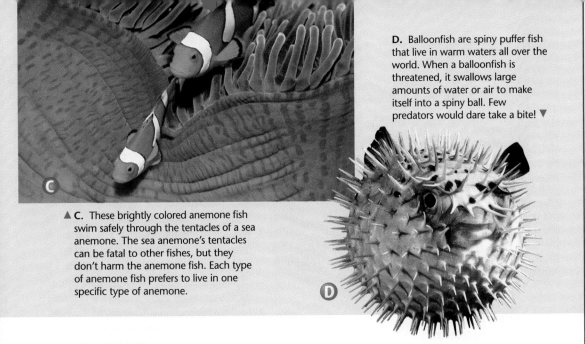

D. Balloonfish are spiny puffer fish that live in warm waters all over the world. When a balloonfish is threatened, it swallows large amounts of water or air to make itself into a spiny ball. Few predators would dare take a bite! ▼

▲ **C.** These brightly colored anemone fish swim safely through the tentacles of a sea anemone. The sea anemone's tentacles can be fatal to other fishes, but they don't harm the anemone fish. Each type of anemone fish prefers to live in one specific type of anemone.

Food for People

 INTEGRATING ENVIRONMENTAL SCIENCE People used to think of oceans and rivers as having a limitless supply of fish. Recently, though, overfishing has drastically reduced populations of the Atlantic codfish, Pacific salmon, and many other fish species. Some countries are trying to stop overfishing. The United States, Canada, and other countries have recently set limits on the amounts of certain kinds of fish that can be caught. In addition, some fishes, such as catfish, are being raised in "fish farms." This practice reduces the demand for fish caught in rivers and oceans.

Section 2 Review

1. Could a fish obtain oxygen if it could not open its mouth? In explaining your answer, describe the role of the fish's gills.
2. How is a shark's skeleton different from a perch's?
3. Describe the ways in which two different fishes are adapted to obtain food.
4. **Thinking Critically** **Predicting** How might a shark's hunting be affected if it were unable to smell?

> **Check Your Progress**
> **CHAPTER PROJECT 3**
> By now you should have decided on the adaptation that you want to model. Select a specific fish in which to model this adaptation. Reference books, software, and magazine articles can help you make this choice. Then assemble your materials and build your model. *(Hint:* You might want to go to a pet store to observe how fish and other vertebrates move.)

Answers to Self-Assessment

Caption Question

Figure 11 All the fishes have bony skeletons and swim bladders. Their bodies are covered with scales, and their gills are in flap-covered pockets on each side of the head.

✓ *Checkpoint*
The buoyant force is greater than the weight of the pencil.

Food for People

 Integrating Environmental Science

Encourage students to brainstorm other ways that might be used to stop overfishing. Ideas could include catch-and-release fishing and fishing bans.
learning modality: verbal

3 Assess

Section 2 Review Answers

1. No, because water gets to the gills through the mouth. The gills remove oxygen from water.
2. The shark's skeleton is made entirely of cartilage. The perch's is mostly made of bone.
3. Answers will vary. Sample: The barracuda has long, sharp teeth with which it can capture prey. The lamprey has sharp teeth and a suction mouth that allow it to attach itself to a host fish and feed on the host's blood and tissue.
4. A shark that could not smell would only be able to hunt animals that it could see. But because sharks do not have very good vision, the shark would not be able to capture as much prey.

> **Check Your Progress**
> **CHAPTER PROJECT 3**
> Review and approve students' adaptation and fish choices. Make sure that the adaptation they have chosen can be easily modeled for the fish and for an amphibian and a reptile. Help students locate reference sources and materials.

Performance Assessment

Concept Mapping Have each student draw a concept map to show the three main types of fish described in this section, their characteristics, and examples.

Home Sweet Home

Preparing for Inquiry

Key Concept Organisms need specific habitats in order to survive.

Skills Objective Students will be able to
◆ make a model habitat.

Time 30 minutes to set up, then 10 minutes per day for two weeks

Advance Planning
◆ Provide sufficient clean water for all the groups. The chlorine may be removed by letting the water stand for two or three days or by treatment with a special chemical available at pet shops.
◆ Make sure other supplies are thoroughly clean. Do not use soap.

Alternative Methods A large fishbowl can be used in place of an aquarium.

Guiding Inquiry

Troubleshooting the Experiment
◆ Keep plenty of chlorine-free water available to add to the tank.
◆ Remove dead organisms and waste immediately. Do not overfeed fish.

Expected Outcome
After a day or two, if the animals have adapted, the snails should be moving about the tank feeding. The fish should be swimming normally and feeding.

Analyze and Conclude
1. **a.** By air entering through the filter and oxygen from plants **b.** From the heater or sunlight **c.** By the plants and by the students
2. The oxygen is used by the fish. Plants release oxygen.
3. In an aquarium, ideal conditions are maintained artificially. In nature, animals have to locate their own food and avoid prey.

Extending Inquiry

More to Explore Questions might include, will the new fish prey on the guppies? Is there enough space?

Home Sweet Home

For an artificial environment to work, it must meet the needs of the organisms that live in it. In this lab, you will build an aquarium for guppies, whose natural environment is warm, fresh water.

Problem

How does an aquarium enable fish to survive?

Skills Focus

making models, posing questions

Materials

gravel	metric ruler	guppies
snails	guppy food	dip net
tap water	thermometer	water plants
aquarium filter	aquarium heater	

rectangular aquarium tank (15 to 20 liters) with cover

Procedure

1. Wash the aquarium tank with lukewarm water—do not use soap. Then place it on a flat surface in indirect sunlight.
2. Rinse the gravel and spread it over the bottom of the tank to a depth of about 3 cm.
3. Fill the tank about two-thirds full with tap water. Position several water plants in the tank by gently pushing their roots into the gravel. Wash your hands after handling the plants.
4. Add more water until the level is about 5 cm from the top.
5. Place the filter in the water and turn it on. Insert an aquarium heater into the tank, and turn it on. Set the temperature to 25°C. **CAUTION:** *Do not touch electrical equipment with wet hands.*
6. Allow the water to "age" by letting it stand for 2 days. Aging allows the chlorine to evaporate.
7. When the water has aged and is at the proper temperature, add guppies and snails to the tank. Include one guppy and one snail for each 4 liters of water. Cover the aquarium. Wash your hands after handling the animals.
8. Observe the aquarium every day for 2 weeks. Feed the guppies a small amount of food daily. Look for evidence that the fish and snails have adapted to their new environment. Also look for the ways they carry out their life activities, such as feeding and respiration. Record your observations.
9. Use a dip net to keep the gravel layer clean and to remove any dead plants or animals.

Analyze and Conclude

1. How does the aquarium meet the following needs of the organisms living in it: (a) oxygen supply, (b) proper temperature, and (c) food?
2. What happens to the oxygen that the fish take in from the water in this aquarium? How is that oxygen replaced?
3. **Apply** How is an aquarium like a guppy's natural environment? How is it different?

More to Explore

Write a plan for adding a different kind of fish to the aquarium. Include a list of questions that you would need to have answered before you could carry out your plan. Get the approval of your teacher before going ahead with your plan.

Safety

Students should be careful carrying the glass aquariums. They should make sure the area around the tank is dry and that their hands are dry before they plug in the electrical equipment. Review the safety guidelines in Appendix A.

Program Resources

◆ **Teaching Resources** Chapter 3 Real-World Lab, pp. 97–98

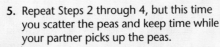

DISCOVER · ACTIVITY

What's the Advantage of Being Green?

1. Count out 20 dried yellow peas and 20 green ones. Mix them up in a paper cup.

2. Cover your eyes. Have your partner gently scatter the peas onto a large sheet of green paper.

3. Uncover your eyes. Have your partner keep time while you pick up as many peas, one at a time, as you can find in 15 seconds.

4. When 15 seconds are up, count how many peas of each color you picked up.

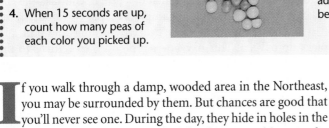

5. Repeat Steps 2 through 4, but this time you scatter the peas and keep time while your partner picks up the peas.

6. Compare your results with those of your partner and your classmates.

Think It Over

Inferring Many frogs are green, and the environment in which they live is mostly green. What advantage does a frog have in being green?

If you walk through a damp, wooded area in the Northeast, you may be surrounded by them. But chances are good that you'll never see one. During the day, they hide in holes in the ground and cracks in rocks. At night they scramble over the decaying leaves on the forest floor, searching for food. Some climb to the tops of bushes and rocks to find their prey. What are these creatures that roam by night? They are red-backed salamanders.

Most of these slender, long-tailed animals are only as long as your longest finger. They may be small, but there are a lot of them. Some northeastern woodlands probably have more red-backed salamanders than all birds and mammals combined.

> ### GUIDE FOR READING
>
> ◆ What is the life cycle of an amphibian like?
>
> ◆ How are amphibians adapted for movement on land?
>
> *Reading Tip* Before you begin to read, write two or three things you already know about amphibians. After you have read this section, add three things you have learned.

Figure 12 Red-backed salamanders are the most common amphibians in some damp northeastern woodlands.

Chapter 3 **B ◆ 95**

Objectives

After completing this lesson, students will be able to

◆ describe the characteristics of amphibians, their life cycles, and amphibian groups;

◆ describe how amphibians are adapted for movement on land and current threats to their survival.

Key Terms amphibian, atria, ventricle, habitat

1 Engage/Explore

Activating Prior Knowledge

Ask students: **Do you know any animals that live part of their life in water and part of their life on land?** *(Students may say frogs, toads, or salamanders.)* **What characteristics do you think allow these animals to do this?** *(Students may say different life stages, such as tadpoles and adults in frogs.)* Make a list of answers on the board. Reexamine this list after students have completed this section.

· · · · · · · · DISCOVER · · · · · · · · ·

Skills Focus inferring
Materials *dried yellow and green peas; paper cup; green construction paper, approximately 1 m × 1 m; clock or watch with second hand*
Time 10 minutes
Tips To intensify the camouflage effect, make sure that the green background closely matches the color of the green peas. Tell students to toss the peas gently onto the paper, so the peas do not scatter onto the floor.
Expected Outcome Students should pick up more yellow peas than green peas from the green background.
Think It Over Being a color that blends in with the environment makes it more difficult for frogs to be seen by predators and thus more likely that they will survive and reproduce.

Gills to Lungs

Building Inquiry Skills: Inferring

Once students are familiar with amphibian metamorphosis, ask: **Why is water essential for amphibian life?** *(Their eggs are laid and hatched in water. Their larvae live in water. Adult amphibians need to stay moist in order to absorb oxygen through their skin.)* Then ask: **How does acquiring lungs change the life of amphibians?** *(They are able to leave the water, breathe air, and live on land.)* **learning modality: verbal**

Amphibian Circulation

Including All Students

Materials 25 red balloons

Time 5 minutes

This activity helps students to understand oxygen uptake in an adult amphibian's circulatory system. Position students at five stations representing parts of the circulatory system—lungs, body, right atrium, left atrium, and ventricle. Place 25 red balloons, representing oxygen, at the lungs station. Slowly clap your hands to indicate heartbeats. At each heartbeat, students change stations in the direction of blood flow. For example, students at the body station will move to the right atrium. Students at the ventricle move to the lungs or back to the body. Students at the lungs will pick up a balloon, and students at the body must drop off a balloon if they are holding one. A student holding a balloon represents oxygen-rich blood. A student without a balloon represents oxygen-poor blood. Continue for 3 or 4 minutes. Ask: **Where in an adult amphibian's circulatory system is oxygen acquired?** *(the lungs and skin)* **Where is oxygen released?** *(in the body)* **Where does mixing of oxygen-rich and oxygen-poor blood occur?** *(in the ventricle)* **learning modality: kinesthetic**

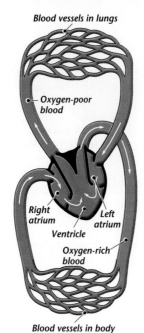

Figure 13 An adult amphibian's circulatory system has two loops. One loop runs from the heart to the lungs and back, and the second runs from the heart to the body and back.

Figure 14 The throat of this "peeper" inflates as he calls out to potential mates.

Gills to Lungs

The red-backed salamander is one kind of amphibian; frogs and toads are others. An **amphibian** is an ectothermic vertebrate that spends its early life in water. The word *amphibian* means "double life," and amphibians have exactly that. **After beginning their lives in the water, most amphibians spend their adulthood on land, returning to water to reproduce.**

Most amphibians lay their eggs in water. Amphibian eggs hatch into larvae that swim and have gills for obtaining oxygen. As they undergo metamorphosis and become adults, most amphibians lose their gills and acquire lungs. Adult amphibians also obtain oxygen and get rid of carbon dioxide through their thin, moist skin.

Amphibian Circulation

The circulatory system of a tadpole—the larval form of a frog or toad—has a single loop, like that of a fish. In contrast, the circulatory system of many adult amphibians has two loops. In the first loop, blood flows from the heart to the lungs and skin, and picks up oxygen. This oxygen-rich blood then returns to the heart. In the second loop, the blood flows to the rest of the body, delivering oxygen-rich blood to the cells.

As you read about the heart, trace the path of blood through the amphibian's circulatory system shown in Figure 13. The hearts of most amphibians have three inner spaces, or chambers. The two upper chambers of the heart, called **atria** (singular *atrium*), receive blood. One atrium receives oxygen-rich blood from the lungs, and the other receives oxygen-poor blood from the rest of the body. From the atria, blood moves into the lower chamber, the **ventricle**, which pumps blood out to the lungs and body. Oxygen-rich and oxygen-poor blood mix in the ventricle.

☑ *Checkpoint* *Compare the functions of the atria and ventricle.*

Reproduction and Development

On spring evenings near a lake or pond, you can usually hear a loud chorus of "peepers," male frogs calling to attract mates. Most frogs and toads have external fertilization—a female frog releases eggs that are then fertilized by the male's sperm. In contrast, most salamanders have internal fertilization—the eggs are fertilized before they are laid.

Background

Facts and Figures Frogs often have unique ways of protecting and caring for their young. One unusual frog rearing, or brooding, behavior is that of the Australian gastric brooding frog. Studies of this timid frog revealed that the mother keeps up to 30 tadpoles at one time in her stomach until they mature. Scientists do not know whether the tadpoles hatch and then swim into her mouth or the eggs hatch in her stomach. The tadpoles live off the nourishment of the yolk sac from their eggs. The mother's stomach stops releasing hydrochloric acid for about 8 weeks. When the young frogs have matured, the mother opens her mouth and the frogs swim out.

Australian gastric brooding frogs were first observed by scientists in 1972, but have not been seen in the past few years. Scientists think these frogs are now extinct.

Amphibian eggs are coated with clear jelly that keeps moisture in and helps protect them from infection. Inside each fertilized egg, a tiny embryo develops. In a few days, larvae wriggle out of the jelly and begin a free-swimming, fishlike life.

Most amphibian parents don't take care of their eggs after fertilization, but some do. For example, in one species of South American river toad, the male presses the fertilized eggs into the skin of the female's back. Skin grows over the eggs, and the young go through the tadpole stage beneath their mother's skin, safe from predators. Tiny frogs eventually hatch out of her skin.

Most amphibians undergo metamorphosis. Trace the process of frog metamorphosis in Figure 15. Hind legs appear first, accompanied by changes in the skeleton, circulatory system, and digestive system. Later the front legs appear. At about the same time, the tadpole loses its gills and starts to breathe with its lungs.

Unlike the tadpoles of frogs and toads, the larvae of salamanders resemble the adults. Most salamander larvae undergo a metamorphosis in which they lose their gills. However, the changes are not as dramatic as those that happen during frog and toad metamorphosis.

Figure 15 During its metamorphosis from tadpole to adult, a frog's body undergoes a series of dramatic changes. *Applying Concepts How do these changes prepare a frog for living on land?*

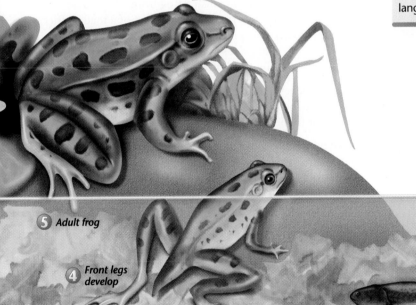

⑤ **Adult frog**

④ **Front legs develop**

③ **Hind legs develop**

② **Legless tadpole**

① **Fertilized eggs**

Language Arts
CONNECTION

When a tadpole becomes an adult frog, it moves to an unfamiliar location—a land environment that is very different from the watery one in which it has been living. While real tadpoles need no instructions for how to accomplish this move, you are about to write an imaginary guidebook for tadpoles that prepares them for their move onto land.

In Your Journal

First, brainstorm what types of information might be useful to the tadpole, such as how solid ground is different from water and where a frog might find food. Then choose four or five of your ideas and write a brief suggestion for each. Write in a lively way, using descriptive language.

Getting Around on Land

Skills Focus making models

Materials *plastic bags, heavy rubber bands, pail of water or sink*

Time 15 minutes

Tips Make sure that students insert only their fingers into the water. No part of their palm should be under water as it will provide too much resistance. Encourage students to experiment with moving their bagged hands through the water with their fingers spread as wide as possible and with their hands balled into a fist. Collect bags and rubber bands after use. Ask students to explain how their hand in the plastic bag is like a frog's webbed foot. *(The plastic acts like the web between the frog's toes.)*

Extend Ask: **How do some kinds of birds benefit from webbed feet?** *(Because these birds spend some part of their lives in water)* **learning modality: kinesthetic**

Frogs and Toads

Including All Students

You may wish to have supervised students obtain additional information about frogs and toads from the Internet, local zoos, or pet shops. **learning modality: visual**

Addressing Naive Conceptions

Ask students if they have heard that someone who touches a toad will get warts. Explain that this belief is merely a superstition—touching a toad's skin will not cause warts. Ask: **Can you think of any reasons why this superstition came about?** *(Toads' skin is bumpy and looks "warty." People assumed that toads' "warts" were contagious. While toads don't cause warts, their secretions can irritate skin, sometimes severely.)* **learning modality: logical/ mathematical**

Webbing Through Water

How does having webbed feet make it easier to swim?

1. Fill a sink or pail with water.
2. Spread your fingers and put your hand into the water just far enough so that only your fingers are under-water. Drag your fingers back and forth through the water.
3. Take your hand out of the water and dry it. Put a small plastic bag over your hand. Secure it around your wrist with a rubber band.

4. Repeat Step 2. Note any difference in the way in which your fingers push the water.

Making Models Use your model to explain how a frog's webbed feet help it move through water.

Getting Around on Land

Because it is not supported by water's buoyancy, a land animal needs a strong skeleton to support its body against the pull of gravity. In addition, a land animal needs some way of moving. Fins work in water, but they don't work on land. **Most adult amphibians have strong skeletons and muscular limbs adapted for movement on land.** Amphibians were the first vertebrates to have legs.

The eyes of amphibians are adapted to life on land. A transparent membrane helps keep them from drying out. Amphibians also have eyelids. Unlike fishes and tadpoles, whose wide-open eyes are always bathed in water, adult amphibians can close their eyes.

Frogs and Toads

When most people hear the word *amphibian,* they first think of frogs and toads—amphibians that are adapted for hopping and leaping. This kind of movement requires powerful hind-leg muscles and a skeleton that can absorb the shock of landing. The feet of frogs and toads have other adaptations, too. The webbed feet and long toes of bullfrogs form swim fins that help the frogs dart through the water. Tree frogs have toe pads with adhesive suckers that provide secure holds as the frogs leap from twig to twig.

It is usually easy to distinguish a frog from a toad. The skin of a frog is smooth and very moist, while that of a toad is drier and bumpy. Many toads have large lumps behind their eyes. These are actually skin glands that ooze a poisonous liquid when the toad is attacked by a predator such as a raccoon.

Although most tadpoles are herbivores, most adult frogs and toads are predators that feed on insects or other small animals. Insects don't usually see the frogs and toads that prey on them, because many frogs and toads are colored in such a way that they blend in with their environment. Green frogs, such as the one shown in *Exploring a Frog,* are brownish-green, making them hard to see in the ponds and meadows where they live. If you did the Discover activity, you learned that it is hard to see something green against a green background. Besides concealing frogs and toads from prey, their coloring also helps protect them from enemies.

☑ *Checkpoint* How can you tell a frog from a toad?

Salamanders

Salamanders are amphibians that keep their tails as adults. Their bodies are long and usually slender. Unlike frogs and toads, the

---

Background

Facts and Figures Some salamanders live in underground streams that flow through caves. Over millions of years, these unusual salamanders acquired adaptations that enabled them to survive in the dark conditions of their environment. As with many cave-dwelling animals, a sense of sight would be of little value to the salamanders.

Their eyes are greatly reduced. Because they are not exposed to sunlight, their skin has no need for protection from the sun and has little pigment. In some species, the skin is transparent, and the salamander's internal organs can be seen through the skin. Cave salamanders have become highly specialized to survive in their own caves.

EXPLORING a Frog

Green frogs are common throughout the eastern United States and southeastern Canada.

Eyes A frog's large eyes give it excellent vision and allow it to see predators while it floats in the water.

Mouth The mouth has teeth and nostril openings. The frog's tongue is attached at the front of its mouth—it flips out to catch insects.

Lungs In the lungs, oxygen enters the blood and carbon dioxide is released into the air.

Skin A frog's skin is smooth and moist. It absorbs some oxygen through its skin.

Ears A frog's ears look like small drumheads located behind its eyes.

Heart Like all amphibians, a green frog has a three-chambered heart.

Kidney

Stomach

Hind Legs Long hind legs and powerful leg muscles make the green frog an excellent leaper.

legs of salamanders are not adapted for jumping. Rather, salamanders stalk and ambush the small invertebrates that they eat. Most salamanders return to water each year to breed and lay their eggs. The eggs hatch into larvae that swim, feed, and soon grow into adults.

Some kinds of salamanders live in water all of their lives, while many other kinds live almost entirely on land. Some salamanders that live only on land do not have lungs. They rely on their thin, moist skins to obtain oxygen from air and to remove carbon dioxide from their blood. These lungless salamanders do not even return to water to reproduce. They lay their eggs in moist places on land, and they look like miniature adults when they hatch, not like larvae with gills.

Chapter 3 **B ◆ 99**

Answers to Self-Assessment

☑ *Checkpoint*

Frogs have smooth, moist skin. Toads have drier, bumpier skin. Many toads have large lumps behind their eyes.

EXPLORING
a Frog

Students can compare and contrast this visual with that of Exploring a Bony Fish in Section 2. Make copies of these figures to hand out so that students can examine them side-by-side. Tell students: **Draw circles around the characteristics of each animal that relate to movement.** *(Frog—hind legs; Fish—fins for balance, tail fin, swim bladder)* **Draw squares around the characteristics that help each sense its environment.** *(Frog—eyes, ears; Fish—lateral line)* **Draw triangles around the characteristics that help each obtain oxygen.** *(Frog—lungs, skin; Fish—gills)* **learning modality: visual**

Salamanders

Building Inquiry Skills: Relating Cause and Effect

Lungless salamanders obtain oxygen entirely through their skin. Ask: **What other animals absorb oxygen directly through their skins?** *(Students may mention roundworms, earthworms, and flatworms.)* Then ask: **What do these organisms have in common?** *(They are all small.)* Ask: **Do you think animals without gills or lungs can grow very large? Why or why not?** Guide students to understand that only small animals can absorb enough oxygen through the skin only. Earthworms and lungless salamanders are close to the size limit for animals that breathe entirely through their skin. **learning modality: verbal**

Ongoing Assessment

Making Diagrams Ask students to make a Venn diagram to compare and contrast frogs and salamanders.

B ◆ 99

Amphibians in Danger

Integrating Environmental Sciences

Students can research an amphibian that lives in their area that is being threatened by loss of habitat. Students can find a list of local endangered amphibians by contacting the U.S. Fish and Wildlife Service. **learning modality: verbal**

Section 3 Review

1. Amphibians have a double life because most begin their lives in the water and then spend their adulthood on land.

2. The adult amphibian skeleton has bones for the four limbs that it uses to move on land. The fish skeleton has no bones for limbs. A fish moves by pushing against water with its fins.

3. Forest destruction has caused a decrease in the number of amphibians. This happens because when a forest is destroyed, amphibians' habitats are destroyed as well.

4. A lungless salamander depends on its skin for obtaining oxygen. If the skin dries out, oxygen can no longer dissolve in the moisture and enter the body.

Check Your Progress

Review students' amphibian choices for appropriateness. Before students begin work on their amphibian model, review their fish model. Discuss with students ways in which amphibians differ from fish and how these differences will be reflected in their amphibian model.

Figure 16 This young red-spotted newt is among the many amphibians in danger from poisons in its environment.

Amphibians in Danger

 INTEGRATING ENVIRONMENTAL SCIENCE All over the world, populations of amphibians are decreasing. One reason is the destruction of amphibian habitats. An animal's **habitat** is the specific environment in which it lives. When a swamp is filled in or a forest is cut, an area that was moist becomes drier. Few amphibians can survive in dry, sunny areas. But habitat destruction does not account for the whole problem, because amphibians are declining even in areas where their habitats have not been damaged.

Because their skins are very thin and their eggs lack shells, amphibians are especially sensitive to changes in the environment. Poisons in the environment, such as insecticides and other chemicals, can pollute the waters that are essential to the life of an amphibian. Even small amounts of these chemicals can weaken adult amphibians, kill amphibian eggs, or cause tadpoles to be deformed.

The decline in amphibians may be a warning that other animals are also in danger. The environmental changes that are hurting amphibians may eventually affect other animals, including humans. To try to save amphibians and prevent harm to other animals, scientists are working to understand what is causing amphibian numbers to decline.

Section 3 Review

1. Why is it said that amphibians have a double life?

2. Compare an adult amphibian's skeleton and method of moving to those of a fish.

3. How has forest destruction affected amphibians? Why has it had this effect?

4. Thinking Critically Relating Cause and Effect A lungless salamander cannot survive if its skin dries out. Explain why.

Check Your Progress

At this point, you should have chosen an amphibian to model. Make sure that you are modeling the same type of adaptation that you did for the fish. (*Hint:* Before you begin constructing your model, make a sketch of what it will look like.)

100 ◆ B

Performance Assessment

Organizing Information Have students create a cycle diagram of the life cycle of a frog.

Background

Facts and Figures In 1935, cane toads were introduced to Australia to control the beetles that attack sugar cane crops. Unfortunately, the toads did eat the cane beetles, but they also ate beneficial insects, frogs, lizards, and even mice. The toads had no natural predators, so their population exploded. Native species have suffered as a result. Cane toads are now a major nuisance for Australians.

Program Resources

 Science Explorer Series *Environmental Science*, Chapter 2
◆ **Teaching Resources** 3-3 Review and Reinforce, p. 87; 3-3 Enrich, p. 88

Media and Technology

 Interactive Student Tutorial CD-ROM B-3

DISCOVER ···················· ACTIVITY····

How Do Snakes Feed?

1. To model how a snake feeds, stretch a sock cuff over a grapefruit "prey" by first pulling on one side and then on the other. Work the grapefruit down into the "stomach." A snake's jawbones can spread apart like the sock cuff.

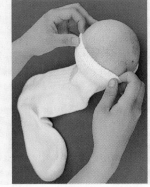

2. Remove the grapefruit and put a rubber band around the sock about 8 cm below the opening. The rubber band represents the firmly joined jawbones of a lizard. Now try to repeat Step 1.

Think It Over

Inferring What is the advantage of having jawbones like a snake's?

The king cobra of Southeast Asia, which can grow to more than 4 meters, is the world's longest venomous snake. When it encounters a predator, a king cobra flattens its neck and rears up. Its ropelike body sways back and forth, and its tongue flicks in and out.

A king cobra's fearsome behavior in response to a predator contrasts with the gentle way it treats its eggs. King cobras are one of the only snakes that build nests. The female builds a nest of grass and leaves on the forest floor. She lays her eggs inside the nest and guards them until they hatch.

Protection from Drying Out

Like other reptiles, king cobras lay their eggs on land rather than in water. A **reptile** is an ectothermic vertebrate that has lungs and scaly skin. In addition to snakes, lizards, turtles, and alligators are also reptiles.

GUIDE FOR READING

◆ What are some adaptations that allow reptiles to live on dry land?

◆ How is a reptile's egg different from an amphibian's egg?

Reading Tip As you read, write brief summaries of the information under each heading.

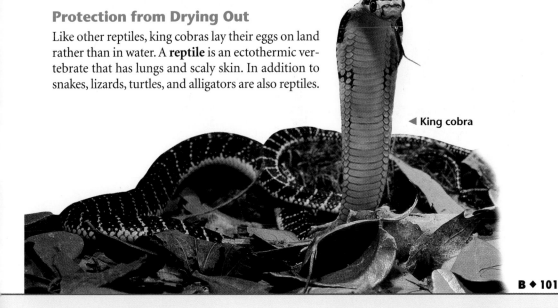

◄ King cobra

READING STRATEGIES

Reading Tip Explain to students that their summaries should state the main ideas of the section as opposed to focusing on its details. Suggest that students rewrite the main idea or topic of each paragraph into a single sentence. Also, point out that key words and concepts in the text are presented in boldface. Students can use their summaries to answer some of the Section 4 Review Questions.

Program Resources

◆ **Teaching Resources** 3-4 Lesson Plan, p. 89; 3-4 Section Summary, p. 90

Media and Technology

 Audiotapes English-Spanish Summary 3-4

Objectives

After completing this lesson, students will be able to

◆ describe some adaptations that allow reptiles to live on dry land;

◆ state how a reptile's egg is different from an amphibian's egg;

◆ list and describe the major groups of reptiles.

Key Terms reptile, urine

1 Engage/Explore

Activating Prior Knowledge

Ask students: **What are some characteristics of snakes?** *(Students may say no legs, poisonous, or fangs.)* List students' answers on the board. After students have become familiar with the information in the section, revisit this list. Help students to decide which of the characteristics are facts and which are "myths." Make revisions as necessary.

········· DISCOVER ·········

Skills Focus inferring
Materials *sock with ribbed cuff, grapefruit, strong rubber band*
Time 10 minutes
Tips Tell students to ease the sock over the grapefruit gently. They might also measure or estimate the diameters of the unstretched sock and the grapefruit to see how they compare. During Step 2 of the activity, use a rubber band that is too small to fit around the grapefruit. Reinforce what students learn by showing them a picture of a snake skull, pointing out that the skull has no large regions of solid bone. Tell students that a snake skull is very delicate, but very mobile.
Expected Outcome Students should infer that the spreading jawbones of the snake allow it to eat larger prey than is possible with the firmly joined jawbones of the lizard.

2 Facilitate

Protection from Drying Out

Addressing Naive Conceptions

Some students may think snakes are slimy. A snake's skin is actually quite dry, especially compared to that of a fish or amphibian. Under supervision, you may allow students to touch the scales of a molted snake skin. They should wash their hands afterwards. **learning modality: kinesthetic**

Building Inquiry Skills: Inferring

Materials *small cut pieces of a sponge, plastic bag, water*

Time 10 minutes over two class periods

To emphasize how eggshells and membranes prevent liquid loss, have students work in small groups to model an egg with a membrane. Provide each group with two pieces of sponge and one resealable plastic bag that will model the shell and membrane. Students should label the bag with their group's name. Have students wet both sponge pieces thoroughly, then put one piece in the plastic bag. They should place the other piece of sponge on top of the sealed bag and leave overnight. The next day, ask students to describe the condition of their sponges. Lead students to infer that the condition of the sponges left outside the bag is similar to what would happen to a developing embryo if the egg did not have a shell and membranes that retain moisture. **cooperative learning**

Unlike amphibians, reptiles can spend their entire lives on dry land. Reptiles were the first vertebrates that were well adapted to live on land, and they were the dominant land animals for about 160 million years. About 7,000 kinds of reptiles are alive today, but they are only a tiny fraction of a group that once dominated the land.

You can think of a land animal as a pocket of water held within a bag of skin. To thrive on land, an animal must have adaptations that keep the water within the "bag" from evaporating in the dry air. **The eggs, skin, and kidneys of reptiles are adapted to conserve water.**

An Egg With a Shell The eggs of reptiles are fertilized internally. While they are still inside the body of the female, fertilized eggs are covered with membranes and a shell. **Unlike an amphibian's egg, a reptile's egg has a shell and membranes that protect the developing embryo and help keep it from drying out.** Reptile eggs look much like bird eggs, except that their shells are soft and leathery, instead of rigid. Tiny holes, or pores, in the shell let oxygen in and carbon dioxide out. Since their eggs conserve water, reptiles—unlike amphibians—can lay their eggs on dry land.

Look carefully at Figure 17 to see how the membranes of a reptile's egg are arranged. One membrane holds the liquid that surrounds the embryo. Like bubble wrap that cushions breakable objects, the liquid keeps the embryo from getting crushed. The liquid also keeps the embryo moist. A second membrane holds the yolk, which provides the embryo with the food its cells must have to grow. A third membrane holds the embryo's wastes.

Figure 17 The egg from which this turtle is hatching provided it with food, moisture, and protection when it was an embryo. *Relating Cause and Effect List the parts of the egg that help keep the embryo from drying out.*

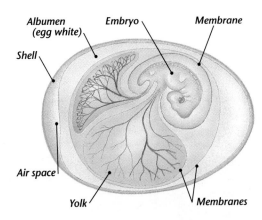

102 ◆ B

History of Science As life evolved on land, there was a general migration and exploitation of drier environments by plants. Plants adapted to habitats that were farther away from a constant water supply. The insects and other animals that fed on these plants soon followed. Amphibians could not take advantage of these dry land plants as a food source because the amphibian life cycle depended on water.

The ancestors of reptiles could move away from water to take advantage of these plants due to the specialized eggs they laid. Once it became possible for animals to live their entire life cycle without depending on constant sources of water, these animals began to adapt to many new environments. Reptiles are one successful group that evolved from these entirely land-dwelling animals. Other such groups are birds and mammals.

Skin and Kidneys Unlike amphibians, which have thin, moist skin, reptiles have dry, tough skins covered with scales. This scaly skin protects reptiles and helps keep water in their bodies. Another adaptation that helps keep water inside a reptile's body is its kidneys, which are organs that filter wastes from the blood. The wastes are then excreted in a watery fluid called **urine**. The kidneys of reptiles concentrate the urine so that they lose very little water.

☑ *Checkpoint* *List two functions of a reptile's skin.*

Obtaining Oxygen from the Air

Reptiles get their oxygen from the air. Like you, most reptiles breathe entirely with lungs. Like adult amphibians, reptiles have two loops in which their blood circulates through their bodies. In the first loop, the blood travels from the heart to the lungs and back to the heart. In the thin, moist surfaces of lung tissue, the oxygen moves into the blood and carbon dioxide moves out. In the second loop, blood travels from the heart to the tissues of the body. In the tissues, oxygen moves out of the blood and carbon dioxide moves into it. Then the blood returns to the heart. Like amphibians, the hearts of most reptiles have three chambers—two atria and one ventricle—and some mixing of oxygen-rich and oxygen-poor blood occurs.

Lizards

Most reptiles alive today are either lizards or snakes. These two groups of reptiles are closely related and share some important characteristics. Both have skin covered with overlapping scales. As lizards and snakes grow, they shed their skins, replacing the worn scales with a new coat. Most lizards and snakes live in warm areas.

Figure 18 The skin color of this chameleon can change in response to factors in its environment, such as changes in temperature.

Answers to Self-Assessment

Caption Question

Figure 17 The shell and membranes

☑ *Checkpoint*

A reptile's skin protects its body and keeps in water.

Lizards, continued

EXPLORING
a Lizard

As students examine the visual essay, remind them that by now they have studied several vertebrate groups. Ask: **What characteristics does the iguana share with the vertebrates you have already studied?** (*Eyes, hearing organs, nostrils for smelling, heart, and kidneys*) Then ask: **What characteristics of the iguana appear to be specialized features of iguanas?** (*Dry, scaly skin, claws, dewlap, crest*)
Extend Encourage interested students to choose another type of lizard to research. They can make a labeled drawing of this lizard showing its unique characteristics as well as those shared with other lizards. **learning modality: logical/ mathematical**

Snakes

Real-Life Learning

Skills Focus observing
Time 50 minutes

Arrange a presentation in which students can "meet a snake," either by taking students to a zoo, or by inviting a guest presenter to your class. Have students write a checklist of key features to observe. If possible, arrange for students to observe the movement of snakes across a variety of surfaces. Refer to Section 3-4 Enrich for information on various types of snake movement. Ask students to describe the kinds of movement they observe. Some students may be fearful of snakes. Allow fearful students to observe from a distance. Make sure the snakes are from nonvenomous and nonaggressive species. Garter snakes and grass snakes are common and can be easily and safely handled. **learning modality: visual**

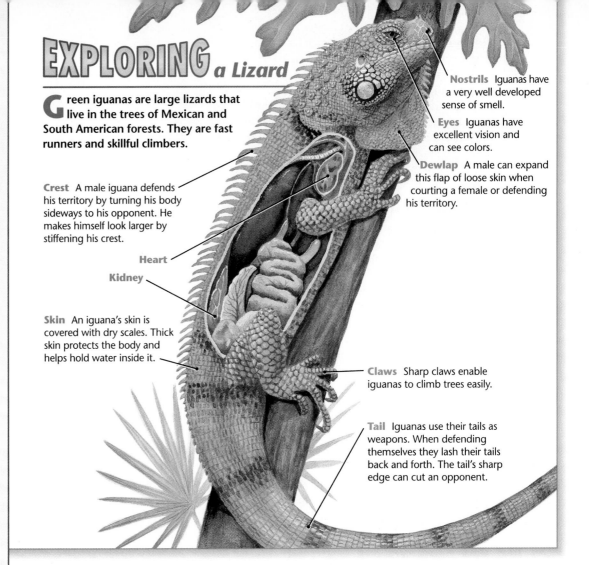

EXPLORING a Lizard

Green iguanas are large lizards that live in the trees of Mexican and South American forests. They are fast runners and skillful climbers.

Nostrils Iguanas have a very well developed sense of smell.

Eyes Iguanas have excellent vision and can see colors.

Dewlap A male can expand this flap of loose skin when courting a female or defending his territory.

Crest A male iguana defends his territory by turning his body sideways to his opponent. He makes himself look larger by stiffening his crest.

Heart

Kidney

Skin An iguana's skin is covered with dry scales. Thick skin protects the body and helps hold water inside it.

Claws Sharp claws enable iguanas to climb trees easily.

Tail Iguanas use their tails as weapons. When defending themselves they lash their tails back and forth. The tail's sharp edge can cut an opponent.

Lizards differ from snakes in one obvious way. Lizards have four legs, usually with claws on the toes. Many lizards have long tails, slender bodies, movable eyelids, and external ears.

A few lizards, including the iguana shown in *Exploring a Lizard,* are herbivores that eat leaves. Most lizards, however, are carnivores that capture food by jumping at it. While large lizards will eat large prey such as frogs and ground-dwelling birds, most small lizards are insect-hunters. Chameleons, which are found in Africa and India, have a sticky tongue adapted for snaring insects. This elastic tongue shoots out rapidly, extending as long as the chameleon's head and body put together!

Background

Facts and Figures Venomous snakes have fascinated people throughout history. The structure of the mouth and position of the venom-delivering fangs vary widely between species. Many "rear-fanged" snakes, such as the South African Boomslang, have venom-conducting fangs at the back of their mouths. Cobras and green mambas have short fangs at the front of their mouths. Rattlesnakes are vipers. Their fangs are quite long and fold up against the roof of the mouth when the snakes' mouths are closed. When vipers open their mouths, their fangs rotate downward into the biting position.

Snakes

Snakes are able to live in almost every sort of habitat, from deserts to swamps. They are similar to lizards, but streamlined, both externally and internally. Snakes have no legs, eyelids, or external ears, and most snakes have only one lung.

Snakes on the Move If you've ever seen a snake slither across the ground, you know that when it moves, its long, thin body bends into curves. Snakes move by contracting, or shortening, bands of muscles that are connected to their ribs and backbones. Alternate contractions of muscles on the right and left sides produce a slithering side-to-side motion.

How Snakes Feed All snakes are carnivores, and some eat large prey. If you did the Discover activity, you learned that a snake's jawbones can spread widely apart. In addition, the bones of a snake's skull can move to let the snake swallow an animal much larger in diameter than itself. Most snakes, however, feed on small rodents, such as mice.

Snakes capture their prey in different ways. The sharp-tailed snakes of western North America, which eat only slugs, have long, curved front teeth for hooking their slippery prey. Some West Indian boas are bat hunters that wait in ambush at the entrances to caves where bats live. At twilight, when the bats fly out of the cave to feed, the snakes snatch them out of the air.

Some snakes, such as rattlesnakes and copperheads, have venom glands attached to hollow teeth called fangs. When these snakes bite a prey animal, venom flows down inside the fangs. The venom enters the flesh of the prey and kills it quickly.

☑ *Checkpoint* How do snakes move?

Figure 19 A wide variety of snakes live on Earth, some adapted to almost every habitat. **A.** The temple viper from Thailand has one of the strongest venoms of any snake. **B.** Although the kingsnake is not venomous, it is quite aggressive—a kingsnake will even attack and eat a rattlesnake. *Making Generalizations How are snakes different from lizards?*

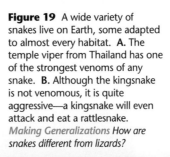

Answers to Self-Assessment

Caption Question

Figure 19 Unlike lizards, snakes lack legs, external ears, and eyelids. Most snakes have only one lung.

☑ *Checkpoint*

Snakes move by alternately contracting the muscles on their right and left sides connecting their ribs and vertebrae. This produces a slithering, side-to-side motion.

Soaking Up Those Rays

Preparing for Inquiry

Key Concept The temperature of ectotherms changes as the animals approach or avoid heat sources in their environment.

Skills Objective Students will be able to
◆ interpret data associated with an ectotherm.

Time 30 minutes

Guiding Inquiry

Invitation Heat flows from a warmer object to a cooler object. Challenge students to consider whether this rule applies to living organisms. Ask: **What do you notice if you lean against a car parked in the sun?**

Introducing the Procedure

As needed, help individual students understand the significance of each type of information in the illustration.

Troubleshooting the Experiment

Students may have trouble relating to Celsius temperatures. Students can convert a few key temperatures in the diagram into degrees Fahrenheit. This may make it easier for them to understand the lizard's behavior. Students can check each other's work.

Expected Outcome

◆ Through their behavior, lizards can maintain their body temperature within a range that is more limited than the temperature range in the environment.

Analyze and Conclude

1. The lizard's body temperature varied from 25–39.5°C. At 8 P.M. it dropped back down to 25°C.

2. The sun's rays, the surrounding air, and surface rocks. Note: In some periods, the air was cooler than the lizard's body temperature and so served to cool it.

3. Air temperature = 40.3°C, ground temperature = 53.8°C. The lizard

---

Skills Lab

Soaking Up Those Rays

In this lab, you will examine and interpret data associated with an ectotherm.

Problem

How do some lizards control their body temperatures in the extreme heat of a desert environment?

Materials

paper   pencil

Procedure

1. The data in the diagram below were collected by scientists studying how lizards control their body temperature. Examine the data.
2. Copy the data table on the next page into your notebook.
3. Organize the data in the diagram by filling in the table, putting the appropriate information in each column. Begin by writing a brief description of each type of lizard behavior.
4. Complete the data table using the information in the diagram.

Analyze and Conclude

1. How did the lizard's body temperature vary from 6 A.M. until 8 P.M.?
2. What are the three sources of heat that caused the lizard's body temperature to rise during the day?
3. During the hottest part of the day, what were the air and ground temperatures? Why do you think the lizard's temperature remained below 40°C?
4. Predict what the lizard's body temperature would have been from 8 P.M. to 6 A.M. Explain your prediction.

6 A.M.–7 A.M.
Emerging from burrow
Air temperature **20°C**
Ground temperature **28°C**
Body temperature **25°C**

7 A.M.–9 A.M.
Basking (lying on ground in sun)
Air temperature **27°C**
Ground temperature **29°C**
Body temperature **32.6°C**

9 A.M.–12 noon
Active (moving about)
Air temperature **27°C**
Ground temperature **30.8°C**
Body temperature **36.6°C**

Program Resources

◆ **Teaching Resources** Chapter 3 Skills Lab, pp. 99–100
◆ **Inquiry Skills Activity Book** Provides teaching and review of all inquiry skills

DATA TABLE

Activity	Description of Activity	Time of Day	Air Temperature (°C)	Ground Temperature (°C)	Body Temperature (°C)
1. Emerging					
2. Basking					
3. Active					
4. Retreat					
5. Stilting					
6. Retreat					

5. Based on what you learned from the data, explain why it is misleading to say that an ectotherm is a "coldblooded" animal.

6. Predict what would happen to your own body temperature if you spent a brief period outdoors in the desert at noon. Predict what your temperature would be if you spent time in a burrow at 7 P.M. Explain your predictions.

7. **Think About It** Why is it helpful to organize data in a data table before you try to interpret the data?

More to Explore

Make one or more bar graphs of the temperature data. Explain what the graphs show you. How do these graphs help you interpret the data?

12 noon–2:30 P.M.
Retreat to burrow
Air temperature **40.3°C**
Ground temperature **53.8°C**
Body temperature **39.5°C**

2:30 P.M.–6 P.M.
Stilting (belly off ground)
Air temperature **34.2°C**
Ground temperature **47.4°C**
Body temperature **39.5°C**

6 P.M.–9 P.M.
Retreat to burrow
Air temperature **25°C**
Ground temperature **26°C**
Body temperature **25°C**

remained cooler by staying in its burrow, which was in the shade and cooler than the ground temperature.

4. Accept all reasonable answers. Students may say that the body temperature will probably remain about 25°C, since the burrow tends to have a stable temperature.

5. "Coldblooded" implies that an animal's body temperature is cold. The lizard's temperature gets as high as 39°C, which is hotter than 100°F.

6. Our body temperatures at both times would remain relatively constant, since human body temperature is controlled by its own internal controls.

7. Organizing data in a table allows us to list all the data in the same place and makes data easier to compare. In this lab, the data table lets us quickly see temperature changes that happened over the course of the day. The table also makes comparing the temperatures at different times of the day easier.

Extending Inquiry

More to Explore On the bar graphs, the temperature is plotted on the *y*-axis; the time of the day on the *x*-axis. The graph of ground temperature shows that the rocks are cool in the morning, become hot at noon, and remain hot until evening. Lizards keep their bodies off the rocks after the rocks become hot. They either retreat, as they did from 12–2:30 P.M., or show stilting behavior. Stilting keeps their bodies away from the heat of the rocks.

Sample Data Table

Activity	Description of Activity	Time	Air Temp °C	Ground Temp °C	Body Temp °C
1. Emerging	leaves burrow	6–7 A.M.	20	28	25
2. Basking	rests on surface	7–9	27	29	32.6
3. Active	moves around	9–12	27	30.8	36.6
4. Retreat	enters burrow	12–12:30 P.M.	40.3	53.8	39.5
5. Stilting	belly away from surface, tail over head	2:30–6	34.2	47.4	39.5
6. Retreat	enters burrow	6	25	26	25

Turtles

Figure 20 Turtles vary greatly in their feeding habits. **A.** The green sea turtle lives entirely at sea and is a carnivore. **B.** The Galapagos tortoise lives on land, where it eats mainly cacti.

Turtles

A turtle is a reptile whose body is covered by a protective shell, which is made from the turtle's ribs and backbone. As you can see in Figure 20, the bony plates of the shell are covered by large scales made from the same material as the skin's scales. Some turtle shells can cover the whole body—a box turtle can draw its head, legs, and tail inside its shell for protection. Turtles like the snapping turtle have much smaller shells. Soft-shelled turtles, as their name suggests, have shells that are as soft as pancakes. Soft-shelled turtles lie in stream beds, concealed from predators, with only their nostrils and eyes above the sand.

The feeding habits of turtles are quite diverse. The largest turtles, the leatherbacks, are carnivores. Leatherbacks, which can weigh over 500 kilograms, are sea turtles that feed mainly on venomous jellyfishes. The stinging cells of the jellyfish can kill other animals, but the leatherback's tough skin seems to be unharmed by them. The giant Galapagos tortoises, on the other hand, are herbivores that feed mainly on cacti. They carefully scrape the prickly spines off before swallowing the cactus. Turtles have sharp-edged beaks instead of teeth. The razor-sharp beaks of soft-shelled turtles can chop fishes in two.

Figure 21 Alligators, left, and crocodiles, right, are the largest reptiles still living on Earth. They are similar in many ways, including appearance. *Comparing and Contrasting How can you tell the difference between an alligator and a crocodile?*

Alligators and Crocodiles

If you walk along a lake in Florida, you just might see an alligator swimming silently in the water. Most of its body lies beneath the surface, but you can see its large, bulging eyes above the surface. Alligators, crocodiles, and their relatives are the largest living reptiles. The American alligator can grow to be more than 5 meters long.

How do you tell an alligator from a crocodile? Look for teeth—but use binoculars and stay far away! Alligators have broad, rounded snouts, with only a few teeth visible. In comparison, crocodiles have pointed snouts, and you can see most of their teeth. Both alligators and crocodiles spend much of their days resting in the sun or lying in the water.

Alligators and crocodiles are carnivores that hunt mostly at night. They have several adaptations to help them capture prey. They use their strong, muscular tails to swim rapidly through the water. Their jaws are equipped with many large, sharp, and pointed teeth. Their jaw muscles are extremely strong when biting down. Although alligators will eat dogs, raccoons, and deer, they usually do not attack humans.

Unlike most other reptiles, crocodiles and alligators care for their eggs and newly hatched young. After laying eggs in a nest of rotting plants, the female stays near the nest. From time to time she comes out of the water and crawls over the nest to keep it moist. After the tiny alligators or crocodiles hatch, the female scoops them up in her huge mouth. She carries them from the nest to a nursery area in the water where they will be safer. For as long as a year, she will stay near her young, which make gulping quacks when they're alarmed. When their mother hears her young quack, she rushes toward them.

☑ *Checkpoint* *How are alligators and crocodiles adapted for catching prey?*

Sharpen your Skills

Drawing Conclusions

Scientists incubated, or **raised, eggs of one alligator species at four different temperatures. When the alligators hatched, the scientists counted the numbers of males and females. The table below shows the results.**

Incubation Temperature	Number of Females	Number of Males
29.4°C	80	0
30.6°C	19	13
31.7°C	13	38
32.8°C	0	106

Use the data to answer these questions.
1. What effect does incubation temperature have on the sex of the alligators?
2. Suppose a scientist incubated 50 eggs at 31°C. About how many of the alligators that hatched would be males? Explain.

Alligators and Crocodiles

Sharpen your Skills

Skills Focus drawing conclusions
Time 15 minutes
Tips So that students can answer Question 1 accurately, make sure they understand the answer is based on the proportion of males to females in the groups of eggs, not the absolute number. To help students answer Question 2, explain that the incubation temperature is the temperature at which the eggs were kept after they were laid, not the temperature at which the female was kept before she laid them. **learning modality: logical/mathematical**

Answers

1. The warmer the incubation temperature, the greater the proportion of males.
2. About half, or 25, would be males, because 31°C is between 30.6°C, at which there were more females than males, and 31.7°C, at which there were more males than females. Accept any answer close to that.

Extend Ask students to think of an experiment that could test whether incubation temperature affects the percentage of eggs that hatch. Do not allow students to perform their experiments. *(Sample experiment: Incubate three groups of 100 eggs at three different temperatures and then count the number of alligators that hatch.)*

Program Resources

◆ **Teaching Resources** 3-4 Review and Reinforce, p. 91; 3-4 Enrich, p. 92

Media and Technology

 Interactive Student Tutorial CD-ROM B-3

Answers to Self-Assessment

Caption Question

Figure 21 Alligators have broad, rounded snouts with only a few teeth visible. Crocodiles have pointed snouts with many teeth visible.

☑ *Checkpoint*

Alligators and crocodiles have strong tails for pursuing prey in water, long snouts, sharp teeth, and strong jaws.

Ongoing Assessment

Writing Invite students to write a paragraph comparing the beaks of soft-shelled turtles with the teeth of alligators and crocodiles. Have them include an explanation of how each adaptation contributes to the animals' ability to successfully acquire food.

 Students can save their paragraphs in their portfolios.

Extinct Reptiles— The Dinosaurs

Addressing Naive Conceptions

Movies have given students a mix of information and misinformation about dinosaurs. Divide students into groups and have them list some of the characteristics they think dinosaurs possessed. Compile the students' lists and assign each characteristic to a category ranging from probably right to probably wrong. Have students do research to determine whether the listed characteristics are accurate. **cooperative learning**

3 Assess

Section 4 Review

1. Dry, watertight skin; an egg with a shell and membranes; kidneys to concentrate urine
2. The shell, membranes, and fluid in a reptile's egg surround and protect the developing embryo.
3. The bones of a snake's skull can move in such a way to make an opening larger in diameter than the snake itself.
4. Endotherms can live in a wider range of climates.

Check Your Progress

CHAPTER PROJECT 3

Check to make sure students have chosen appropriate and safe materials for building their reptile model. Be sure that students are modeling the same adaptation in all three models.

Performance Assessment

Organizing Information Have students make a table with column heads "Characteristic," "Amphibians," and "Reptiles." The row labels are "Eggs" and "Skin." In the second column, students should describe how this feature functions in amphibians. In the third column, students should describe how the same feature is different in reptiles, enabling them to live on dry land.

Figure 22 *Brachiosaurus,* the largest dinosaur, grew to be over 22.5 meters long—longer than two school buses put together. *Observing What adaptation is demonstrated by the legs of* Brachiosaurus *and many other dinosaurs?*

Extinct Reptiles—The Dinosaurs

Millions of years ago, huge turtles and fish-eating reptiles swam in the oceans. Flying reptiles soared through the skies. And from about 225 million years ago until 65 million years ago, reptiles were the major form of vertebrate life on land. Snakes and lizards basked on warm rocks. And there were dinosaurs of every description. Unlike today's reptiles, dinosaurs may have been endothermic. Some dinosaurs, such as the *Brachiosaurus* in Figure 22, were the largest land animals that have ever lived.

Dinosaurs were the earliest vertebrates that had legs positioned directly beneath their bodies. This adaptation allowed them to move more easily than animals, such as salamanders, whose legs stick out to the sides of their bodies. Most herbivorous dinosaurs, such as *Brachiosaurus,* walked on four legs; most carnivores, such as the huge *Tyrannosaurus rex,* ran on two legs.

Dinosaurs became extinct about 65 million years ago, long before humans appeared on Earth. Several theories try to explain their disappearance, but no one is sure why they became extinct. A change in climate from warm to cool probably played a role. One leading theory suggests that a huge meteorite, a chunk of rock sailing through space, crashed into Earth. The impact sent up thick clouds of dust that blocked out the sun. The decrease in sunlight not only made Earth cooler, it also decreased plant growth, thus limiting food supplies. Dust from massive volcanic eruptions may also have blocked out sunlight. The dinosaurs were unable to survive in these changed conditions and died out.

Today, it's only in movies that dinosaurs shake the ground with their footsteps. But in a way, dinosaurs still exist. Birds may be descended from certain small dinosaurs. Some biologists think that birds are dinosaurs with feathers.

Section 4 Review

1. Describe three adaptations that enabled reptiles to live on land.
2. Explain how the structure of a reptile's egg protects the developing embryo.
3. Explain how snakes are able to eat large prey.
4. **Thinking Critically Making Generalizations** If some dinosaurs had been endotherms, what advantage might they have had over other reptiles?

Check Your Progress

CHAPTER PROJECT 3

Assemble the materials you need in order to build your reptile model. Make sure that your model clearly shows how the animal is adapted for the same function as your fish and amphibian. Begin preparing a written explanation of the adaptations that your three models demonstrate. Your written explanation should include labeled diagrams.

Background

Facts and Figures Some scientists believe that dinosaurs were probably endotherms. This belief gathered support when *Deinonychus* (day NON ik us) was discovered in 1964. This dinosaur was bipedal and could move with speed and agility. These characteristics require a great deal of energy, possibly indicating endothermy.

Answers to Self-Assessment

Caption Question

Figure 22 They had legs positioned directly beneath their bodies.

SECTION 5 Vertebrate History in Rocks

DISCOVER

ACTIVITY

What Can You Tell From an Imprint?

1. Flatten some modeling clay into a thin sheet on a piece of paper.

2. Firmly but gently press two or three small objects into different sections of the clay. The objects might include such things as a key, a leaf, a feather, a pencil, a postage stamp, a flower, or a raisin. Don't let anyone see the objects you are using.

3. Carefully remove the objects from the clay, leaving only the objects' imprints.

4. Exchange your sheet of imprints with a partner. Try to identify the objects that made the imprints.

Think It Over

Observing In general, what types of objects made the clearest imprints? If those imprints were fossils, what could you learn about the objects by looking at their "fossils"? What couldn't you learn?

Millions of years ago, in an ancient pond, some fish died and their bodies settled into the mud on the bottom. Soon heavy rains fell, and more mud washed into the pond, covering the fish. The fish's soft tissues decayed, but their bones remained. After many thousands of years, the mud hardened into rock, and the fish bones became the fossils shown here.

GUIDE FOR READING

◆ What can scientists learn from studying fossils?

Reading Tip Predict what you will learn in this section. Then read to see whether your prediction is correct.

◀ Fossilized fish

READING STRATEGIES

Reading Tip Suggest students use the title of the section and skim the section photos and illustrations to predict the section's content. Then have them write down what they want to learn. After students finish reading the section, direct them to write down what they learned. Check that students have learned all that they had wanted to. If not, suggest other resources for interested students.

Program Resources

◆ **Teaching Resources** 3-5 Lesson Plan, p. 93; 3-5 Section Summary, p. 94

SECTION 5 Vertebrate History in Rocks

Objectives

After completing this lesson, students will be able to

◆ describe how fossils are formed and what scientists can learn from studying fossils.

Key Terms fossil, sedimentary rock, paleontologist

1 Engage/Explore

Activating Prior Knowledge

Distribute some fossils. Ask: **What do you think made the patterns you see in the rocks?** (*Students may infer that the patterns are the remains or traces of dead animals or plants that lived long ago.*) **What can you infer about the organism that made these imprints and where it lived? Does it resemble any living organism that you know?** (*Answers will vary.*) Have students write brief descriptions of the fossils.

DISCOVER

Skills Focus observing
Materials *modeling clay; paper; small objects of various textures and degrees of rigidity*

ACTIVITY

Time 15 minutes
Tips Each student should use some objects that will make a clear impression, such as coins, and some that will not, such as feathers.
Expected Outcome Harder objects, such as the key, will be easiest to identify. Imprints of soft objects with recognizable outlines, such as the leaf, will also be easy to recognize.
Think It Over The objects that made the clearest imprints were firm and had distinct borders. If the imprints were fossils, you could learn the size and shape of the object that made them. You could not learn what was inside the object or organism, what it ate, or why it died.

2 Facilitate

Fossils in Sedimentary Rock

Including All Students

Materials *plastic jar with lid, marbles, pea gravel, sand, powdered clay*

 **ACTIVITY**

Time 10 minutes

If students who lack proficiency in English have difficulty understanding the text description of sedimentary rock formation, this activity will help them understand the process. Students will simulate the effect of moving water on different sizes of rocks. Have students half-fill the jar with the pebbles, gravel, sand, and clay. Tell students these represent different sizes of rocks. Then, have them fill the jar with water and securely fasten the lid. Students should shake the jar until the solid contents are suspended. Then they should quickly set the jar down and record the order in which the materials settle to the bottom. *(Pebbles first, then the gravel, then the sand, then much later, the clay)* Ask: **What is the relationship between the size of the rock and the length of time it takes to settle?** *(The larger the rock, the faster it settles.)* **limited English proficiency**

Building Inquiry Skills: Calculating

Sedimentary deposits can be thousands of meters thick. For example, part of the Florida Peninsula consists of limestone deposits more than 4,000 meters thick. Ask students to consider the following: Suppose this limestone accumulated at a rate of 1 cm every 50 years. How many years did it take for 4,000 meters of limestone to accumulate? *(4,000 m $\times$ 100 cm/m $\times$ 50 yr/cm = 20 million years)* **learning modality: logical/ mathematical**

Fossils in Sedimentary Rock

A **fossil** is the hardened remains or other evidence of a living thing that existed a long time in the past. Sometimes a fossil is an imprint in rock, such as an animal's footprint or the outline of a leaf. Other fossils are the remains of bones or other parts of living things—a chemical process has taken place in which the organism's tissues have become replaced by hard minerals. Because most living tissues decay rapidly, only a very few organisms become preserved as fossils.

Fossils occur most frequently in the type of rock known as sedimentary rock. **Sedimentary rock** is made of hardened layers of sediments—particles of clay, sand, mud, or silt. Have you ever

SCIENCE & History

Discovering Vertebrate Fossils

People have been discovering fossils since ancient times. However, it is only within the last few centuries that people have understood that fossils are the remains of extinct organisms. Here are some especially important fossil discoveries.

1822
Dinosaur Tooth

In a quarry near Lewes, England, Mary Ann Mantell discovered a strange-looking tooth embedded in stone. Her husband Gideon drew the picture of the tooth shown here. The tooth belonged to the dinosaur *Iguanodon*.

| 1675 | 1725 | 1775 | 1825 |

1677
Dinosaur-Bone Illustration

Robert Plot, the head of a museum in England, published a book that had an illustration of a huge fossilized thighbone. Plot thought that the bone belonged to a giant human, but it probably was the thighbone of a dinosaur.

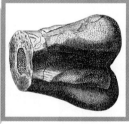

1811
Sea Reptile

Along the cliffs near Lyme Regis, England, 12-year-old Mary Anning discovered the fossilized remains of the giant sea reptile now called *Ichthyosaurus*. Mary became one of England's first professional fossil collectors.

Background

History of Science Aristotle recognized that fossils were evidence of past life, but he thought the organisms had grown in the rocks. During medieval times, from about A.D. 500 to 1500, the belief that Earth was created in six days led to the dismissal of fossils as simply odd mineral formations that happened to resemble living things by chance.

Leonardo da Vinci was one of the first scholars to understand how fossils were formed. He noticed that certain fossils he was studying not only looked like the live animal but were also buried in the rock in lifelike positions.

It was not until the late eighteenth century, when the English engineer William Smith recognized that certain fossils are limited to particular layers in the Earth's crust, that paleontology became the study of the development of organisms over time.

washed a dirty soccer ball and seen sand and mud settle on the bottom of the sink? If you washed a dozen soccer balls, the sink bottom would be covered with a layer of sediment. Sediments build up in many ways. For example, wind can blow a thick layer of sand onto dunes. Sediments can also form when muddy water stands in an area for a long time. Muddy sediment in the water will eventually settle to the bottom and build up.

Over a very long time, layers of sediments can be pressed and cemented together to form rock. As sedimentary rock forms, traces of living things that have been trapped in the sediments are sometimes preserved as fossils.

☑ *Checkpoint* **What are two ways in which fossils form?**

In Your Journal

If you could interview the discoverer of one of these fossils, what questions would you ask about the fossil and how it was found? Write a list of those questions in your journal. Then use reference materials to try to find the answers to some of them.

1902
Tyrannosaurus

A tip from a local rancher sent Barnum Brown, a fossil hunter, to a barren, rocky area near Jordan, Montana. There Brown found the first relatively complete *Tyrannosaurus rex* skeleton.

1991
Dinosaur Eggs in China

Digging beneath the ground, a farmer on Green Dragon Mountain in China uncovered what may be the largest nest of fossil dinosaur eggs ever found. A paleontologist chips carefully to remove one of the eggs from the rock.

| 1875 | 1925 | 1975 | 2025 |

1861
Bird Bones

A worker in a stone quarry in Germany discovered *Archaeopteryx,* a feathered, birdlike animal that also had many reptile characteristics.

1964
Deinonychus

In Montana, paleontologist John Ostrom discovered the remains of a small dinosaur, *Deinonychus.* This dinosaur was probably a predator who could move rapidly. This fossil led scientists to hypothesize that dinosaurs may have been endotherms.

Chapter 3 **B ◆ 113**

B ◆ 113

Interpretation of Fossils

Real-Life Learning

Paleontologists can also infer how species have changed by studying other types of preserved remains. Tell students that whole organisms may be preserved in materials such as ice, tar, and amber. If possible, bring a piece of amber containing plant or animal remains to class for students to examine. **learning modality: visual**

3 Assess

Section 5 Review

1. Compare a fossil organism with present-day organisms

2. Sediments carried by water or wind build up over time. Gradually, they can be pressed and cemented into rock.

3. A leaf falls into soft sediment and is covered. Soft tissues of the leaf decay, leaving an imprint of the leaf. The sediment hardens and becomes rock, with the fossil imprint inside.

4. Fossil A is probably older because it is buried deeper. Additional evidence: The rocks can be dated through measurement of radioactive decay products.

Science at Home

Ask: **What could you conclude if the newspapers in the top layer were older than those in the bottom layer?** *(Something must have disturbed the stack.)* **How is this similar to what can happen to rock layers?** *(Rock layers can be disturbed by natural events so that their original order is altered.)* **learning modality: verbal**

Performance Assessment

Organizing Information Have students draw flowcharts that show the stages in the making of a fossil. Students can save their flowcharts in their portfolios.

Figure 23 The diagram shows fossils in layers of sedimentary rocks. *Interpreting Diagrams Which rock layer probably contains the oldest fossils? Explain.*

Interpretation of Fossils

What information can scientists learn from fossils? **Paleontologists** (pay lee uhn TAHL uh jihsts), the scientists who study extinct organisms, examine fossil structure and make comparisons to present-day organisms. **By studying fossils, paleontologists can infer how a species changed over time.** One important piece of information that paleontologists can learn from a fossil is its approximate age.

One method for estimating a fossil's age takes advantage of the process in which sediments form. Think about sediments settling out of water—the lowest layers are deposited first, and newer sediments settle on top of the older layers. Therefore, fossils in higher layers of rock are often younger than fossils in lower layers.

However, rock layers can become tilted or even turned upside down. Natural events such as earthquakes and human events such as construction can change the position of rock layers. Therefore, a fossil's position in rock is not always a reliable indication of its age. Scientists must usually rely on other methods to help determine a fossil's age. For example, fossils—and the rocks in which they are found—contain some radioactive chemical elements. These radioactive elements decay, or change into other chemical elements, over a known period of time. The more there is of the decayed form of the element, the older the fossil.

Paleontologists have used fossil evidence to piece together the history of the major groups of vertebrates. As new fossils are found, paleontologists will reinterpret the fossil evidence and possibly revise their ideas about when different animal groups first appeared and how the groups may be related to one another.

Section 5 Review

1. How can paleontologists use fossils to determine how a species changed over time?
2. Describe how sedimentary rock forms.
3. Describe the process by which a leaf becomes fossilized.
4. **Thinking Critically** **Inferring** Fossil A is found in a rock layer 200 meters below the surface of the ground. Fossil B is found in the same rock formation, but at a depth of 150 meters. Which fossil is probably older? What additional evidence would help verify the fossils' ages?

Science at Home

Does your family store newspapers or magazines in a stack? With someone in your family, check the dates of the newspapers in the stack. Going from the top of the pile to the bottom, are the newspapers in any particular order? If the oldest newspapers are on the bottom and the newest on top, you can relate this to the way in which sediments are laid down. Ask family members to imagine that two fossils were trapped in different newspapers. Explain which fossil would probably be older, and why.

114 ◆ B

Program Resources

◆ **Teaching Resources** 3–5 Review and Reinforce, p. 95; 3–5 Enrich, p. 96

Media and Technology

 Interactive Student Tutorial CD-ROM B-3

Answers to Self-Assessment

Caption Question Figure 23

The lowest layer probably contains the oldest fossils. Because it is the lowest layer, it was probably deposited first.

SECTION 1 — What Is a Vertebrate?

Key Ideas
- Vertebrates have a backbone that is part of an endoskeleton. The endoskeleton supports, protects, and gives shape to the body.
- Most fishes, amphibians, and reptiles are ectotherms. Mammals and birds are endotherms.

Key Terms

chordate	notochord	cartilage
vertebra	ectotherm	endotherm

SECTION 2 — Fishes

Key Ideas
- A fish is an ectothermic vertebrate that lives in the water, has fins, usually has scales, and obtains oxygen through gills.
- Major groups of fishes include jawless fishes, cartilaginous fishes, and bony fishes.

Key Terms
fish
swim bladder
buoyant force

SECTION 3 — Amphibians

Key Ideas
- An amphibian is a moist-skinned, ectothermic vertebrate. Most amphibians spend their early lives in water and adulthood on land, returning to water to reproduce.
- Major groups of amphibians include frogs, toads, and salamanders.
- Adult amphibians have strong skeletons and muscular limbs adapted for moving on land.

Key Terms

amphibian	atrium	ventricle
habitat		

SECTION 4 — Reptiles

Key Ideas
- A reptile is an ectothermic vertebrate that has lungs and scaly skin. Reptiles can spend their entire lives on dry land.
- The leathery eggs, scaly skin, and the kidneys of reptiles are adapted to conserving water.
- Major groups of reptiles include lizards, snakes, turtles, and alligators and crocodiles.

Key Terms
reptile
urine

SECTION 5 — Vertebrate History in Rocks

INTEGRATING EARTH SCIENCE

Key Ideas
- Sedimentary rock forms from hardened layers of sediments such as clay, mud, or sand.
- Fossils are found primarily in sedimentary rock.
- Paleontologists study fossils to infer how organisms, including vertebrates, have changed over time. Scientists are always reinterpreting fossil evidence.

Key Terms

fossil	sedimentary rock	paleontologist

USING THE INTERNET ACTIVITY

www.science-explorer.phschool.com

Program Resources

- **Teaching Resources** Chapter 3 Project Scoring Rubric, p. 76; Chapter 3 Performance Assessment Teacher Notes, pp. 180–181; Chapter 3 Performance Assessment Student Worksheet, p. 182; Chapter 3 Test, pp. 183–186

Media and Technology

 Interactive Student Tutorial CD-ROM B-3

 Computer Test Bank Test B-3

Reviewing Content:
Multiple Choice
1. b **2.** b **3.** c **4.** d **5.** d

True or False
6. true **7.** tooth **8.** true **9.** in water
10. fossils

Checking Concepts

11. At some time during their lives, chordates have a notochord, a nerve cord running down their back, and slits in their throat area.

12. Fishes reproduce sexually. Most have external fertilization.

13. A frog begins life as an egg, surrounded by jelly, laid in water or a moist environment. The egg hatches into a fishlike tadpole, which gradually develops into an adult frog. Hind legs appear, then front legs. Lungs replace gills as organs for obtaining oxygen. The tadpole loses its tail, and finally develops into an adult that lives on land. The adult frog returns to water to mate and lay eggs, completing the cycle.

14. A fish has a circulatory system with one loop and a simple heart. Amphibians have a circulatory system with two loops and a three-chambered heart.

15. The membranes and shell protect the embryo and hold water inside the egg. One membrane holds cushioning liquid that surrounds the embryo; the yolk holds food for the embryo; and another membrane holds wastes.

16. Both lizards and snakes have skin covered with overlapping scales, which is shed as the animal grows. Lizards have legs, eyelids, and external ears, but snakes do not. Most snakes have only one lung.

17. A snake moves in a wavelike pattern because of alternating contractions of muscles on opposite sides of its body.

18. A huge meteorite crashing into Earth, or massive volcanic eruptions, may have sent up a thick cloud of dust that blocked out the sun. The dinosaurs could not survive in the changed conditions and died out.

Reviewing Content

 For more review of key concepts, see the Interactive Student Tutorial CD-ROM.

Multiple Choice
Choose the letter of the best answer.

1. Which fishes do not have jaws, scales, or paired fins?
   a. sharks
   b. lampreys and hagfishes
   c. sturgeons
   d. ocean sunfish

2. A bony fish uses a swim bladder to
   a. propel itself through water.
   b. regulate its buoyancy.
   c. remove wastes.
   d. pump water over its gills.

3. Adult frogs must return to the water to
   a. catch flies.
   b. obtain all their food.
   c. reproduce.
   d. moisten their gills.

4. Which of the following animals breathes with lungs?
   a. shark   **b.** lamprey
   c. larval salamander **d.** lizard

5. Fossils are rare because
   a. there were few living things in ancient times.
   b. scientists have only searched for fossils in Africa and the United States.
   c. most fossils have sunk to the ocean floor.
   d. the bodies of dead organisms decay rapidly.

True or False
If the statement is true, write true. If it is false, change the underlined word or words to make the statement true.

6. Birds and mammals are <u>endotherms</u>.

7. If a shark loses a <u>fin</u>, another one will move into its place.

8. <u>Buoyant force</u> is the force that pushes upward against an underwater object.

9. Amphibians usually begin their lives <u>on land</u>.

10. Paleontologists are scientists who study <u>fishes</u>.

Checking Concepts

11. Describe the main characteristics of chordates.
12. How do fish reproduce?
13. Describe the life cycle of a frog.
14. How is an amphibian's circulatory system different from that of a fish?
15. Explain how the structure of a reptile's egg protects the embryo inside.
16. Compare and contrast lizards and snakes.
17. Why does a snake move in a wavelike pattern rather than in a straight line?
18. What may have caused the dinosaurs to become extinct?
19. Describe two methods that scientists use to determine the age of a fossil.
20. **Writing to Learn** Write a description of an hour in the life of a shark. Before you begin to write, list the events you want to include, and arrange those events in the sequence in which you want them to occur. As you write, use words such a *then* and *a moment later* to let your readers know that the shark is progressing from one activity to another.

Thinking Visually

21. **Compare/Contrast Table** Copy the table comparing fish groups onto a separate sheet of paper. Then complete the table and add a title. (For more on compare/contrast tables, see the Skills Handbook.)

Kind of Fish	Kind of Skeleton	Jaws?	Scales	Example
Jawless Fishes	a. _?_	no	b. _?_	c. _?_
d. _?_	e. _?_	f. _?_	toothlike scales	shark
Bony Fishes	bone	g. _?_	h. _?_	i. _?_

---

19. The age of a fossil can be determined by its position in the rock layers, or by the decay of radioactive elements in the rock or fossil.

20. Answers will vary. Students' narrative should include realistic details about a shark, such as constant motion, searching for prey, reacting to the smell of blood, and so forth. Check for accurate, realistic events arranged in a logical sequence, with transitions between ideas.

Thinking Visually

21. **a.** cartilage **b.** none **c.** lamprey or hagfish **d.** cartilaginous fishes **e.** cartilage **f.** yes **g.** yes **h.** yes **i.** Sample: trout, tuna, or goldfish

Applying Skills

22. The manipulated variable is the water temperature. The responding variable is the breathing rate of the fish.

23. The breathing rate at 18°C is lower than the breathing rate at 22°C.

24. The goldfish breathing rate is directly

Applying Skills

A scientist performed an experiment on five goldfish to test the effect of water temperature on "breathing rate"—the rate at which the fish open and close their gill covers. The graph shows the data that the scientist obtained at four different temperatures. Use the graph to answer Questions 22–24.

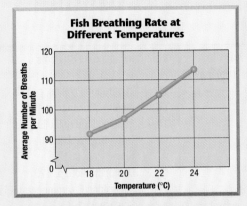

Fish Breathing Rate at Different Temperatures

Y-axis: Average Number of Breaths per Minute (90, 100, 110, 120)
X-axis: Temperature (°C) (18, 20, 22, 24)

22. **Controlling Variables** Identify the manipulated variable and the responding variable in this experiment.
23. **Interpreting Data** How does the breathing rate at 18°C compare to the breathing rate at 22°C?
24. **Drawing Conclusions** Based on the data shown in the graph, what is the relationship between water temperature and goldfish breathing rate?

Thinking Critically

25. **Comparing and Contrasting** Compare the ways a tadpole and an adult frog obtain oxygen.
26. **Applying Concepts** Imagine that you are in the hot desert sun with a wet paper towel. You must keep the towel from drying out. What strategy can you copy from reptiles to keep the towel wet?

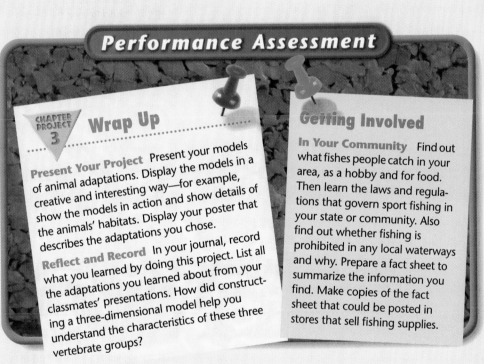

Performance Assessment

Wrap Up
CHAPTER PROJECT 3

Present Your Project Present your models of animal adaptations. Display the models in a creative and interesting way—for example, show the models in action and show details of the animals' habitats. Display your poster that describes the adaptations you chose.

Reflect and Record In your journal, record what you learned by doing this project. List all the adaptations you learned about from your classmates' presentations. How did constructing a three-dimensional model help you understand the characteristics of these three vertebrate groups?

Getting Involved

In Your Community Find out what fishes people catch in your area, as a hobby and for food. Then learn the laws and regulations that govern sport fishing in your state or community. Also find out whether fishing is prohibited in any local waterways and why. Prepare a fact sheet to summarize the information you find. Make copies of the fact sheet that could be posted in stores that sell fishing supplies.

related to water temperature. The lower the water temperature, the slower the breathing rate, and vice versa.

Thinking Critically

25. A tadpole obtains oxygen through its gills, while an adult frog gets oxygen from its lungs and through its skin.
26. Wrap the towel in a material such as foil or plastic wrap that will keep water from escaping.

Performance Assessment

Wrap Up
Present Your Project
When students demonstrate their models for the class, some models may not perform the intended function as smoothly as they are designed to do. Locomotion can be a difficult adaptation to successfully demonstrate. Look for realistic and thoughtful ideas. Remind students that the poster can support their ideas. Posters can be flowcharts that convey additional information about the specific adaptation.
Reflect and Record Guide students to first record the adaptations that prompted their choices of models. Also, have them record the other adaptations their classmates modeled. After all students have presented their projects, you may wish to take a census of the class to find out what adaptations were modeled most.

Getting Involved

In Your Community Consider contacting your local cooperative extension office or state fish and game department to find those who are willing to participate in the activity. Create a list of addresses and phone numbers of the willing experts. Group students according to the length of the list. Have them work together to find the information and organize the fact sheets. Use this updated list each time you assign this activity to students.

4 Birds and Mammals

Sections	Time	Student Edition Activities	Other Activities
CHAPTER PROJECT 4 **Bird Watch** p. 119	Ongoing (2–3 weeks)	Check Your Progress, pp. 129, 132, 146 Wrap Up, p. 149	**TE** Chapter 4 Project Notes, pp. 118–119
1 Birds pp. 120–129 ◆ Identify the common characteristics of birds. ◆ Explain how birds are adapted to and affect their environments.	5 periods/ 2–3 blocks	**Discover** What Are Feathers Like? p. 120 **Skills Lab: Drawing Conclusions** Looking at an Owl's Leftovers, pp. 124–125 **Try This** Eggs-amination, p. 127	**TE** Including All Students, pp. 121, 122 **TE** Integrating Physics, p. 122 **TE** Inquiry Challenge, p. 126 **TE** Building Inquiry Skills: Observing, p. 126 Classifying, p. 127 **TE** Demonstration, p. 126 **TE** Integrating Environmental Science, p. 128 **IES** "India Beyond the Golden Age," pp. 36–38 **ISLM** B-4, "Adaptations of Birds"
2 ◆ INTEGRATING PHYSICS **The Physics of Bird Flight** pp. 130–132 ◆ Explain how a bird is able to fly.	2 periods/ 1 block	**Discover** What Lifts Airplanes and Birds Into the Air? p. 130 **Try This** It's Plane to See, p. 131	
3 What Is a Mammal? pp. 133–140 ◆ Describe the characteristics all mammals share.	4 periods/ 2 blocks	**Discover** What Are Mammals' Teeth Like? p. 133 **Try This** Insulated Mammals, p. 135 **Sharpen Your Skills** Classifying, p. 137 **Science at Home** p. 138 **Real-World Lab: You, the Consumer** Keeping Warm, p. 139	**TE** Including All Students, p. 136 **TE** Inquiry Challenge, p. 136
4 Diversity of Mammals pp. 141–146 ◆ Identify the characteristic used to classify mammals as monotremes, marsupials, or placental mammals.	3 periods/ 1½ blocks	**Discover** How Is a Thumb Useful? p. 141	**TE** Building Inquiry Skills: Observing, p. 143 **TE** Inquiry Challenge, p. 144
Study Guide/Chapter Review pp. 147–149	1 period/ ½ block		**ISAB** Provides teaching and review of all inquiry skills

For Standard or Block Schedule The Resource Pro® CD-ROM gives you maximum flexibility for planning your instruction for any type of schedule. Resource Pro® contains Planning Express®, an advanced scheduling program, as well as the entire contents of the Teaching Resources and the Computer Test Bank.

CHAPTER PLANNING GUIDE

Program Resources	Assessment Strategies	Media and Technology
TR Chapter 4 Project Teacher Notes, pp. 102–103 **TR** Chapter 4 Project Overview and Worksheets, pp. 104–107 **TR** Chapter 4 Project Scoring Rubric, p. 108	**SE** Performance Assessment: Wrap Up, p. 149 **TE** Check Your Progress, pp. 129, 132, 146 **TR** Chapter 4 Project Scoring Rubric, p. 108	Science Explorer Internet Site
TR 4-1 Lesson Plan, p. 109 **TR** 4-1 Section Summary, p. 110 **TR** 4-1 Review and Reinforce, p. 111 **TR** 4-1 Enrich, p. 112 **TR** Chapter 4 Skills Lab, pp. 125–126 **SES** Book M, *Motion, Forces, and Energy,* Chapter 6 **SES** Book E, *Environmental Science,* Chapter 2	**SE** Section 1 Review, p. 129 **SE** Analyze and Conclude, p. 125 **TE** Ongoing Assessment, pp. 121, 123, 127 **TE** Performance Assessment, p. 129 **TR** 4-1 Review and Reinforce, p. 111	Exploring Life Science Videodisc, Unit 3 Side 2, "Backbones" Exploring Life Science Videodisc, Unit 3 Side 2, "How Does Everything Fit?" Audiotapes: English-Spanish Summary 4-1 Transparency 16, "Circulation in Fishes, Amphibians, and Birds" Transparency 17, "Exploring a Bird" Interactive Student Tutorial CD-ROM, B-4
TR 4-2 Lesson Plan, p. 113 **TR** 4-2 Section Summary, p. 114 **TR** 4-2 Review and Reinforce, p. 115 **TR** 4-2 Enrich, p. 116	**SE** Section 2 Review, p. 132 **TE** Ongoing Assessment, p. 131 **TE** Performance Assessment, p. 132 **TR** 4-2 Review and Reinforce, p. 115	Exploring Physical Science Videodisc, Unit 3 Side 2, "How an Airplane Flies" Audiotapes: English-Spanish Summary 4-2 Transparency 18, "Bird Flight" Interactive Student Tutorial CD-ROM, B-4
TR 4-3 Lesson Plan, p. 117 **TR** 4-3 Section Summary, p. 118 **TR** 4-3 Review and Reinforce, p. 119 **TR** 4-3 Enrich, p. 120 **TR** Chapter 4 Real-World Lab, pp. 127–129	**SE** Section 3 Review, p. 138 **SE** Analyze and Conclude, p. 139 **TE** Ongoing Assessment, pp. 135, 137 **TE** Performance Assessment, p. 138 **TR** 4-3 Review and Reinforce, p. 119	Exploring Life Science Videodisc, Unit 3 Side 2, "Backbones" Exploring Life Science Videodisc, Unit 3 Side 2, "How Does Everything Fit?" Audiotapes: English-Spanish Summary 4-3 Interactive Student Tutorial CD-ROM, B-4
TR 4-4 Lesson Plan, p. 121 **TR** 4-4 Section Summary, p. 122 **TR** 4-4 Review and Reinforce, p. 123 **TR** 4-4 Enrich, p. 124	**SE** Section 4 Review, p. 146 **TE** Ongoing Assessment, pp. 143, 145 **TE** Performance Assessment, p. 146 **TR** 4-4 Review and Reinforce, p. 123	Exploring Life Science Videodisc, Unit 3 Side 2, "pH in Aquaria" Audiotapes: English-Spanish Summary 4-4 Interactive Student Tutorial CD-ROM, B-4
TR Chapter 4 Performance Assessment pp. 187–189 **TR** Chapter 4 Test, pp. 190–193	**SE** Chapter Review, pp. 147–149 **TR** Chapter 4 Performance Assessment, pp. 187–189 **TR** Chapter 4 Test, pp. 190–193 **CTB** Chapter 4 Test	Computer Test Bank, Test B-4 Interactive Student Tutorial CD-ROM, B-4 Got It! Video Quizzes

Key: **SE** Student Edition   **TE** Teacher's Edition   **TR** Teaching Resources
      CTB Computer Test Bank   **SES** Science Explorer Series Text   **ISLM** Integrated Science Laboratory Manual
      ISAB Inquiry Skills Activity Book   **PTA** Product Testing Activities by *Consumer Reports*   **IES** Interdisciplinary Explorations Series

Meeting the National Science Education Standards and AAAS Benchmarks

National Science Education Standards	Benchmarks for Science Literacy	Unifying Themes

National Science Education Standards

Science as Inquiry (Content Standard A)

◆ **Recognize and analyze alternative explanations and predictions** Students may suggest explanations for observed animal behavior. *(Chapter Project)*

◆ **Design and conduct a scientific investigation** Students implement a plan to investigate the effectiveness of wool as an insulator. Additionally, they will design their own experiment to test the insulation properties of wool to model fur as an adaptation to varying climates. *(Real-World Lab)*

Physical Science (Content Standard B)

◆ **Motions and Forces** The flight of birds depends on lift and can be described using principles from physics. *(Section 2)*

Life Science (Content Standard C)

◆ **Diversity and Adaptations of Organisms** Many characteristics of birds and mammals are adaptations that allow the animals to live in different environments. This is reflected in differences in physical and behavioral traits. *(Sections 1–4)*

◆ **Structure and Function** The structural features of both birds and mammals are related to their life-supporting functions. The physical adaptations of different animals correspond to different behaviors. *(Sections 1–4)*

Benchmarks for Science Literacy

5A Diversity of Life Birds and mammals are classified as distinct groups based on morphological structures. Some characteristics of individual species determine further classifications. *(Sections 1–4; Real-World Lab; Skills Lab; Chapter Project)*

5C Basic Functions The major anatomical systems of both birds and mammals correspond to specialized functions. The behavior, diet, and habitat of animals are related to physical adaptations of the species, such as feathers and fur. *(Sections 1–4)*

5F Evolution of Life The origins of both birds and mammals can be studied through the fossil record and by comparing the specialized structures of animals with different adaptations. *(Sections 1, 3)*

12D Communication Skills Students organize and create simple tables and graphs. They may describe, in words, what the tables and graphs show. Students can analyze any variation in results. *(Real-World Lab; Skills Lab)*

Unifying Themes

◆ **Scale and Structure** Birds and mammals possess many specialized systems, each serving a specific function. *(Sections 1–4)*

◆ **Unity and Diversity** Birds and mammals have some similar characteristics, such as endothermy and a four-chambered heart. Birds share many characteristics that distinguish the group from mammals. However, within the group there is great diversity. Mammals also share many similar characteristics distinguishing them from birds, but show great diversity within the group. *(Sections 1–4; Skills Lab)*

◆ **Systems and Interactions** The interaction of the respiratory and circulatory systems in both birds and mammals provides these organisms with abundant energy. The interaction of a complex nervous system with keen senses allows fast movement and reaction. *(Sections 1, 3)*

◆ **Modeling** Students create models demonstrating the ability of wool to provide insulation. *(Real-World Lab)*

Media and Technology

Exploring Physical Science Videodisc

◆ **Section 2** "How an Airplane Flies" introduces viewers to the forces that act on an airplane during flight.

Exploring Life Science Videodisc

◆ **Section 1** "Backbones" compares the systems and functions of vertebrates as they have evolved over time.

◆ **Section 3** "How Does Everything Fit?" demonstrates the important interactions among all types of animals and humans.

◆ **Section 4** "pH in Aquaria" demonstrates the difficulty of creating natural conditions.

Interactive Student Tutorial CD-ROM

◆ **Chapter Review** Interactive questions help students to self-assess their mastery of key chapter concepts.

Student Edition Connection Strategies

◆ **Section 1** **Visual Arts Connection**, p. 121
  Integrating Physics, p. 122
  Integrating Environmental Science, p. 129

◆ **Section 2** **Integrating Physics**, p. 130

◆ **Section 3** **Science and Society**, p. 140

USING THE INTERNET

www.science-explorer.phschool.com

Visit the Science Explorer Internet site to find an up-to-date activity for Chapter 4 of *Animals*.

ACTIVITY	Time (minutes)	Materials *Quantities for one work group*	Skills
Section 1			
Discover, p. 120	15	**Nonconsumable** feathers, hand lens	Observing
Skills Lab, pp. 124–125	50	**Consumable** owl pellet **Nonconsumable** hand lens, dissecting needle, metric ruler, forceps	Drawing Conclusions
Try This, p. 127	20	**Consumable** uncooked egg, water **Nonconsumable** bowl, hand lens	Observing
Section 2			
Discover, p. 130	10	**Consumable** notebook paper **Nonconsumable** scissors, metric ruler, book	Predicting
Try This, p. 131	30	**Consumable** sheets of different kinds of paper (letter, construction, foil-covered), tape, glue, staples **Nonconsumable** paper clips, string, rubber bands	Making Models
Section 3			
Discover, p. 133	15	**Consumable** cracker **Nonconsumable** hand mirror	Inferring
Try This, p. 135	15	**Consumable** shortening, paper towels **Nonconsumable** rubber gloves, bucket or sink full of cold water	Inferring
Sharpen Your Skills, p. 137	15	No special materials are required.	Classifying
Real-World Lab, p. 139	35	**Consumable** hot tap water, graph paper, room temperature tap water **Nonconsumable** scissors, 1-L beaker, 3 thermometers, clock or watch, a pair of wool socks, 3 250-mL containers with lids	Controlling Variables, Interpreting Data
Section 4			
Discover, p. 141	15	**Consumable** masking tape, paper **Nonconsumable** pencil, various objects such as books and shoes	Inferring

A list of all materials required for the Student Edition activities can be found on pages T14–T15. You can order Materials Kits by calling 1-800-828-7777 or by accessing the Science Explorer Internet site at **www.science-explorer.phschool.com.**

Scientists learn about birds and mammals through careful observation. Watching a bird feeder will exercise students' ability to accurately observe and record observations. By watching a feeder, students can learn about bird communication, territoriality, and food choice.

Purpose In this project, students will model the skills and observations required for the careful study of any group of animals. They will observe the interaction between birds, and record feeding behavior and food preference in different birds.

Skills Focus Students will be able to
◆ observe and identify birds at a feeder;
◆ classify behaviors;
◆ create data tables;
◆ interpret data from their experiment.

Project Time Line During the first week, students select the feeder location and begin to observe and identify the species. During the second week, students make a list of bird species and begin to record common behaviors. In week three, students concentrate on feeding behaviors. Finally, students devise a way to present the information they have collected.

Before beginning the project, see Chapter 4 Project Teacher Notes on pages 102–103 in Teaching Resources for more details on carrying out the project. Distribute to students the Chapter 4 Project Overview, Worksheets, and Scoring Rubric on pages 104–108 in Teaching Resources.

Possible Materials
◆ a commercial bird feeder or materials to construct a feeder
◆ birdseed
◆ string or wire for hanging bird feeder
◆ field guide for bird identification
◆ guide to bird behaviors

Launching the Project To introduce the project and to stimulate student interest, ask: **What birds have you seen in your neighborhood?**

CHAPTER

4 Birds and Mammals

WHAT'S AHEAD

Integrating Physics

SECTION
1 Birds

Discover **What Are Feathers Like?**
Skills Lab **Looking at an Owl's Leftovers**
Try This **Eggs-amination**

SECTION
2 The Physics of Bird Flight

Discover **What Lifts Airplanes and Birds Into the Air?**
Try This **It's Plane to See**

SECTION
3 What Is a Mammal?

Discover **What Are Mammals' Teeth Like?**
Try This **Insulated Mammals**
Sharpen Your Skills **Classifying**
Real-World Lab **Keeping Warm**

118 ◆ B

Allow time for students to read the description of the project in their texts and the Chapter Project Overview on pages 104–105 in Teaching Resources. Then encourage discussions on bird feeders, bird behavior, and materials that could be used to construct a feeder; then answer initial questions students may have. Pass out copies of the Chapter 4 Project Worksheets on pages 106–107 in Teaching Resources for students to review.

Placement of the bird feeders should be discussed with the class. It is important to place the feeders so that they are easily refilled with food and easily observed. They should also be placed in or close to trees or shrubs so that birds have a safe place to go if they are startled.

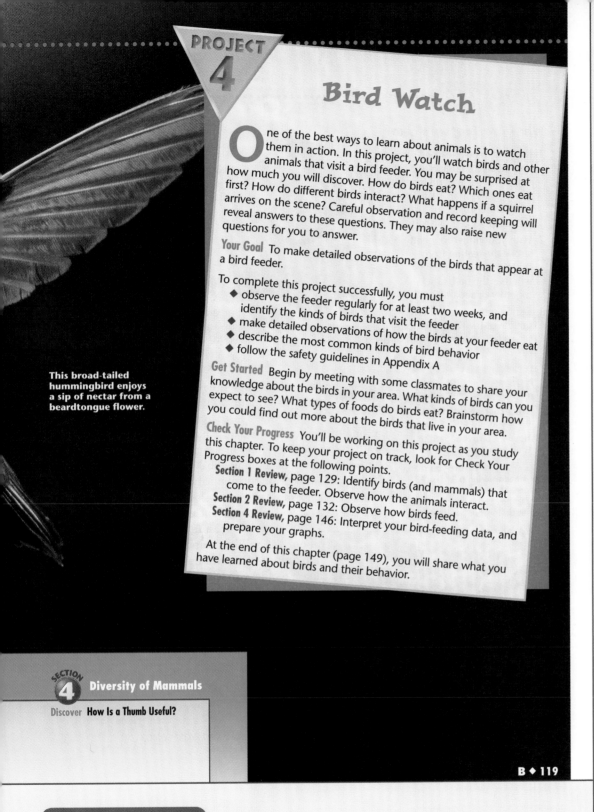

Bird Watch

One of the best ways to learn about animals is to watch them in action. In this project, you'll watch birds and other animals that visit a bird feeder. You may be surprised at how much you will discover. How do birds eat? Which ones eat first? How do different birds interact? What happens if a squirrel arrives on the scene? Careful observation and record keeping will reveal answers to these questions. They may also raise new questions for you to answer.

Your Goal To make detailed observations of the birds that appear at a bird feeder.

To complete this project successfully, you must
◆ observe the feeder regularly for at least two weeks, and identify the kinds of birds that visit the feeder
◆ make detailed observations of how the birds at your feeder eat
◆ describe the most common kinds of bird behavior
◆ follow the safety guidelines in Appendix A

Get Started Begin by meeting with some classmates to share your knowledge about the birds in your area. What kinds of birds can you expect to see? What types of foods do birds eat? Brainstorm how you could find out more about the birds that live in your area.

Check Your Progress You'll be working on this project as you study this chapter. To keep your project on track, look for Check Your Progress boxes at the following points.
Section 1 Review, page 129: Identify birds (and mammals) that come to the feeder. Observe how the animals interact.
Section 2 Review, page 132: Observe how birds feed.
Section 4 Review, page 146: Interpret your bird-feeding data, and prepare your graphs.

At the end of this chapter (page 149), you will share what you have learned about birds and their behavior.

This broad-tailed hummingbird enjoys a sip of nectar from a beardtongue flower.

Program Resources

◆ **Teaching Resources** Chapter 4 Project Teacher's Notes, pp. 102–103; Chapter 4 Project Overview and Worksheets, pp. 104–107; Chapter 4 Project Scoring Rubric, p. 108

The feeders should be refilled daily. Harmful molds can grow in wet seeds. If the birdseed gets wet, immediately discard it, wash and dry the feeder, and refill with fresh seed.

Have students observe and record the numbers of a particular species and the interaction of those birds with members of other species. They should collect and interpret bird-feeding data, taking note of what type of seed seems to be preferred by particular species. It is also important to note the birds' interaction with other animals, such as dogs or squirrels.

Performance Assessment

The Chapter 4 Project Scoring Rubric on page 108 of Teaching Resources will help you evaluate how well students complete the Chapter 4 Project. You may wish to share the scoring rubric with your students so they are clear about what will be expected of them. Students will be assessed on
◆ how thoroughly they research the birds of the area so that they use appropriate feeders, food, and locations;
◆ the completeness of their observation entries, including what birds appeared, interactions, and foods eaten;
◆ how well they apply chapter concepts to their observations;
◆ the thoroughness and organization of their presentations;
◆ the organization of their written analyses.

Objectives

After completing the lesson, students will be able to
◆ identify the common characteristics of birds;
◆ explain how birds are adapted to and affect their environments.

Key Terms birds, contour feather, down feather, insulator, crop, gizzard

1 Engage/Explore

Activating Prior Knowledge

Brainstorm a list of expressions about birds and write them on the board. (*Samples: birds of a feather flock together; bird's-eye view; birdlike appetite*) Ask students whether these are scientifically valid. List students' ideas on the board. Later, after students have read the section, ask them to look at the expressions again. Students should reevaluate the accuracy of each expression on the basis of what they have learned.

 **DISCOVER**

Skills Focus observing
Materials *feathers, hand lens*

Time 15 minutes
Tips Try to have a variety of contour feathers. Good sources are wooded areas, beaches, pet stores, bird sanctuaries, or biological supply houses. Fresh feathers should be frozen for 72 hours to kill organisms. Point out the shaft and barbs of a feather.
Expected Outcome Feathers have a central shaft with a vane made up of flexible barbs that link together but can be pulled apart.
Think It Over The barbs rejoin easily; this helps birds smooth their feathers quickly to fly or swim.

120 ◆ B

DISCOVER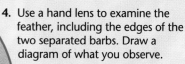

What Are Feathers Like?

1. Examine a feather. Observe its overall shape and structure. Use a hand lens to examine the many hairlike barbs that project out from the feather's central shaft.

2. With your fingertip, gently stroke the feather from bottom to top. Observe whether the barbs stick together or separate.

3. Gently separate two barbs in the middle of the feather. Rub the separated edges with your fingertip.

4. Use a hand lens to examine the feather, including the edges of the two separated barbs. Draw a diagram of what you observe.

5. Now rejoin the two separated barbs by gently pulling outward from the shaft. Then wash your hands.

Think It Over
Observing Once barbs have been separated, is it easy to rejoin them? How might this be an advantage to the bird?

GUIDE FOR READING

◆ What characteristics do birds have in common?

◆ How are birds adapted to their environments?

Reading Tip Before you read, look at *Exploring a Bird* on page 123 and make a list of unfamiliar terms. As you read, write definitions for the terms.

One day in 1861, in a limestone quarry in what is now Germany, Hermann von Meyer was inspecting rocks. Meyer, who was a fossil hunter, spotted something dark in one of the rocks. It was the blackened fossil imprint of a feather! Excited, Meyer began searching for a fossil of an entire bird. Though it took a month, he eventually found what he was looking for—a skeleton surrounded by the clear imprint of many feathers. The fossil was given the scientific name *Archaeopteryx* (ahr kee AHP tur iks), meaning "ancient, winged thing."

Paleontologists estimate that *Archaeopteryx* lived about 145 million years ago. *Archaeopteryx* didn't look much like the birds you know. It looked more like a reptile with wings. While no modern bird has any teeth, *Archaeopteryx* had a mouthful of them. No modern bird has a long, bony tail, either, but *Archaeopteryx* did. However, unlike any reptile, extinct or modern, *Archaeopteryx* had feathers—its wings and tail were covered with them. Paleontologists think that *Archaeopteryx* and today's birds descended from some kind of reptile, possibly from a dinosaur.

Figure 1 The extinct bird *Archaeopteryx* may have looked like this.

READING STRATEGIES

Reading Tip After students write definitions for unfamiliar terms, instruct them to write sentences in which they use each term. Then have students rewrite the sentences on a separate sheet of paper, omitting the key terms and inserting a blank line. Direct partners to exchange papers and fill in the missing terms.

Study and Comprehension Encourage students to set their own purposes for reading this section by rewriting section headings as questions. To demonstrate, change the heading "Feathers" to "Why are feathers important to birds?" After reading the section, have students discuss and compare answers to their questions.

Figure 2 John James Audubon painted this little blue heron in 1832. (© Collection of the New York Historical Society)

What Is a Bird?

Modern **birds** all share certain characteristics. **A bird is an endothermic vertebrate that has feathers and a four-chambered heart, and lays eggs.** Birds have scales on their feet and legs, evidence of their descent from reptiles. In addition, most birds can fly.

The flight of birds is an amazing feat that people watch with delight and envy. All modern birds—including ostriches, penguins, and other flightless birds—evolved from ancestors that could fly.

The bodies of birds are adapted for flight. For example, the bones of a bird's forelimbs form wings. In addition, many of a bird's bones are nearly hollow, making the bird's body extremely lightweight. Flying birds have large chest muscles that move the wings. Finally, feathers are a major adaptation that help birds fly.

☑ *Checkpoint* **List four ways in which birds are adapted for flight.**

Feathers

The rule is this: If it has feathers, it's a bird. Feathers probably evolved from reptiles' scales. Both feathers and reptile scales are made of the same tough material as your fingernails.

Birds have different types of feathers. If you've ever picked up a feather from the ground, chances are good that it was a contour feather. A **contour feather** is one of the large feathers that give shape to a bird's body. The long contour feathers that extend beyond the body on the wings and tail are called flight feathers. When a bird flies, these feathers help it balance and steer.

Chapter 4 **B ◆ 121**

Visual Arts CONNECTION

John James Audubon (1785–1851) was an American artist who painted pictures of birds and other kinds of animals. Audubon grew up in France. Even as a child he loved to sketch the birds that he observed while roaming through the forest. Later, as an adult in America, he began to study and draw birds seriously, traveling to various parts of the country in search of different varieties of birds.

Audubon's four-volume work, *The Birds of America,* published between 1827 and 1838, contains 435 pictures showing 489 different bird species. Audubon's paintings, such as that of the little blue heron in Figure 2, are known for their accuracy and remarkable detail as well as their beauty.

In Your Journal

List five observations that you can make about the little blue heron in Audubon's painting, such as the shape of its bill and the pattern of color on its body. Then describe the heron's environment.

2 Facilitate

What Is a Bird?

Including All Students

To help students understand the characteristics of birds, pair students who are still mastering English with students who are proficient in English. Have each pair list the following terms: *endothermic, vertebrate, feathers, four-chambered heart,* and *egg-laying.* Challenge student pairs to write brief definitions of each term and to list three or four animals that share these characteristics. *(Sample: Vertebrates have backbones and include lizards, giraffes, and fish.)* **limited English proficiency**

Visual Arts CONNECTION

Invite each student to choose a bird in *The Birds of America* and compare its picture with the picture and description of the same bird in a field guide. Ask how each book might be useful in identifying an unknown bird. Also, ask students what the Audubon print shows better than the field guide, and vice versa.

In Your Journal Students should observe that the heron has a long, pointed, mostly blue bill; long, curved neck; black head and tail; blue wings; and long, thin legs. **learning modality: visual**

Answers to Self-Assessment

☑ *Checkpoint*

Bird adaptations for flight include forelimb bones that form wings, bones that are nearly hollow, large chest muscles, and feathers.

Ongoing Assessment

Oral Presentation Ask students to name at least four characteristics all birds share. *(Accept any four: endothermic, vertebrates, feathers, four-chambered hearts, lay eggs, scales on their feet and legs)*

Feathers

Integrating Physics

Materials *3 plastic containers, 3 ice cubes, clock, insulating materials such as down feathers, shredded paper, cotton balls, shredded plastic foam, aluminum foil, plastic wrap*

Time 35 minutes

Have students work in groups to test different insulators. Each group should wrap an ice cube in one of the insulators, place it in a container, and observe it every 5 minutes for 30 minutes. Ask: **What variables must be the same in all your experiments?** *(The size of the ice cube, the temperature of the container)* Invite students to predict which insulator will be the most effective. Groups can compare data and draw conclusions about which insulator is the most effective.** cooperative learning**

Food and Body Temperature

Including All Students

Materials *saltine cracker, plastic jar, several small pebbles*

Time 10 minutes

This activity benefits students who have difficulty seeing, because it conveys concepts through tactile experiences. It also helps other students who need extra help to understand how a gizzard works. Direct students to place a saltine cracker in a plastic jar along with several small pebbles. Have them put the lid on the jar and shake it for 30 seconds. Students who have difficulty seeing may open the jar and feel the cracker. Then ask: **What happened to the cracker?** *(It broke into smaller pieces.)* **How is the jar like a gizzard?** *(Both grind food using stones.)* **How are they different?** *(The gizzard is a muscular wall that squeezes as it grinds the food. The jar is a hard container that has to be shaken to grind the food.)*
learning modality: kinesthetic

Figure 3 Birds are the only animals that have feathers. **A.** Down feathers act as insulation to trap warmth next to a bird's body. **B.** Contour feathers, like this one from a Steller's jay, give a bird its shape and help it to fly. *Observing Where do you see down feathers and contour feathers on the family of Emperor geese above?*

In Figure 3, you can see that a contour feather consists of a central shaft and many hairlike projections, called barbs, that are arranged parallel to each other. If you examined a contour feather in the Discover activity, you know that you can "unzip" its flat surface by pulling apart the barbs. When birds fly, their feathers sometimes become "unzipped." To keep their flight feathers in good condition, birds often pull the feathers through their bills in an action called preening. Preening "zips" the barbs back together again, smoothing the ruffled feathers.

Integrating Physics

In addition to contour feathers, birds have short, fluffy **down feathers** that are specialized to trap heat and keep the bird warm. Down feathers are found right next to a bird's skin, at the base of contour feathers. Down feathers are soft and flexible, unlike contour feathers. Down feathers mingle and overlap, trapping air. Air is a good **insulator**—a material that does not conduct heat well and therefore helps prevent it from escaping. By trapping a blanket of warm air next to the bird's skin, down feathers slow the rate at which the skin loses heat. In effect, down feathers cover a bird in lightweight long underwear.

Checkpoint Why do you think quilts and jackets are often stuffed with down feathers?

Food and Body Temperature

Birds have no teeth. To capture, grip, and handle food, birds primarily use their bills. Each species of bird has a bill shaped to help it feed quickly and efficiently. For example, the pointy, curved bill of a hawk acts like a meathook. A hawk holds its prey with its claws and uses its sharp bill to pull off bits of flesh. In contrast, the straight, sharp bill of a woodpecker is a tool for chipping into wood. When a woodpecker chisels a hole in a tree and finds a tasty insect, the woodpecker spears the insect with its long, barbed tongue.

After a bird eats its food, digestion begins. Each organ in a bird's digestive system is adapted to process food. Many birds have an internal storage tank, or **crop,** that allows them to store food inside the body after swallowing it. Find the crop in *Exploring a Bird,* and notice that it is connected to the stomach.

Background

Integrating Science The origin of feathers is not clearly understood. The most common belief is that feathers are modified scales. The scales on the leg of the bird are made of keratin and form the same way a reptile's scales do. In the early stages of development, scales and feathers are very similar to each other. This evidence leads scientists to believe that feathers evolved from early reptilian scales. In fact, many paleontologists believe that today's birds evolved from a certain type of dinosaur. Fossils that were recently discovered in China seem to reveal two different species of feathered dinosaurs. The scientists who studied these fossils think that the feathers served as insulation, because they doubt that the dinosaurs could fly. It is hoped that someday scientists will know more about how feathers evolved.

The first part of the stomach is long and has thin walls. Here food is bathed in chemicals that begin to break it down. Then the partially digested food moves to a thick-walled, muscular part of the stomach called the **gizzard,** which squeezes and grinds the partially digested food. Remember that birds do not have teeth—their gizzard performs the grinding function of teeth. The gizzard may contain small stones that the bird has swallowed. These stones help with the grinding by rubbing against the food and crushing it.

EXPLORING *a Bird*

If you are strolling through a grassy field or meadow in spring, you might hear the beautiful song of a meadowlark. Notice how a meadowlark's body is adapted for flight and for a high level of activity.

Air Sacs A bird's lungs are connected to a series of air sacs. Air sacs help provide the bird's body with the rich supply of oxygen it needs.

Bill A meadowlark uses its bill to catch insects and pick up seeds.

Contour Feathers Contour feathers give a bird its shape. Without its contour feathers, a bird cannot fly.

Crop

Heart Like all birds, meadowlarks have a four-chambered heart that keeps oxygen-rich blood separate from oxygen-poor blood. Thus the blood arriving at the tissues carries the most oxygen possible.

Gizzard The muscular gizzard churns food and grinds it to a paste.

EXPLORING

a Bird

Ask students to find the structures in the visual essay that help the bird fly. Most will select the feathers and wings. Point out other structures. Ask: **How do the air sacs and heart work as a bird flies?** *(The air sacs provide the oxygen that the heart pumps to the body.)* Have students find the structures that are parts of the bird's digestive system. Ask: **How does the crop benefit the bird?** *(It allows the bird to store food.)* Have students trace the path through the digestive system. *(From the bill to the crop, to the stomach, to the gizzard, to the intestines)*
Extend Meadowlarks live in grassy environments and move mostly by flying. Have students examine photos of birds that are adapted for other forms of movement, such as ocean birds that dive and swim. Students can compare the bills, feathers, and body shapes of these birds. **learning modality: visual**

Cultural Diversity

Birds appear in the folklore of many cultures. In the folklore of ancient Egypt, an indestructible bird called a phoenix rose from the ashes of its own funeral pyre. The Yosei are fairies in Japanese folklore that appear as cranes or swans. In Siberian folklore, the Zonget is a goddess who appears as an Arctic bird and decides whether hunted birds and animals will be caught. Ask students: **How are other birds used as symbols?** *(Sample: Doves symbolize peace; peacocks symbolize vanity.)* **learning modality: verbal**

Answers to Self-Assessment

Caption Question

Figure 3 Down feathers are found on the young geese. Contour feathers are found on the adults.

☑ *Checkpoint*

Quilts and jackets are often stuffed with down feathers because the feathers are good insulators. This makes the garments very warm.

Looking at an Owl's Leftovers

Preparing for Inquiry

Key Concept Conclusions about an animal's diet can be drawn by examining the parts that are not digested.

Skills Objective The students will be able to

◆ draw conclusions about the diet of owls by studying the pellets they cough up.

Time 50 minutes

Advance Planning Order owl pellets from a biological supply company. If possible, obtain one for each student and a few extras.

Guiding Inquiry

Invitation Have students think about what they discard when they eat. Ask: **What do you have left over when you eat a chicken wing? What about an apple?** *(Bones, apple core)* Inform students that other animals also leave behind parts of their food, and these leftovers can be studied to determine what the animal ate.

Introducing the Procedure

◆ Before students begin dissecting, allow them to use dissecting needles to examine a cookie with nuts, chocolate chips, or raisins. Warn students not to eat the cookies.

◆ Encourage students to examine the outside of the pellet before making hypotheses.

◆ Owls may eat lizards or snakes. Provide pictures of lizard and snake bones to help students identify them.

Troubleshooting the Experiment

◆ Explain that the pellets have been decontaminated. Have reluctant students work with a partner and perform the roles of data collection and record keeping.

◆ It is helpful to break pellets into pieces and soak them in water to loosen the materials before beginning the dissection.

Like all animals, birds use the food they eat for energy. Because birds are endotherms, they need a lot of energy to maintain their body temperature. It also takes an enormous amount of energy to power the muscles used in flight. Each day an average bird eats food equal to about a quarter of its body weight. When people say, "You're eating like a bird," they usually mean that you're eating very little. But if you were actually eating as a bird does, you would be eating huge meals. You might eat 100 hamburger patties in one day!

Skills Lab

Drawing Conclusions

LOOKING AT AN OWL'S LEFTOVERS

In this lab, you will gather evidence and draw conclusions about an owl's diet.

Problem

What can you learn about owls' diets from studying the pellets that they cough up?

Materials

owl pellet   hand lens   dissecting needle
metric ruler   forceps

Procedure

1. An owl pellet is a collection of undigested materials that an owl coughs up after a meal. Write a hypothesis describing what items you expect an owl pellet to contain. List the reasons for your hypothesis.

2. Use a hand lens to observe the outside of an owl pellet. Record your observations.

3. Use one hand to grasp the owl pellet with forceps. Hold a dissecting needle in your other hand, and use it to gently separate the pellet into pieces. **CAUTION:** *Dissecting needles are sharp. Never cut material toward you; always cut away from your body.*

4. Using the forceps and dissecting needle, carefully separate the bones from the rest of the pellet. Remove any fur that might be attached to bones.

Background

Facts and Figures Birds can have unusual ways of obtaining food. Hummingbirds sip nectar while hovering in midair. Woodpecker finches use a broken piece of cactus spine to pry grubs and insects out of tree bark. African secretary birds stamp snakes with their feet before eating them. Owls use a keen sense of hearing to listen for prey. In the dark, an owl can accurately locate a mouse rustling in the leaves and grass. Some vultures can smell a potential meal from a great distance.

Delivering Oxygen to Cells

Cells must receive plenty of oxygen to release the energy contained in food. Flying requires much energy. Therefore, birds need a highly efficient way to get oxygen into their body and to their cells. Birds have a system of air sacs in their body that connects to the lungs. The air sacs enable birds to extract much more oxygen from each breath of air than other animals can.

The circulatory system of a bird is also efficient at getting oxygen to the cells. Unlike amphibians and most reptiles,

Shrew	House mouse	Meadow vole	Mole	Rat
Upper jaw has at least 18 teeth; teeth are brown. Skull length is 23 mm or less.	Upper jaw has 2 biting teeth and extends past lower jaw. Skull length is 22 mm or less.	Upper jaw has 2 biting teeth that are smooth, not grooved. Skull length is more than 23 mm.	Upper jaw has at least 18 teeth. Skull length is 23 mm or more.	Upper jaw has 2 biting teeth. Upper jaw extends past lower jaw. Skull length is 22 mm or more.

5. Group similar bones together in separate piles. Observe the skulls, and draw them. Record the number of skulls, their length, and the number, shape, and color of the teeth.

6. Use the chart on this page to determine what kinds of skulls you found. If any skulls do not match the chart exactly, record which animal the skulls resemble most.

7. Try to fit together any of the remaining bones to form complete or partial skeletons. Sketch your results.

8. Wash your hands thoroughly with soap when you are finished.

Analyze and Conclude

1. How many animals' remains were in the pellet? What data led you to that conclusion?

2. Combine your results with those of your classmates. Which three animals were eaten most frequently? How do these results compare to your hypothesis?

3. Owls cough up about two pellets a day. Based on your class's data, what can you conclude about the number of animals an owl might eat in one month?

4. **Think About It** In this lab, you were able to examine only the part of the owl's diet that it did not digest. How might this fact affect your confidence in the conclusions you reached?

More to Explore

Design a study that might tell you how an owl's diet varies at different times of the year. Give an example of a conclusion you might expect to draw from such a study.

Chapter 4 **B ◆ 125**

◆ Some pellets may not contain identifiable skulls because the skulls were coughed up in a different pellet. Few other animal remains are likely to be present in a pellet containing a skull.

Expected Outcome
Students should find a varying number of identifiable animal remains in their pellets.

Analyze and Conclude
1. Answers will vary. Students should explain that the number of each type of bone can help determine the number of animals eaten. For example, each skull represents one animal. Each pair of femurs represents one animal.
2. Combined data should give an estimate of total number and type of animals in the pellets.
3. The estimated total of animals found in all pellets divided by the number of pellets dissected gives an average number of animals per pellet. Students can multiply this number by 2 to find the average number of animals eaten per day. Then, multiply the average number per day by 30 to find the average number of animals eaten per month.
4. Students may explain that they are less confident in their results because they will probably underestimate the number of animals eaten each month.

Extending Inquiry
More to Explore A sample study might be to analyze pellets collected on the last two days of each month for a year. From this study, students would expect to conclude that an owl's diet varies during the year. In winter, hibernating animals will be absent. Animals such as house mice, which are always active, may be common in the diet all year.

Program Resources
◆ **Teaching Resources** Chapter 4 Skills Lab, pp. 125–127
◆ **Inquiry Skills Activity Book** Provides teaching and review of all inquiry skills

Delivering Oxygen to Cells

Inquiry Challenge

Have students find their pulse rates and count how many times they breathe in 1 minute. Then have able students run in place for 1 minute. (CAUTION: *Students with medical problems that preclude running should be excused.*) Have students retake their pulse and breathing rates. Ask them to form hypotheses about what happens to a bird's heart and breathing rate when it flies. Ask: **What feature helps birds get more oxygen to their muscles?** (*Air sacs and four-chambered heart*) **learning modality: kinesthetic**

Nervous System and Senses

Building Inquiry Skills: Observing

Materials *binoculars*
Time 30 minutes

Take students outdoors to observe the way birds rely on their nervous systems. Students can use binoculars to observe and record specific activities, such as taking off, pecking, preening, or calling. They should also identify the senses that the bird probably used to perform the behavior. In class, place students in small groups and have them compile a master list of observations. **learning modality: visual**

Reproducing and Caring for Young

Demonstration

Materials *3 uncooked chicken eggs, a heavy book, clay, cotton balls*
Time 10 minutes

Place the eggs in clay supports, small ends up, in a triangular pattern. Pad between the eggs with cotton. Ask students to predict what will happen when you place a book on the eggs. Demonstrate this. Then ask: **How do strong eggs benefit birds?** (*They will not break if they roll or when a bird sits on them.*) **learning modality: visual**

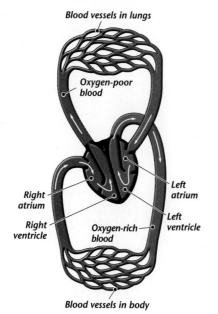

Figure 4 Birds have hearts with four chambers. Notice how the left side of the heart is completely separate from the right side. This separation prevents oxygen-rich blood from mixing with oxygen-poor blood. *Comparing and Contrasting Contrast a bird's circulatory system with that of an amphibian, as shown on page 96, Figure 13. How do the circulatory systems differ?*

Blood vessels in lungs

Oxygen-poor blood

Right atrium

Right ventricle

Left atrium

Left ventricle

Oxygen-rich blood

Blood vessels in body

whose hearts have three chambers, birds have hearts with four chambers—two atria and two ventricles. Trace the path of blood through a bird's two-loop circulatory system in Figure 4. The right side of a bird's heart pumps blood to the lungs, where the blood picks up oxygen. Oxygen-rich blood then returns to the left side of the heart, which pumps it to the rest of the body. The advantage of a four-chambered heart is that there is no mixing of oxygen-rich and oxygen-poor blood. Therefore, blood that arrives in the body's tissues has plenty of oxygen.

Nervous System and Senses

In order to fly, birds must have very quick reactions. To appreciate why, imagine how quickly you would have to react if you were a sparrow trying to land safely on a tree branch. You approach the tree headfirst, diving into a maze of tree branches. As you approach, you only have an instant to find a place where you can land safely and avoid crashing into those branches. If birds had slow reactions, they would not live very long.

A bird can react so quickly because of its well-developed brain and finely-tuned senses of sight and hearing. The brain of a bird controls such complex activities as flying, singing, and finding food. Most birds have keener eyesight than humans. A flying vulture, for example, can spot food on the ground from a height of more than one and a half kilometers. Some birds have excellent hearing, too. How could keen hearing help an owl search for prey in a dark forest?

Reproducing and Caring for Young

Like reptiles, birds have internal fertilization and lay eggs. Bird eggs are similar to reptile eggs, except that their shells are harder. In most bird species, the female lays the eggs in a nest that has been prepared by one or both parents.

Bird eggs will only develop at a temperature close to the body temperature of the parent bird. A parent bird usually incubates the eggs by sitting on them to keep them warm. In some species, incubating the eggs is the job of one parent. Female robins, for example, incubate their delicate blue eggs. In other species, such as pigeons, the parents take turns incubating the eggs.

Birds differ in the length of time that it takes for their chicks to develop until hatching. Sparrow eggs take only about 12 days. Chicken eggs take about 21 days, and albatross eggs take about 80 days. In general, the larger the bird species, the longer its incubation time.

Background

Facts and Figures The incubation period for bird eggs depends on the species of bird. Warblers, which are small birds, incubate their eggs for just 10 days. Albatrosses, which are large birds, incubate their eggs for about 10 weeks. The award for the most energy-efficient brooding strategy, however, has to go to the cowbird. Cowbirds do not incubate their eggs at all, but instead lay their eggs in the nests of other birds. Even though the cowbird egg is larger than the other birds' eggs, the unknowing foster parents incubate the egg of the intruder anyway. When the cowbird egg hatches, the cowbird chick is usually much larger than the other chicks. The cowbird chick eventually becomes so large that it pushes the smaller rival chicks out of the nest or takes their food. The foster parents raise the lone cowbird chick, never realizing that it is not their own.

Figure 5 This masked northern weaver bird is literally weaving a nest out of grass. The finished baglike nest will have only a small, weaver bird-sized hole in it. The small entrance helps keep the eggs and young safe from predators.

When it is ready to hatch, a chick pecks its way out of the eggshell. Some newly hatched chicks, such as bluebirds and robins, are featherless, blind, and so weak they can barely lift their heads to beg for food. Other chicks, such as ducks, chickens, and pheasants, are covered with down and can run about soon after they have hatched. Most parent birds feed and protect their young at least until they are able to fly.

☑ *Checkpoint* *How do bird eggs differ from reptile eggs?*

Diversity of Birds

With almost 10,000 species, birds are the most diverse land-dwelling vertebrates. **In addition to adaptations for flight, birds have adaptations—such as the shapes of their legs, claws, and bills—for living in widely diverse environments.** For example, the long legs and toes of wading birds, such as herons and cranes, make wading easy, while the toes of perching birds, such as goldfinches and mockingbirds, can automatically lock onto a branch or other perch. The bills of ducks enable them to filter tiny plants and animals from water. Birds also have adaptations for flying, finding mates, and caring for their young. You can see a variety of bird adaptations in *Exploring Birds* on the next page.

Eggs-amination

Like reptile eggs, bird eggs protect the developing embryo, provide food for it, and keep it from drying out.

1. Look at the surface of a chicken egg with a hand lens. Then gently crack the egg into a bowl. Do not break the yolk.

2. Note the membrane attached to the inside of the shell. Then look at the blunt end of the egg. What do you see?

3. Fill one part of the eggshell with water. What do you observe?

4. Find the egg yolk. What is its function?

5. Look for a small white spot on the yolk. This marks the spot where the embryo would have developed if the egg had been fertilized.

6. Wash your hands with soap.

Observing Draw a labeled diagram of the egg that names each structure and describes its function.

Skills Focus observing
Materials *uncooked egg, bowl, hand lens, water*
Time 20 minutes
Tips Uncooked eggs can carry bacteria. Tell students not to put eggs in their mouths. Suggest using only a little water in Step 3.
Answers There is an air pocket between the shell and the membrane. The water stays in the shell. The yolk provides food.
Observing Diagrams should identify the white spot, shell, yolk, egg white, and membrane. The egg and its shell keep water inside, protect the embryo, and provide nourishment (yolk).
Extend Have students gently roll an uncooked egg on a hard surface, and infer how the shape of an egg protects the embryo. (*The egg rolls in a circle, so it is less likely to roll out of the nest.*)
learning modality: visual

Diversity of Birds

Building Inquiry Skills: Classifying

Materials *pictures of birds, paper, tape, scissors*
Time 20 minutes

Provide pictures showing the legs and feet of various birds. Have students classify the pictures into two or three groups on the basis of the characteristics of the legs and feet—for example, webbed feet; long, sharp claws. Have students cut out the pictures and group them, then tape them to a sheet of paper.

Portfolio Students can save their pictures in their portfolios. **learning modality: visual**

Media and Technology

🗔 **Transparencies** "Circulation in Fishes, Amphibians, and Birds," Transparency 16

💿 **Exploring Life Science Videodisc**
Unit 3, Side 2, "How Does Everything Fit?"
Chapter 1

Answers to Self-Assessment

Caption Question

Figure 4 The amphibian's heart has three chambers, so oxygen-rich and oxygen-poor blood can mix somewhat. The bird's heart has four chambers that separate oxygen-rich and oxygen-poor blood.

☑ *Checkpoint*

Bird eggs are harder than reptile eggs and are usually laid in a nest.

Ongoing Assessment

Oral Presentation Call on students to briefly describe the functions and locations of a bird's four-chambered heart and air sacs.

Diversity of Birds,
continued

EXPLORING
Birds

Invite volunteers to read aloud the description of the birds in the visual essay. When all descriptions have been read, ask:

◆ **What adaptations do the woodpecker and spoonbill have that help them eat the food in their environments?** (*The woodpecker has a sharp beak that chisels into trees. The spoonbill has a long, flat bill that it sweeps underwater to catch small animals.*)

◆ **How do the kestrel's eyes help it find food?** (*The placement of the eyes allows the kestrel to watch the ground while flying.*)

◆ **How are the leg and body proportions of the ostrich adaptations?** (*The ostrich's legs are long compared to its body; it cannot fly to escape predators, and its long legs help it run quickly.*)

Extend Challenge students to consider birds adapted to extreme environments such as penguins in Antarctica or roadrunners in the desert. Have students draw conclusions about the adaptations that allow these birds to survive.
learning modality: visual

Why Birds Are Important

Integrating Environmental Science

Emphasize to students the important roles birds play in helping to pollinate plants and eliminate pests. Encourage them to protect and care for birds in their own neighborhood. As trees are cut down, nesting habitats are lost. Building a birdhouse gives some kinds of homeless birds a place to nest. Have students research a particular bird and then design and build a birdhouse for birds that live in their neighborhood.
learning modality: verbal

EXPLORING Birds

Every bird has adaptations that help it live in its environment. Note how the bill and feet of each of these birds are adapted to help the bird survive.

▲ **Bee-Eaters**
This rainbow bee-eater feeds on bees and other insects, which it catches as it flies. Bee-eaters, which are found in Africa, Europe, Australia, and Asia, help control insect pests such as locusts.

▲ **Long-Legged Waders**
The roseate spoonbill is found in the southern United States and throughout much of South America. The spoonbill catches small animals by sweeping its long, flattened bill back and forth underwater.

▲ **Woodpeckers**
The pileated woodpecker is the largest woodpecker in North America—adults average about 44 centimeters in length. This woodpecker feeds on insects it finds in holes it has chiseled into trees.

Ostriches
The ostrich, found in Africa, is the largest living bird. It cannot fly, but it can run at speeds greater than 60 kilometers per hour. Its speed helps it escape from predators. ▼

Birds of Prey
The American kestrel, a small falcon, catches its food by hovering in the air and scanning the ground. When it sees prey, such as an insect, the kestrel swoops down and grabs it. Kestrels are found worldwide. ▼

Background

Facts and Figures Animal species are disappearing all over the world. Many people do not realize that there may be threatened species in their backyards and neighborhoods. Some very hardy species of birds, such as sparrows and pigeons, have done very well in urbanized areas. However, recent studies have identified a new threat to these city dwellers—the effective hunting skills of the domestic cat. Cats are wonderful predators.

They can climb trees and remove fledglings from nests. They are excellent ambushers, and lie in wait or sneak up on unwary prey. As a result of the cats' efficient hunting strategies, populations of songbirds are declining all over the United States. The situation will only get worse as cat populations continue to increase. This problem has no immediate solution, but the answer may be as simple as putting bells on cats.

◄ Owls
Owls are predators that hunt mostly at night. Sharp vision and keen hearing help owls find prey in the darkness. Razor-sharp claws and great strength allow larger owls, like this eagle owl, to prey on animals as large as deer.

▲ Perching Birds
There are over 5,000 species of perching birds. They represent more than half of all the bird species in the world. The painted bunting, a seed-eating bird, lives in the southern United States and northern Mexico.

Why Birds Are Important

A walk through the woods or a park would be dull without birds. You wouldn't hear their musical songs, and you wouldn't see them flitting gracefully from tree to tree. But people benefit from birds in practical ways, too. Birds and their eggs provide food, while feathers are used to stuff pillows and clothing.

INTEGRATING ENVIRONMENTAL SCIENCE Birds also play an important role in the environment. Nectar-eating birds, like hummingbirds, carry pollen from one flower to another, thus enabling some flowers to reproduce. Seed-eating birds, like painted buntings, carry the seeds of plants to new places. This happens when the birds eat the fruits or seeds of a plant, fly to a new location, and then eliminate some of the seeds in digestive wastes. In addition, birds are some of the chief predators of pest animals. Hawks and owls eat many rats and mice, while many perching birds feed on insect pests.

 **Section 1 Review**

1. What characteristics do modern birds share with reptiles? How are birds different from reptiles?
2. Choose two different bird species and describe how they are adapted to obtain food in their environment.
3. Predict how the size of crop harvests might be affected if all birds disappeared from Earth.
4. **Thinking Critically** Comparing and Contrasting Compare contour feathers with down feathers, noting both similarities and differences.

 Check Your Progress
By now you should have set up your bird feeder. As you begin making observations, use a field guide to identify the species of birds. Count and record the number of each species that appears. Also observe the birds' behaviors. How long do birds stay at the feeder? How do birds respond to other birds and mammals? Look for signs that some birds are trying to dominate others.

CHAPTER PROJECT 4

Chapter 4 **B ◆ 129**

---

3 Assess

Section 1 Review Answers

1. Shared characteristics: a vertebral column, breathe oxygen, lay eggs, and have scaly legs. Differences: Birds—endotherms, feathers, four-chambered hearts. Reptiles—ectotherms, lack feathers, and most have three-chambered hearts.
2. Students can use birds in the visual essay *Exploring Birds*. Sample: The woodpecker has a strong, pointy bill that can peck holes into trees. The spoonbill has long legs adapted to wading and a bill shaped to catch prey in the water.
3. Crop harvests would probably decrease, because birds would not be eating insect pests or spreading pollen and seeds.
4. Both are lightweight and made of the same material. Contour feathers are larger and have barbs that lock tightly and smoothly together. Down feathers have soft and fluffy barbs.

Check Your Progress CHAPTER PROJECT 4
After students install their bird feeders, provide field guides to help them identify the species they observe. Check to see that students are recording appropriate observations. As students proceed with their observations, meet with them regularly to discuss their progress.

Program Resources

Science Explorer Series
Environmental Science, Chapter 2
◆ **Teaching Resources** 4-1 Review and Reinforce, p. 111; 4-1 Enrich, p. 112
◆ **Integrated Science Laboratory Manual** B-4, "Adaptations of Birds"
◆ **Interdisciplinary Exploration Series** "India Beyond the Golden Age," pp. 36–38

Media and Technology

Interactive Student Tutorial CD-ROM B-4

Performance Assessment

Writing Have each student write a paragraph describing at least six adaptations of birds. Students should describe feathers; the four-chambered heart; feeding and digestive-system adaptations; nervous system and senses; and reproductive adaptations.

SECTION 2 The Physics of Bird Flight

Objective

After completing the lesson, students will be able to

◆ explain how a bird is able to fly.

Key Term lift

1 Engage/Explore

Activating Prior Knowledge

Ask students to describe and demonstrate how they have seen birds fly. (*Some students will flap their arms up and down, while others will glide with their arms outstretched.*) Have students notice this difference and speculate how some birds seem to fly without putting forth any effort at all.

 DISCOVER

Skills Focus predicting
Materials *notebook*
paper, scissors, metric ruler, book
Time 10 minutes
Tips The paper should be curled so that the free edge of the strip faces away from the student. Make sure students hold the book so that their breath flows across the top of the paper strip. Students should not blow down on the paper. Before students attempt the activity, ask them to predict what will happen. Then have them complete Step 3 and determine if their predictions were accurate.
Expected Outcome When students blow gently across the paper, it lifts slightly. When students blow hard across the paper, it lifts higher and remains in a horizontal position.
Think It Over The air flowing over the bird's wing might lift the bird up into the air.

SECTION 2 The Physics of Bird Flight

DISCOVER — ACTIVITY

What Lifts Airplanes and Birds Into the Air?

1. Cut a strip of notebook paper 5 centimeters wide and 28 centimeters long. Insert about 5 centimeters of the paper strip into the middle of a book. The rest of the paper strip should hang over the edge.

2. Hold the book up so that the paper is below your mouth.

3. Blow gently across the top of the paper and watch what happens to the paper. Then blow harder.

Think It Over
Predicting If a strong current of air flowed across the top of a bird's outstretched wing, what might happen to the bird?

GUIDE FOR READING

◆ How is a bird able to fly?

Reading Tip Before you read, look at Figure 6 on page 131. Then predict how a bird's wing is similar to that of an airplane.

From ancient times, people have dreamed of soaring into the air like birds. When people first started experimenting with flying machines, they tried to glue feathers to their arms or to strap on feathered wings. Many failures, crash-landings, and broken bones later, these people had learned that feathers by themselves weren't the secret of flight. If an object is to fly, it must be lightweight. Another key to flying—for birds and insects as well as for airplanes—lies in the shape of wings and the way in which air moves across them.

How Air Moves Across a Wing

All objects on land are surrounded by an invisible ocean of air. Air is a mixture of gas molecules that exert pressure on the objects they surround. You see the results of air pressure when

▼ Owl in flight

READING STRATEGIES

Reading Tip Remind students that predicting involves making educated guesses. Show them an illustration of an airplane wing. Lead them to look closely at the shapes of the two wings, the airflow patterns around the wings, and the functions the wings perform. On the board, make a list of the students' conclusions of similarities of the two types of wings.

Study and Comprehension Have students use the text to write summaries of how a bird is able to fly. Consider asking volunteers to read their summaries aloud.

Vocabulary Most students will recognize the word *lift*, but may be unfamiliar with its scientific definition. Have them write down two definitions for *lift*, including the one in the text, and compare the definitions.

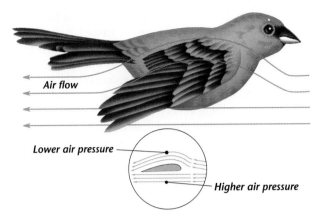

Figure 6 Air moves faster across a wing's upper surface than across its lower surface. The fast-moving air exerts less pressure than the slow-moving air. *Relating Cause and Effect* How does this difference in pressure help a bird to fly?

Air flow

Lower air pressure

Higher air pressure

you blow up a balloon. The pressure of the air molecules pushing on the sides of the balloon makes the balloon expand.

Moving air exerts less pressure than air that is not moving. The faster air moves, the less pressure it exerts. In the Discover activity, the air blowing across the top of the paper was in motion. The moving air above the paper exerted less pressure than the air beneath it, so the paper rose.

Like the paper, a wing is surrounded by air molecules that exert pressure on the wing's surfaces. The lower surface of a wing—whether it belongs to a bird, an insect, or an airplane—is flatter than the upper surface. This difference between the shapes of the upper and lower surfaces of a wing helps birds, insects, and airplanes to fly. In Figure 6, you can see that the curved upper surface of a wing is a little longer than the flatter lower surface. When the wing moves forward, air travels the longer distance over the upper wing in the same amount of time as it takes to travel the shorter distance beneath the wing. Therefore, the air moves faster over the upper surface.

Because fast-moving air exerts less pressure than air that is moving slowly, the air above the wing exerts less pressure than the air beneath the wing. **The difference in pressure above and below the bird's wing produces an upward force that causes the wing to rise.** That upward force is called **lift**.

Checkpoint How is the air pressure above a moving wing different from the air pressure below the wing?

Birds in Flight

Wing shape alone does not enable a bird to fly—it must have some way of getting off the ground. To do this, a bird pushes off with its legs. The bird must also move forward, since lift depends

It's Plane to See

Use this activity to discover how wing shape is important for flight.

1. Work with a partner to design a paper airplane with wings shaped like those of a bird. You can use any of these materials: paper, tape, glue, paper clips, string, rubber bands, and staples. Draw a sketch of your design.

2. Construct your "birdplane" and make one or two trial flights. If necessary, modify your design and try again.

3. Compare your design with those of other groups. Which designs were most successful?

Making Models In what ways was the flight of your airplane like the flight of a bird? In what ways was it different?

Chapter 4 **B ◆ 131**

Program Resources

◆ **Teaching Resources** 4-2 Lesson Plan, p. 113; 4-2 Section Summary, p. 114

Media and Technology

 Audiotapes English-Spanish Summary 4-2

 Transparencies "Bird Flight," Transparency 18

Answers to Self-Assessment

Caption Question

Figure 6 The difference in pressure produces lift, which makes the wings rise into the air.

Checkpoint

The air pressure above a moving wing is lower than the air pressure below a moving wing.

---

2 Facilitate

How Air Moves Across a Wing

Using the Visuals: Figure 6

Emphasize that the higher pressure under the wing creates an upward force. Guide students to trace the airflow in the figure with their fingers. **learning modality: visual**

Skills Focus making models

Materials *sheets of different kinds of paper (letter, construction, foil-covered), tape, glue, paper clips, string, rubber bands, staples*

Time 30 minutes

Tips Elicit students' ideas for a design that allows air to flow rapidly over the nose and wing.

Making Models Sample: Both flights were the result of lift. However, a bird flaps its wings, while an airplane glides.

Extend Have students select a factor such as distance or time and compute the average for all their flights. **learning modality: kinesthetic**

Birds in Flight

Addressing Naive Conceptions

Explain that a bird does not simply flap its wings straight up and down; it rotates its wings upward, pulls them in, and opens up the spaces between its flight feathers. On the downward stroke, the bird turns its wings in the other direction with feathers closed so that the wing pushes flat against the air. **learning modality: verbal**

Ongoing Assessment

Writing Have students briefly describe how lift is created. (*The fast-moving air above the bird's wing exerts less pressure than the air below it. This creates an upward force—lift.*)

B ◆ 131

3 Assess

Section 2 Review Answers

1. Lift is an upward force caused by the difference in air pressure above and below a bird's wing.

2. A bird pushes off with its legs and pulls its wings down to move its body forward and upward.

3. Flapping flight requires a lot of wing movement and energy. Gliding and soaring require less energy. Gliding birds coast downward; soaring birds move upward on rising warm air currents.

4. The shape of a wing helps create the air patterns that cause lift. The loss of too many contour feathers will change the shape of the wing, reducing lift and preventing flight.

Check Your Progress
CHAPTER PROJECT 4

At this point, students should have a list of the various species of birds that visit their feeders. While students continue general observations, they should also concentrate on observing specific feeding behaviors. Feeding behavior includes how birds perch while eating, how birds use their beaks, and rituals such as head bobbing. Review students' notebooks and monitor their progress.

Performance Assessment

Drawing Have students draw and label the wing of a flying bird. Tell them to show the direction in which the air moves over the wing using arrows, and clearly label areas of high and low pressure. *(Students' drawings should indicate that air moves over the wing from front to back. The area of low pressure is over the wing, and the area of high pressure is under the wing.)*

---

on air moving over its wings. So, at the same time that the bird pushes off from the ground, it sharply pulls its wings down. This downstroke provides the power that pushes the bird forward and upward.

Once they are in the air, birds fly in a variety of ways. All birds flap their wings at least part of the time. Flapping requires a lot of energy. Most small birds, such as sparrows, depend heavily on flapping flight. Canada geese and many other birds that travel long distances also use flapping flight.

Unlike flapping flight, soaring and gliding flight involve little wing movement. Birds soar and glide with their wings extended, as shown in Figure 7. When soaring, birds rise up into the sky on currents of warm air. In contrast, when gliding, birds coast downward through the air. Because they require less wing movement, soaring and gliding use less energy than flapping.

Sometimes birds fly with a combination of soaring and gliding. They "take the elevator up" by flying into a current of warm, rising air. The birds stretch their wings out and circle round and round within the column of rising air. High in the atmosphere the column of warm air grows cooler and ceases to rise. At this point the soaring bird "gets off the elevator" and begins gliding downward until it reaches the next "up elevator" of rising air. Predatory birds that spot their food from the air, such as hawks, often soar and glide.

The peregrine falcon, a predatory bird, is one of the fastest fliers. It catches its prey—often other birds such as pigeons—in flight. When it is pursuing prey, a peregrine's speed may reach 300 kilometers per hour. But it is not always useful for birds to fly fast. Birds that are migrating, or traveling long distances, take it slow but steady, usually flying 30 to 70 kilometers per hour. You will learn more about bird migrations in Chapter 5.

Figure 7 As it glides above the ocean's surface, this gannet searches for a school of mackerel or herring. When its search is successful, it will dive into the water to claim its catch.

  Section 2 Review

1. How is lift related to air pressure?

2. Explain how a bird takes off from the ground and begins to fly.

3. Compare and contrast flapping flight, soaring, and gliding.

4. Thinking Critically **Relating Cause and Effect** If a bird loses too many contour feathers, it can no longer fly. Relate this to the feathers' role in giving shape to a bird's wing.

Check Your Progress
CHAPTER PROJECT 4

As you continue your bird-feeder observations, pay careful attention to the way in which two or three different kinds of birds feed. Note the shapes of their beaks and how they use their beaks to pick up and crack seeds. Note how each bird's head moves during feeding. Also note whether certain birds prefer particular kinds of seeds. Write your detailed observations in your notebook.

Program Resources

◆ **Teaching Resources** 4-2 Review and Reinforce, p. 115; 4-2 Enrich, p. 116

Media and Technology

Interactive Student Tutorial CD-ROM B-4

Exploring Physical Science Videodisc Unit 3, Side 2, "How an Airplane Flies"

Chapter 6

What Is a Mammal?

SECTION 3

What Is a Mammal?

DISCOVER ······················· ACTIVITY

What Are Mammals' Teeth Like?

1. Wash your hands before you begin. Then, with a small mirror, examine the shapes of your teeth. Observe the incisors (the front teeth); the pointed canine teeth; the premolars that follow the canine teeth; and the molars, which are the large teeth in the rear of your jaws.

2. Compare and contrast the structures of the different kinds of teeth.

3. Use your tongue to feel the cutting surfaces of the different kinds of teeth in your mouth.

4. Bite off a piece of cracker and chew it. Observe the teeth that you use to bite and chew. Wash your hands when you are finished.

Think It Over

Inferring What is the advantage of having teeth with different shapes?

High in the Himalaya Mountains of Tibet, several yaks inch their way, single file, along a narrow cliff path. The cliff plunges thousands of meters to the valley below, so one false step can mean disaster. But the sure-footed yaks, carrying heavy loads of grain, slowly but steadily cross the cliff and make their way through the mountains.

Yaks, which are related to cows, have large lungs and a complex system of chest muscles that enables them to breathe deeply and rapidly. These structures allow yaks to obtain the oxygen necessary to survive at high altitudes. People who live in the mountains of central Asia have depended on yaks for thousands of years. Not only do yaks carry materials for trade, they also pull plows and provide milk. Mountain villagers weave blankets from yak hair and make shoes and ropes from yak hides.

The yak is a member of the group of vertebrates called **mammals,** a diverse group that share many characteristics. **All mammals are endothermic vertebrates with a four-chambered heart, and skin covered with fur or hair. The young of most mammals are born alive, and every young mammal is fed with milk produced in its mother's body.** In addition, mammals have teeth of different shapes that are adapted to their diets.

GUIDE FOR READING

◆ What characteristics do all mammals share?

Reading Tip As you read this section, write one or two sentences summarizing the information under each heading.

▼ Himalayan yak

Chapter 4 **B ◆ 133**

READING STRATEGIES

Reading Tip Remind students to use their own words when summarizing the information under each heading.

Concept Mapping Have students use a concept map to organize information about the characteristics of mammals. Draw the framework for the map on the board and have students fill in each oval with information.

Program Resources

◆ **Teaching Resources** 4-3 Lesson Plan, p. 117; 4-3 Section Summary, p. 118

Objective

After completing the lesson, students will be able to
◆ describe the characteristics all mammals share.

Key Terms mammal, incisor, canine, premolar, molar, diaphragm, mammary gland

1 Engage/Explore

Activating Prior Knowledge

Ask students who have mammals as pets to describe their pets' physical characteristics and behavior. Students can use their descriptions as a basis for making generalizations about the characteristics of mammals. If any of their generalizations are incorrect, make sure that students correct them after they have read the chapter.

········· DISCOVER ·········

Skills Focus inferring
Materials *hand mirror, cracker*
Time 15 minutes
Tips Tell students that the tooth arrangement from the middle of the row to the back is 2 incisors, 1 canine, 2 premolars, and 3 molars. Suggest that students wash their hands before they feel their teeth with their fingers. Ask: **Which teeth are sharp and good for cutting or tearing food?** *(Incisors and canines)* **For grinding up food?** *(Premolars and molars)* After students eat the cracker, ask: **How did you use your incisors?** *(To bite into the cracker)* **How did you use your molars?** *(To grind or chew up the cracker)* Remind students to wash their hands after this activity.
Think It Over Teeth with different shapes are adapted for different functions. This means that a wider variety of foods can be eaten.

Mammals First Appear

Building Inquiry Skills: Inferring

Remind students that small, early mammals lived during the time of the dinosaurs. Ask students to infer what might be some advantages of being small during the time large dinosaurs lived. *(Sample: Small animals could hide in small spaces to avoid the dinosaurs. Small animals would be hard to spot as they ran along the ground.)* **learning modality: verbal**

Cultural Diversity

Nearly all cultures use domesticated mammals. The yak in Tibet, the ox in Western Europe, and the llama in South America transport loads and help farmers plow fields. Ask students: **What domesticated mammals have been used in the United States?** *(Students may mention cows, oxen, or horses.)* Tell students mammals also provide milk and meat, rich sources of protein. In some cultures, such as that of the Masai people in East Africa, the cow is so highly valued that it is used as currency. **learning modality: verbal**

Fur and Hair

Building Inquiry Skills: Comparing and Contrasting

Provide students with pictures of different mammals, including some with a lot of hair and some with very little. Include pictures of the animals' heads and faces. Ask students: **Are there some kinds of hair that all these mammals have?** *(Students may notice that most mammals have whiskers around the eyes, lips, and muzzle.)* **learning modality: visual**

Today there are about 6,000 different species of mammals. There are mammals that you may never have seen, such as kangaroos and wildebeests, as well as familiar mammals such as dogs, cats, bats, and mice.

Mammals First Appear

Two hundred and seventy million years ago, before dinosaurs appeared, and long before birds appeared, there was a group of animals that had a blend of reptilian and mammalian characteristics. They were more like reptiles than mammals, but they resembled mammals in some ways, such as in the shapes of their teeth. These mammal-like reptiles, which became extinct about 160 million years ago, were the ancestors of the true mammals.

The earliest mammals were small, mouse-sized animals that lived in habitats dominated by dinosaurs. These early mammals may have been nocturnal, or active mainly at night, presumably the time when the dinosaurs were inactive or asleep. It was only after the dinosaurs disappeared, about 65 million years ago, that large mammals first evolved.

Most mammals, such as kangaroos and giraffes, became specialized to live on land. Other mammals, such as dolphins, became adapted to life in Earth's waters, while still others, the bats, became adapted to flight.

Fur and Hair

All mammals have fur or hair at some point in their lives. Like a bird's down feathers, thick fur provides lightweight insulation

Figure 8 The amount of fur or hair covering a mammal's body varies greatly. **A.** Hippopotamuses live in hot regions such as Africa year-round and have little hair. **B.** Gray wolves live in the northern half of North America and have thick fur coats during the cold winter months. During the summer, however, their coats are thinner. *Comparing and Contrasting Compare the function of a mammal's fur or hair to that of down feathers.*

134 ◆ B

that prevents body heat from escaping. Fur and hair help mammals maintain a stable body temperature in cold weather. Each strand of hair or fur is composed of dead cells strengthened with the same tough material that strengthens feathers. Hair grows from living cells located below the surface of the skin.

The amount of hair that covers the skin of a mammal varies a great deal from group to group. Some mammals, such as whales and manatees, have only a few bristles. Others, including dogs and weasels, have thick, short fur. The fur of sea otters is thickest of all—on some areas of its body, a sea otter can have 150,000 hairs per square centimeter! Human bodies are covered with hair, but in places the hairs are spaced widely apart.

In general, animals that live in cold regions have thicker coats of fur than animals in warmer environments, as you can see by contrasting the hippopotamus and wolf in Figure 8. Mammals such as wolves and rabbits that live in places where cold and warm seasons alternate usually grow thicker coats in winter than in summer.

Fur is not the only adaptation that allows mammals to live in cold climates. Mammals also have a layer of fat beneath their skins. Fat, like fur and feathers, is an insulating material that keeps heat in the body. Recall that mammals are endotherms, which means that their bodies produce enough heat to maintain a stable body temperature regardless of the temperature of their environment.

☑ *Checkpoint* *What is the major function of fur or hair?*

B ◆ 135

Insulated Mammals

In this activity, you will discover whether or not fat is an effective insulator.

1. Put on a pair of rubber gloves.
2. Spread a thick coating of solid white shortening on the outside of one of the gloves. Leave the other glove uncoated.
3. Put both hands in a bucket or sink filled with cold water.

Inferring Which hand got cold faster? Explain how this activity relates to mammalian adaptations.

Answers to Self-Assessment

☑ *Checkpoint*

Fur and hair prevent heat from escaping, and help maintain a stable body temperature in cold weather.

Caption Question

Figure 8 Fur, hair, and down feathers all provide insulation by trapping air close to the skin.

Using the Visuals: Figure 8

Have students examine the picture of the wolf closely to see if they can recognize more than one type of fur. If the students have a pet dog or cat at home, they can also examine its fur. Ask: **What is the function of the short, woolly hairs?** *(insulation)* **What is the function of the long, smooth hairs?** *(Protect the undercoat)*

TRY THIS

Skills Focus inferring
Materials *rubber gloves, shortening, bucket or sink full of cold water, paper towels*
Time 15 minutes
Tips Explain to students that shortening is a form of fat which has been processed for cooking. Have students work in pairs to coat each other's gloves. When students are experimenting with reactions to temperature, be sure they do not use water that is dangerously cold.
Inferring The hand in the glove without the shortening felt cold faster. Shortening is a fat and acts as an insulator. The glove with shortening keeps heat in the hand, just as animal fat keeps heat in the body of an animal.
Extend Have students coat the second glove with twice as much shortening as the first and compare to test whether more fat keeps them warmer. **learning modality: kinesthetic**

Ongoing Assessment

Writing Invite students to predict how the fur or hair of a mammal living in the Arctic tundra would differ from the fur or hair of a mammal living in the Amazon rain forest. *(The fur or hair of the mammal living in the tundra will probably be thicker than the fur or hair of the animal living in the rain forest.)*

Teeth

Including All Students

Students who are mastering English may  need extra help to remember the names for the types of teeth. Obtain models or preserved jaws of a herbivore and a carnivore, such as a cow and a cat. Label the four types of teeth and have students say the names as they touch the teeth. Have students use the structure of the teeth to determine which animal is a carnivore and which is a herbivore. **limited English proficiency**

Getting Oxygen to Cells

Building Inquiry Skills: Observing

Have students place a hand flat on their abdomens about 6 cm above the navel. Ask students to describe the movement of their rib cages and diaphragms when they take a deep breath and then let it out. *(The diaphragm and ribs expand when they take a deep breath and contract when they let it out.)* **learning modality: kinesthetic**

Nervous System and Senses

Inquiry Challenge

Materials *orange peel, cloves, vanilla extract, small containers, blindfold*
Time 30 minutes

Group students. Have each group design a simple experiment to answer a question about the senses using these materials. *(Sample: Can humans find their way using only their sense of smell?)* Groups should write plans for your approval before they perform the experiment. Have students predict the outcome, perform the experiment, and draw a conclusion. **cooperative learning**

Teeth

Endotherms need a lot of energy to maintain their body temperature, and that energy comes from food. Mammals' teeth are adapted to chew their food, breaking it into small bits that make digestion easier. Unlike reptiles and fishes, whose teeth usually all have the same shape, most mammals have teeth with four different shapes. **Incisors** are flat-edged teeth used to bite off and cut parts of food. **Canines** are sharply pointed teeth that stab food and tear into it. **Premolars** and **molars** grind and shred food into tiny bits.

The size, shape, and hardness of a mammal's teeth reflect its diet. For example, the canines of carnivores are especially large and sharp. Large carnivores, such as lions and tigers, use their canines as meat hooks that securely hold the prey while the carnivore kills it. The molars of herbivores, such as deer and woodchucks, have upper surfaces that are broad and flat—ideal for grinding and mashing plants.

Figure 9 Lions have sharp, pointed teeth. Note the especially long canine teeth. *Inferring What kind of diet do lions eat?*

Getting Oxygen to Cells

To release energy, food molecules must combine with oxygen inside cells. Therefore, a mammal needs an efficient way to get oxygen into the body and to the cells that need it.

Like reptiles and birds, all mammals breathe with lungs—even mammals such as whales that live in the ocean. Mammals breathe in and out because of the combined action of rib muscles and a large muscle called the **diaphragm** located at the bottom of the chest. The lungs have a huge, moist surface area where oxygen can dissolve and then move into the bloodstream.

Like birds, mammals have a four-chambered heart and a two-loop circulation. One loop pumps oxygen-poor blood from the heart to the lungs and then back to the heart. The second loop pumps oxygen-rich blood from the heart to the tissues of the mammal's body, and then back to the heart.

✓ *Checkpoint* *How do mammals take air into their bodies?*

Nervous System and Senses

The nervous system and senses of an animal receive information about its environment and coordinate the animal's movements. The brains of mammals enable them to learn, remember, and behave in complex ways. Squirrels, for example, feed on

136 ◆ B

Background

Facts and Figures The evolution of mammal teeth is fairly easy for paleontologists to trace by studying fossils. The earliest form of a mammal molar was shaped like a triangle. Opossum molars still have this shape. As mammals diversified, they ate different types of food. For example, the anteater is a mammal that specializes in eating insects such as ants. The anteater's elongated skull and tongue allow it to remove insects from underground nests. Its lower jaw has become smaller and it has fewer teeth.

nuts. In order to do this, they must crack the nutshell to get to the meat inside. Squirrels learn to use different methods to crack different kinds of nuts, depending on where the weak points in each kind of shell are located.

The senses of mammals are highly developed and adapted for the ways that individual species live. Tarsiers, which are active at night, have huge eyes that enable them to see in the dark. Humans, monkeys, gorillas, and chimpanzees are able to see objects in color. This ability is extremely useful because these mammals are most active during the day when colors are visible.

Most mammals hear well. Bats even use their sense of hearing to navigate. Bats make high-pitched squeaks that bounce off objects. The echoes give bats information about the shapes of objects around them and about how far away the objects are. Bats use their hearing to fly at night and to capture flying insects.

Most mammals have highly developed senses of smell. Many mammals, including dogs and cats, use smell to track their prey. By detecting the scent of an approaching predator, antelopes use their sense of smell to protect themselves.

Movement

One function of a mammal's nervous system is to direct and coordinate complex movement. No other group of vertebrates can move in as many different ways as mammals can. Like most mammals, camels and leopards have four limbs and can walk and run. Other four-limbed mammals have specialized ways of moving. For example, kangaroos hop, gibbons swing by their arms from branch to branch, and flying squirrels glide down from high perches. Moles use their powerful front limbs to burrow through the soil. Bats, in contrast, are adapted to fly through the air—their front limbs are wings. Whales, dolphins, and other sea mammals have no hind limbs—their front limbs are flippers adapted for swimming in water.

Sharpen your Skills

Classifying

Unlike humans, birds and bats both fly. Does this mean that bats are more closely related to birds than to humans? Use the diagrams below to find out. The diagrams show the front-limb bones of a bird, a bat, and a human. Examine them carefully, noting similarities and differences. Then decide which two animals are more closely related. Give evidence to support your classification.

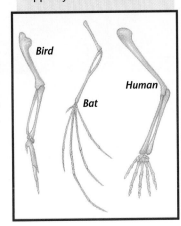

Bird

Bat

Human

Figure 10 Mammals, like these springboks, have large brains. A springbok's brain processes complex information about its environment and then quickly decides on an appropriate action.

Chapter 4 **B ◆ 137**

Answers to Self-Assessment

Caption Question

Figure 9 Lions eat a diet of meat.

☑ *Checkpoint*

Mammals take air into their bodies through their lungs. They breathe in and out because of the action of rib muscles and the diaphragm.

Classifying

Time 15 minutes

Tips Tell students to try to find corresponding bones in all three limbs, and decide which of the bones are most similar.

Expected Outcome The bat and human both have bones for five fingers; they are more similar than the bat and the bird.

Extend Challenge students to identify the functions of a human's finger bones and the corresponding bones of a bat.

Movement

Building Inquiry Skills: Comparing and Contrasting

Show students photographs of a porpoise, a rabbit, a bat, a gazelle, and other mammals with interesting styles of movement. After they observe the photographs, ask students to infer what adaptations each animal has that help or affect its movement. (*The porpoise is streamlined for swimming in the sea. The rabbit has strong legs for hopping. The gazelle has long slender legs to run fast. The bat uses its hands covered with skin to fly.*) **learning modality: logical/mathematical**

Ongoing Assessment

Oral Presentation Call on students to describe how they use their senses to protect themselves from harm. (*Examples: touch—pull hand away from hot stove, smell—food is spoiled, hearing—car is coming*)

Reproducing and Caring for Young

Addressing Naive Conceptions

Students may think that mammals, fishes, and amphibians are equally successful at raising their young. Actually, young mammals are more likely to survive because they receive protection and food from a parent. The survival rate of fish and amphibians is very low, but fish and amphibians produce many offspring, assuring survival of the species.
learning modality: verbal

3 Assess

Section 3 Review Answers

1. All mammals are endothermic vertebrates, have four-chambered hearts, have skin with fur or hair, and produce milk.
2. Mammals and birds are endothermic; they are vertebrates; and they have four-chambered hearts. Unlike birds, mammals have fur or hair, have teeth, and give milk to their young.
3. Sharp, pointy teeth are adapted to biting and tearing flesh. Broad, flat teeth are adapted to grinding and chewing plants.
4. A bat's sense of hearing allows it to navigate at night and find prey.
5. Mammals are endothermic and have fur or hair and a layer of fat beneath their skin.

Science at Home

Show students the nutrition facts listed on a milk label so they will know what to look for.

Figure 11 This young giraffe is feeding on milk produced by its mother, as do all young mammals.

Reproducing and Caring for Young

Like reptiles and birds, mammals have internal fertilization. Although a few kinds of mammals lay shelled eggs, the young of most mammals develop within their mothers' bodies and are never enclosed in an eggshell. All mammals, even those that lay eggs, feed their young with milk produced in **mammary glands**. In fact, the word *mammal* comes from the term *mammary*.

Young mammals are usually quite helpless for a long time after being born. Many are born without a coat of insulating fur. Their eyes are often sealed and may not open for weeks. For example, black bear cubs are surprisingly tiny when they are born. The blind, nearly hairless cubs have a mass of only 240 to 330 grams—about as small as a grapefruit. The mass of an adult black bear, in contrast, ranges from about 120 to 150 kilograms—about 500 times as large as a newborn cub!

Young mammals usually stay with their mother or both parents for an extended time. After black bear cubs learn to walk, they follow their mother about for the next year, learning how to be a bear. They learn things that are important to their survival, such as which mushrooms and berries are good to eat and how to rip apart a rotten log and find good-tasting grubs within it. During the winter, when black bears go through a period of inactivity, the young bears stay with their mother. The following spring, she will usually force them to live independently.

Section 3 Review

1. List five characteristics that all mammals share.
2. Name three ways in which mammals are similar to birds. Then list three ways in which they are different.
3. Relate the shape of any mammal's teeth to its diet.
4. Explain how a keen sense of hearing is an advantage to a bat.
5. **Thinking Critically** **Making Generalizations** What characteristics enable mammals to live in colder environments than reptiles can?

Science at Home

With a family member, examine the nutrition facts listed on a container of whole milk. What types of nutrients does whole milk contain? Discuss why milk is an ideal source of food for young, growing mammals.

Performance Assessment

Drawing Invite students to sketch a mammal or describe it in writing. They should then list the characteristics it has that are unique to mammals.
(Answers will vary depending on the mammal chosen and the detail achieved in students' sketches.)

Background

Facts and Figures Milk contains all of the water, nutrients, and calories that a young mammal needs. Milk is made up of water; lactose, a sugar found only in milk; fat, which supplies energy; and protein. Milk also has antibodies that help the young fight infection. The nursing young control the amount of milk produced. The more that the young nurse, the more milk the mothers' mammary glands make.

Program Resources

◆ **Teaching Resources** 4-3 Review and Reinforce, p. 119; 4-3 Enrich, p. 120
◆ **Teaching Resources** Real-World Lab Chapter 4, pp. 128–129

Media and Technology

 Interactive Student Tutorial CD-ROM B-4

KEEPING WARM

Any time you wear a sweater or socks made of wool, you are using a mammalian adaptation to keep yourself warm. Suppose a manufacturer claims that its wool socks keep your feet as warm when the socks are wet as when they are dry. In this investigation, you will test that claim.

Problem

Do wool products provide insulation from the cold? How well does wool insulate when it is wet?

Skills Focus

controlling variables, interpreting data

Materials

tap water, hot
beaker, 1 L
clock or watch
a pair of wool socks
tap water, room temperature
3 containers, 250 mL, with lids

scissors
3 thermometers
graph paper

Procedure

1. Put one container into a dry woolen sock. Soak a second sock with water at room temperature, wring it out so it's not dripping, and then slide the second container into the wet sock. Both containers should stand upright. Leave the third container uncovered.

2. Create a data table in your notebook, listing the containers in the first column. Provide four more columns in which to record the water temperatures during the experiment.

3. Use scissors to carefully cut a small "X" in the center of each lid. Make the X just large enough for a thermometer to pass through.

4. Fill a beaker with about 800 mL of hot tap water. Then pour hot water nearly to the top of each of the three containers. **CAUTION:** *Avoid spilling hot water on yourself or others.*

5. Place a lid on each of the containers, and insert a thermometer into the water through the hole in each lid. Gather the socks around the thermometers above the first two containers so that the containers are completely covered.

6. Immediately measure the temperature of the water in each container, and record it in your data table. Take temperature readings every 5 minutes for at least 15 minutes.

Analyze and Conclude

1. Graph your results using a different color to represent each container. Graph time in minutes on the horizontal axis and temperature on the vertical axis.

2. Compare the temperature changes in the three containers. Relate your findings to the insulation characteristics of mammal skin coverings.

3. **Apply** Suppose an ad for wool gloves claims that the gloves keep you warm even if they get wet. Do your findings support this claim? Why or why not?

Design an Experiment

Design an experiment to compare how wool's insulating properties compare with those of other natural materials (such as cotton) or manufactured materials (such as acrylic). Obtain your teacher's approval before conducting your experiment.

Sample Data Table

Container	Temp. 0 min (°C)	Temp. 5 min (°C)	Temp. 10 min (°C)	Temp. 15 min (°C)
No Sock	45	36	29	25
Wet Sock	47	44	39	36
Dry Sock	46	44	41	38

Safety

Students should walk slowly when carrying glass containers or hot water to avoid breakage or spills. Students should be cautious when putting holes in lids with scissors. Students should be careful handling glass thermometers and not force thermometers through the holes in lids. They can make a larger hole if the thermometer does not fit. Review the safety guidelines in Appendix A.

Real-World Lab

You, the Consumer

Keeping Warm

Preparing for Inquiry

Key Concept Wool is an insulator that helps an animal or object stay warm.

Skills Objective Students will be able to

◆ control variables and determine whether dry and wet wool have different insulating properties.

Time 35 minutes

Advance Planning Make sure groups use identical containers, such as plastic yogurt cups.

Guiding Inquiry

Invitation Discuss different uses of insulation.

Introducing the Procedure Students will compare temperature changes to find whether wet or dry wool insulates better.

Troubleshooting the Experiment Supply a large container of hot water so it will all be the same temperature, around 40–45°C.

Expected Outcome The containers should cool in this order: no sock, wet sock, dry sock.

Analyze and Conclude

1. Students should graph data with time on the *x*-axis, temperature on the *y*-axis.

2. The temperature changed most in the uncovered container, then the wet, then the dry. Wool keeps animals warm even when it is wet.

3. Sample: Yes. Wet gloves will keep you warmer than no gloves.

Extending Inquiry

Design an Experiment Remind students to use materials of the same thickness.

Animals and Medical Research

Purpose
To discuss the issue of using animals in medical research.

Role-Play

Time 90 minutes

◆ Stimulate discussion with a role-playing scenario. A family member has a life-threatening illness. Scientists have developed a treatment for the illness, but it must be tested on animals before it can be approved for human use. Should the research be done? Choose volunteers to play the roles of family members, doctors, members of the Food and Drug Administration, and people who oppose the use of animals in medical research.

◆ Guide students in their understanding of the practical and moral obligations of each character. Remind them that doctors have a responsibility to protect the health and well-being of their patients. The FDA was established to protect the safety of the American people as a whole.

◆ To help students make a decision, they can think about the following issues:

1. What is the potential benefit of the proposed research? How high are the potential benefits to humanity?

2. How many animals will be tested? Research can be categorized as using no animals, a few animals (fewer than 20) or many animals (more than 20).

3. Will the animals be killed? How much pain will they experience? What animals will be involved?

◆ Prior to the role-playing exercise, invite students to interview community members involved in this issue. Students might contact universities or hospitals to speak with medical researchers or local veterinarians and humane society representatives. Suggest they prepare a list of questions before they call. Encourage students to share their findings with classmates

Animals and Medical Research

In laboratories around the world, scientists search for cures for cancer, AIDS, and other diseases. Scientists use millions of animals each year in research—mostly to test drugs and surgical procedures. Finding treatments could save millions of human lives. However, these experiments can hurt and even kill animals.

The Issues

Why Is Animal Testing Done? If you have ever used an antibiotic or other medicine, animal testing has helped you. The United States Food and Drug Administration requires that new medicines be tested on research animals before they can be used by humans. Through testing, researchers can learn whether a drug works and what doses are safe. Because of animal research, many serious diseases can now be treated or prevented. New treatments for AIDS, cancer, and Alzheimer's disease will also depend on animal testing.

Which Animals Are Used for Testing? Most often mice, rats, and other small mammals are used. These animals reproduce rapidly, so scientists can study many generations in a year. Since apes and monkeys are similar to humans in many ways, they are often used to test new treatments for serious diseases. In other cases, researchers use animals that naturally get diseases common to humans. Cocker spaniels, for example, often develop glaucoma, an eye disease that can cause blindness. Surgeons may test new surgical treatments for the disease on cocker spaniels.

What Happens to Research Animals? In a typical laboratory experiment, a group of animals will first be infected with a disease. Then they will be given a drug to see if it can fight off the disease. In many cases, the animals suffer, and some die. Some people are concerned that laboratory animals do not receive proper care.

What Are the Alternatives? Other testing methods do exist. For example, in some cases, scientists can use computer models to test drugs or surgical treatments. Another testing method is to mix drugs with animal cells grown in petri dishes. Unfortunately, neither computer models nor cell experiments are as useful as tests on living animals.

You Decide

1. Identify the Problem

In a sentence, describe the controversy over using animals in medical research.

2. Analyze the Options

Review the different positions. Is animal testing acceptable? Is it acceptable for some animals but not for others? Is animal research never acceptable? List the benefits and drawbacks of each option.

3. Find a Solution

Suppose you are a scientist who has found a possible cure for a type of cancer. The drug needs to be tested on research animals first, but you know that testing could harm the animals. What would you do? Support your opinion with sound reasons.

and incorporate the results in the role-playing and You Decide writing activity.

You Decide

◆ Students' responses to Identify the Problem and Analyze the Options should be based on the concepts and issues presented in the text. In response to Find a Solution, students may discuss issues raised in the role-playing.

◆ Make sure students understand that there are no "correct" opinions or solutions. As with many complex social issues, no single solution satisfies everyone. Provide examples of other difficult social issues as models.

Background

Reference Against Animal Research
Peter Singer. *Animal Liberation*. New York. Random House. 1990.
Reference Supporting Animal Research
Julian Groves. *Hearts and Minds: The Controversy over Laboratory Animals*. Philadelphia. Temple University Press. 1997.

4 Diversity of Mammals

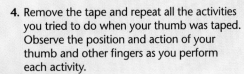

DISCOVER .... ACTIVITY

How Is a Thumb Useful?

1. Tape the thumb of your writing hand to your palm so that you cannot move your thumb. The tape should keep your thumb from moving but allow your other fingers to move freely.

2. Pick up a pencil with the taped hand and try to write your name.

3. Keep the tape on for 5 minutes. During that time, try to use your taped hand to do such everyday activities as lifting a book, turning the pages, and untying and retying your shoes.

4. Remove the tape and repeat all the activities you tried to do when your thumb was taped. Observe the position and action of your thumb and other fingers as you perform each activity.

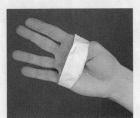

Think It Over

Inferring Humans, chimpanzees, and gorillas all have thumbs that can touch the other four fingers. What advantage does that kind of thumb give to the animal?

How is a koala similar to a panda? Both are furry, cuddly-looking mammals that eat leaves. How is a koala different from a panda? Surprisingly, koalas and pandas belong to very different groups of mammals—koalas are marsupials, and pandas are placental mammals. **Members of the three groups of mammals—monotremes, marsupials, and placental mammals—are classified on the basis of how their young develop.**

GUIDE FOR READING

◆ What characteristic is used to classify mammals into three groups?

Reading Tip As you read this section, write a definition in your own words for each new science term.

Giant panda (left) and koala (right)

Chapter 4   **B ◆ 141**

Diversity of Mammals

Objective

After completing the lesson, students will be able to
◆ identify the characteristic used to classify mammals as monotremes, marsupials, or placental mammals.

Key Terms monotreme, marsupial, gestation period, placental mammal, placenta

1 Engage/Explore

Activating Prior Knowledge

Show students a photograph of a kangaroo and ask them where they would expect to find the animal's young. (*In the pouch*) Have students list other methods for the development of young animals. (*Within eggs, within the mother*) Lead students to conclude that mammals can be classified based on their adaptations for the development of their young.

.... DISCOVER ....

Skills Focus inferring
Materials *masking tape, pencil, paper, various objects such as books and shoes*
Time 15 minutes
Tips Have students work in pairs. Make sure that their taped thumbs will be comfortable for 5 minutes. Ask: **How does your thumb help you write?** (*It allows you to grasp and control the pencil.*) Then ask students what other ways they use their thumbs. (*Students may use their thumbs to hold food, climb, or handle tools*) Develop a list of activities that would be difficult or impossible without an opposable thumb.

Think It Over A thumb that can touch the other fingers allows an animal to grasp food and other objects.

---

2 Facilitate

Monotremes

Using the Visuals: Figure 12

As students study the two monotremes, ask: **What characteristics that you can see make these two animals different?** *(Spiny anteater—spines, long, pointy nose; duck-billed platypus—webbed feet, a bill, furry body)* Students may infer that these animals are unrelated because they are so different. Then ask: **What do these animals have in common that makes them different from many other mammals?** *(They both lay eggs.)* Ask: **How does this affect their classification?** *(Both animals are monotremes, because monotremes are the only mammals whose young hatch from eggs.)* Guide students to understand that mammals are classified into different groups based on how their young develop, not on how the mammals look. **learning modality: visual**

Marsupials

Building Inquiry Skills: Inferring

Encourage students to infer the functions of a female marsupial's pouch. *(It keeps the newborn warm, protects it from predators, and contains the mother's nipples, which are the newborn's source of food. It helps the mother protect and care for her young while leaving her forepaws, hindpaws, and mouth free to find food, defend against predators, and move from place to place.)* **learning modality: logical/mathematical**

Figure 12 The spiny anteater, left, and the duck-billed platypus, right, could share the "Weirdest Mammal" award. Both are monotremes, the only mammals whose young hatch from eggs.

Monotremes

If you held a "Weirdest Mammal in the World" contest, two main contenders would be spiny anteaters and duck-billed platypuses. There are two species of spiny anteaters and only one species of duck-billed platypus, all living in Australia and New Guinea. These are the only species of monotremes that are alive today. **Monotremes** are mammals that lay eggs.

Spiny Anteaters These monotremes look like pincushions with long noses. They have sharp spines scattered throughout their brown hair. As their name implies, spiny anteaters eat ants, which they dig up with their powerful claws.

A female spiny anteater lays one to three leathery-shelled eggs directly into the pouch on her belly. After the young hatch, still in the pouch, they drink milk that seeps out of pores on the mother's skin. They stay in the pouch until they are six to eight weeks old, when their spines start to irritate the mother anteater, and she scratches them out of her pouch.

Duck-billed Platypuses The duck-billed platypus has webbed feet and a bill, but it also has fur and feeds its young with milk. Platypuses, which live in the water, construct a maze of tunnels in muddy banks. The female lays her eggs in an underground nest. The eggs hatch about two weeks later. After they hatch, the tiny offspring feed by lapping at the milk that oozes onto the fur of their mother's belly.

Marsupials

Koalas, kangaroos, bandicoots, wallabies, and opossums are some of the better known marsupials. **Marsupials** are mammals whose young are born alive, but at an early stage of development, and they usually continue to develop in a pouch on their

---

Background

Facts and Figures Australia has many animals that are not found anywhere else in the world. This is because Australia has been geographically isolated for millions of years as the continent drifted into its current position. Marsupials are common throughout Australia, where there are marsupial equivalents of moles, anteaters, and even antelopes. Placental mammals are very rare, however.

mother's body. Marsupials were once widespread, but today they are found mostly in South America, Australia, and New Guinea. Opossums are the only marsupials found in North America.

Marsupials have a very short **gestation period,** the length of time between fertilization and birth. Opossums, for example, have a gestation period of only about 13 days. Newborn marsupials are tiny—the newborns of one opossum species are only about 10 millimeters long! When they are born, marsupials are blind, hairless, and pink. They crawl along the wet fur of their mother's belly until they reach her pouch. Once inside, they find one of her nipples and attach to it. They remain in the pouch at least until they have grown enough to peer out of the pouch opening.

Kangaroos The largest marsupials are kangaroos, which are found in Australia and nearby islands. Some male kangaroos are over 2 meters tall—taller than most humans. Kangaroos have powerful hind legs for jumping and long tails that help them keep their balance. A female kangaroo gives birth to only one baby, called a joey, at a time. Kangaroos are herbivores, so they eat foods such as leaves and grasses.

Opossums The common opossum is an omnivore that comes out of its nest at dusk to search for fruits, plants, insects, or other small animals to eat. Opossums are good climbers. They can grasp branches with their long tails. If a predator attacks it, an opossum will often "play dead"—its body becomes limp, its mouth gapes open, and its tongue lolls out of its mouth. Female opossums may give birth to 21 young at a time, but most female opossums have only 13 nipples. The first 13 young opossums that get into the pouch and attach to nipples are the only ones that survive.

Checkpoint *What do the young of marsupials do immediately after they are born?*

Placental Mammals

Unlike a monotreme or a marsupial, a **placental mammal** develops inside its mother's body until its body systems can function independently. In *Exploring Placental Mammals* on the next page, you can see some members of this group.

Figure 13 Gray kangaroos, above, and opossums, below, are marsupials, mammals whose young live for a time in the mother's pouch. *Classifying How do marsupials differ from monotremes?*

Answers to Self-Assessment

Caption Question

Figure 13 Marsupials give birth to live young. Monotremes lay eggs.

Checkpoint
The young of marsupials crawl into their mother's pouch immediately after birth.

Placental Mammals

Building Inquiry Skills: Observing

Materials *pair of breeding mice; 2 wire cages or aquariums with mesh tops; 2 water bottles with metal spouts; large bag of rodent bedding; rodent food; water*

Time 5 minutes daily for 4 to 6 weeks

 Obtain a breeding pair of mice. Caution students to wash their hands before and after touching the mice, food, or bedding. Demonstrate that the mice must be handled very gently and should not be taken out except when the cage is being cleaned, so that they cannot bite or run away. Let students place 2 cm of bedding in each cage. Stress the importance of adequate food and water and a clean cage. Assign students turns cleaning the cage, replacing the bedding, and supplying food and water. Encourage students to predict how the parents will care for their offspring. Keep both mice in the same cage for 2 weeks or until you notice that the female mouse is pregnant. Then move the male to the other cage. Signs of pregnancy: a large belly, red and swollen teats, and building a nest. The gestation period is about 2 weeks. Have students record daily observations of the pregnant mouse's behavior, and continue the observations when the young are born. Caution students not to touch the young, or the mother will remove the young from the nest and they will die. The young mice can be taken from the mother when they are 4 weeks old and able to walk around the cage. **cooperative learning**

Ongoing Assessment

Oral Presentation Ask students to name three characteristics all mammals have in common and the distinguishing characteristic of each group of mammals.

Placental Mammals, continued

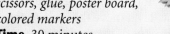

Placental Mammals

To help students focus on the major points presented in this visual essay and make comparisons among the groups of animals shown, organize students into small groups. Ask them to share their observations about the characteristics of the mammals on this page, such as *the young grow inside the mother's body and the young receive food and oxygen and eliminate wastes through the placenta.* On index cards, have students write the name of each mammal along with several of its observable characteristics. Students may exchange cards and quiz each other. **learning modality: visual**

Inquiry Challenge

Materials *magazines, scissors, glue, poster board, colored markers*

ACTIVITY

Time 30 minutes

Tips To help students learn about classifying mammals, ask them to bring magazines from home that contain pictures of mammals. Organize students in small groups. Have groups look through the magazines and cut out as many pictures of mammals as they can find. Challenge students to observe as many traits about each mammal as they can. Students may work in pairs or small groups to list their observations. When their lists are complete, have students evaluate the traits they listed and classify animals based on these criteria. Then, encourage them to compare their criteria with those used to classify placental mammals in *Exploring Placental Mammals.* **learning modality: logical/mathematical**

EXPLORING *Placental Mammals*

From tiny moles to huge elephants, placental mammals exhibit a great variety of size and body form. Note how each group is adapted for obtaining food or for living in a particular environment.

▲ Insect-eaters
Star-nosed moles and their relatives have sharp cutting surfaces on all of their teeth. Star-nosed moles spend much of their time in water searching for prey with their sensitive, tentacled snouts.

Flying Mammals ▲
Bats fly, but they are mammals, not birds. The wings of bats are made of a thin skin that stretches from their wrists to the tips of their long finger bones.

▲ Rabbits and Hares
Leaping mammals like this black-tailed jack rabbit have long hind legs specialized for spectacular jumps. Rabbits and hares have long, curved incisors for gnawing.

Rodents ▲
Rodents are gnawing mammals such as rats, beavers, squirrels, mice, and the North American porcupine shown here. Their teeth are adapted to grind down their food. The four incisors of most rodents keep growing throughout their lives but are constantly worn down by gnawing.

▲ Primates
This group of mammals with large brains includes humans, monkeys, and apes such as this chimpanzee. Many primates have opposable thumbs—thumbs that can touch the other four fingers. An opposable thumb makes the hand capable of complex movements, such as grasping and throwing.

144 ◆ B

Background

Facts and Figures

◆ The manatee is an endangered mammal. Fewer than 2,000 manatees remain. These large, docile marine mammals are threatened by collisions with boats and the loss of their habitat to human development of the coastline.

◆ Two famous gorillas, Koko and Michael, are part of a project to teach a modified form of American Sign Language to gorillas. These gorillas are able to use hundreds of signs. They also use their hands to grasp a paintbrush and have produced several paintings.

▲ Toothless Mammals
Sloths, such as the one shown here, are toothless mammals, as are armadillos. Although a few members of this group have small teeth, most have none.

▲ Hoofed Mammals
Mammals with hooves are divided into two groups—those with an even number of toes and those with an odd number of toes. Cows, deer, and pigs all have an even number of toes, while horses and zebras belong to the odd-numbered group.

Carnivores ▶
This river otter belongs to the group known as carnivores, or meat eaters. Other mammals in this group include dogs, cats, raccoons, bears, weasels, and seals. Large canine teeth and toes with claws help carnivores catch and eat their prey.

Marine Mammals
Whales, manatees, and these Atlantic spotted dolphins are ocean-dwelling mammals that evolved from cowlike, land-dwelling ancestors. The bodies of marine mammals show no external trace of hind limbs, although hind limbs have been found in their fossilized ancestors. ▼

Mammals With Trunks ▲
Elephants' noses are long trunks that they use for collecting food and water.

Chapter 4 **B ◆ 145**

Addressing Naive Conceptions

Some students may think that bats are birds because they can fly. They may also think that dolphins are fish because they live in the ocean. Stress to students that one of the reasons why bats and dolphins are classified as mammals, not birds or fish, is that they feed their young with milk. Ask: **Can you think of other reasons why bats are not birds and dolphins are not fishes?** *(Sample answer: Bats do not have feathers, and dolphins have lungs, not gills.)* **learning modality: logical/mathematical**

Including All Students

To help students whose native language is not English, remind students that the English word *mammal* comes from the same Latin root as the word *mammary*. Have students with other native languages provide the words for *mammal* in those languages. *(Examples: mamífero [Spanish], mammifère [French], honyuu [Japanese])* Write these words on the board and try to identify any root word similarities. Ask students to propose other words for mammals based on other mammalian characteristics. **limited English proficiency**

Ongoing Assessment

Oral Presentation Ask students to name five mammals and state the group to which each belongs. Have them describe characteristics of the animal that place it in that group.

3 Assess

Section 4 Review Answers

1. Monotreme young develop from eggs laid by the mother. Marsupial young are born alive at an early stage of development, then crawl into the mother's pouch, where they continue to grow and develop. Placental mammals develop inside the mother's body, attached to a placenta.

2. Food and oxygen from the mother pass through the placenta to the young. Wastes from the young pass through the placenta to the mother and are eliminated by her body.

3. Sample answer: Carnivores are meat eaters with sharp claws and sharp canine teeth. Insect eaters have sharp cutting surfaces on all teeth. Rodents are gnawing mammals with teeth adapted for grinding. Their incisors grow throughout their lives.

4. Feeding in large herds protects hoofed mammals from predators. It is likely that one animal in a group will see a predator and warn others, and predators who will tackle a lone animal might avoid a large herd.

Check Your Progress

CHAPTER PROJECT 4

While students continue to observe, they should begin to plan how the observations will be analyzed and presented. Review graphing techniques for the benefit of students who are less familiar with this method of organizing mathematical data. Suggest students group their observations to establish the habits of specific birds of related species.

Performance Assessment

Organizing Information Direct students to create concept maps to help them classify various mammals as marsupials, monotremes, or placental mammals.

 Students can save their concept maps in their portfolios.

Figure 14 Young mammals usually require much parental care. On a rocky slope in Alaska, this Dall's sheep, a placental mammal, keeps a close watch on her lamb.

The name of this group comes from the **placenta,** an organ in pregnant female mammals that passes materials between the mother and the developing embryo. Food and oxygen pass from the mother to her young through the placenta. Wastes pass from the young through the placenta to the mother, where they are eliminated by her body. The umbilical cord connects the young to the placenta. Most mammals, including humans, are placental mammals.

Placental mammals are classified into groups on the basis of characteristics such as how they eat, how they move, and where they live. For example, whales, dolphins, and porpoises all form one group of mammals that have adaptations for swimming. The mammals in the carnivore group, which includes cats, dogs, otters, and seals, are all predators that have enlarged canine teeth. Primates, which include monkeys, apes, and humans, all have large brains and eyes that face forward. In addition, the forelimbs of many primates have adaptations for grasping. For example, the human thumb can touch all four other fingers. As you learned if you did the Discover activity, it is difficult to grasp objects if you cannot use your thumb.

Placental mammals vary in the length of their gestation periods. Generally, the larger the placental mammal, the longer its gestation period. For example, African elephants are the largest land-dwelling placental mammals. The gestation period for an elephant averages about 21 months. A house mouse, on the other hand, gives birth after a gestation period of only about 20 days.

Section 4 Review

1. Explain the difference in the development of the young of monotremes, marsupials, and placental mammals.
2. What is the function of the placenta?
3. Describe the feeding adaptations of three groups of placental mammals.
4. **Thinking Critically** **Inferring** Many hoofed mammals feed in large groups, or herds. What advantage could this behavior have?

Check Your Progress

CHAPTER PROJECT 4

Continue to observe bird behavior at your bird feeder and record your observations in your notebook. Now is the time to plan your presentation. You may want to include the following information in your presentation: drawings of the different birds you observed, detailed descriptions of bird behaviors, and other interesting observations you made. *(Hint: Prepare bar graphs to present numerical data, such as the number of times that different species visited the feeder.)*

Program Resources

◆ **Teaching Resources** 4-4 Review and Reinforce, p. 123; 4-4 Enrich, p. 124

Media and Technology

 Interactive Student Tutorial CD-ROM B-4

1 Birds

Key Ideas

◆ Birds are endothermic vertebrates that have feathers and a four-chambered heart and lay eggs. Most birds can fly.

◆ Contour feathers give shape to a bird's body and aid in flight. Down feathers provide insulation.

◆ Birds care for their young by keeping the eggs warm until hatching and by protecting the young at least until they can fly.

◆ Birds have adaptations, such as the shapes of their toes and bills, for living and obtaining food in different environments.

Key Terms
bird
contour feather
down feather
insulator
crop
gizzard

2 The Physics of Bird Flight

INTEGRATING PHYSICS

Key Ideas

◆ Air flowing over the curved upper surface of a moving wing exerts less downward pressure than the upward pressure from the air flowing beneath the wing. The difference in pressure produces lift that causes the wing to rise.

◆ Birds fly in three basic ways—flapping flight, soaring, and gliding. Flapping flight requires more energy than soaring or gliding.

Key Term
lift

3 What Is a Mammal?

Key Ideas

◆ Mammals are vertebrates that are endothermic, have skin covered with hair or fur, feed their young with milk from the mother's mammary glands, and have teeth of different shapes adapted to their diets.

◆ A mammal's fur or hair provides insulation that helps reduce the loss of body heat.

◆ Mammals use a large muscle called the diaphragm to breathe in and out. Mammals have a four-chambered heart and a two-loop circulation.

Key Terms
mammal   incisors   canines
premolars   molars   diaphragm
mammary gland

4 Diversity of Mammals

Key Ideas

◆ Mammals are classified into three groups on the basis of how their young develop. Monotremes lay eggs. Marsupials give birth to live young who continue to develop in the mother's pouch. The young of placental mammals develop more fully before birth than do the young of marsupials.

◆ Placental mammals are divided into groups on the basis of adaptations, such as those for feeding and moving.

Key Terms
monotreme
marsupial
gestation period
placental mammal
placenta

USING THE INTERNET
www.science-explorer.phschool.com

Program Resources

◆ **Teaching Resources** Chapter 4 Project Teacher's Notes, pp. 102–103; Chapter 4 Project Overview and Worksheets, pp. 104–107; Chapter 4 Project Scoring Rubric, p. 108; Chapter 4 Performance Assessment Teacher Notes, pp. 187–188; Chapter 4 Performance Assessment Student Worksheet, p. 189; Chapter 4 Test, pp. 190–193

Media and Technology

Interactive Student Tutorial CD-ROM B-4

Computer Test Bank Test B-4

Reviewing Content
Multiple Choice
1. c **2.** a **3.** b **4.** b **5.** c

True or False
6. true **7.** true **8.** faster **9.** true
10. Monotremes

Checking Concepts
11. The bones are lightweight and the forelimb bones are modified into wings.
12. The upper surfaces of the wings are more curved than the lower surfaces. Consequently, as air moves over the wing, the air moving over the upper surface travels at a speed greater than the air moving across the lower surface. Because of the difference in speed, the air on the upper surface exerts less pressure, so the wing rises.
13. Warm air rises, and soaring birds are carried upward by the rising air. When the air cools, the birds glide downward until they find another column of rising air.
14. Incisors are thin, with sharp cutting edges, and are used for biting. Molars are thick, with broad surfaces used for grinding.
15. Accept any two: They are endotherms; their fur insulates them; they have a layer of insulating fat.
16. Mammals have complex nervous systems and senses that are capable of directing and coordinating complicated movements.
17. Accept any one: Their bodies show no external trace of hind limbs; they have flippers instead of legs or arms; their bodies are streamlined.
18. The scenes that students describe should contain realistic details about the anteaters, such as their having a spiny coat, eating ants, laying eggs into a pouch, and so forth.

Thinking Visually
19. a. as eggs **b.** in their mother's pouch
c. at advanced stage of development
d. milk from nipples in mother's pouch
e. milk from nipples **f.** spiny anteater
g. kangaroo **h.** human

C H A P T E R 4 R E V I E W

Reviewing Content

 For more review of key concepts, see the Interactive Student Tutorial CD-ROM.

Multiple Choice
Choose the letter of the best answer.

1. Which of these characteristics is found only in birds?
 a. scales
 b. wings
 c. feathers
 d. four-chambered heart
2. A four-chambered heart is an advantage because
 a. it keeps oxygen-rich and oxygen-poor blood separate.
 b. it allows oxygen-rich and oxygen-poor blood to mix.
 c. blood can move through it quickly.
 d. it slows the flow of blood.
3. What causes the lift that allows a bird's wing to rise?
 a. reduced air pressure beneath the wing
 b. reduced air pressure above the wing
 c. air that is not moving
 d. jet propulsion
4. Which muscle helps mammals move air into and out of their lungs?
 a. air muscle **b.** diaphragm
 c. placenta **d.** gestation
5. Kangaroos, koalas, and opossums are all
 a. monotremes.
 b. primates.
 c. marsupials.
 d. placental mammals.

True or False
If the statement is true, write true. If it is false, change the underlined word or words to make the statement true.

6. *Archaeopteryx* shows the link between birds and reptiles.
7. A bird's <u>gizzard</u> grinds food.
8. The <u>slower</u> air moves, the less pressure it exerts.
9. Fur and <u>down</u> feathers have a similar function.
10. <u>Marsupials</u> are mammals that lay eggs.

Checking Concepts
11. Explain how the skeleton of a bird is adapted for flight.
12. How is a bird's ability to fly related to the shape of its wings?
13. Explain how soaring birds like vultures use rising air currents in their flight.
14. Contrast the structure and function of incisors and molars.
15. Identify and explain two ways in which mammals are adapted to live in cold climates.
16. How is a mammal's ability to move a function of its nervous system?
17. What is one way in which the bodies of dolphins are different from those of land mammals?
18. Writing to Learn You are a documentary filmmaker preparing to make a short film about spiny anteaters. First, think of a title for the film. Then plan two scenes that you would include in the film and write the narrator's script. Your scenes should show what the animals look like and what they do.

Thinking Visually
19. Compare/Contrast Table The table below compares three groups of mammals. Copy the table onto a separate sheet of paper. Then complete it and add a title. (For more on compare/contrast tables, see the Skills Handbook.)

Characteristic	Monotremes	Marsupials	Placental Mammals
How Young Begin Life	a. _?_	b. _?_	c. _?_
How Young Are Fed	milk from pores or slits on mother's skin	d. _?_	e. _?_
Example	f. _?_	g. _?_	h. _?_

Applying Skills
20. Students' graphs should plot data accurately.
21. Longest—elephants and chimpanzees; Shortest—harp seal
22. In general, the larger the mammal, the more time it spends caring for its young. The harp seal is the exception.

Thinking Critically
23. Since rodents' front teeth grow constantly, they might continue to grow and become very long.

24. Endothermic animals have four-chambered hearts. In a four-chambered heart, oxygenated blood does not mix with deoxygenated blood, and therefore the blood that reaches the body tissues is carrying a large amount of oxygen. Oxygen is needed to release the energy that enables endothermy.
25. While most mammals do not lay eggs, most reptiles do. Therefore, egg-laying is a characteristic that is more reptilian than mammalian.

Applying Skills

The data table below shows the approximate gestation period of several mammals and the approximate length of time that those mammals care for their young after birth. Use the information in the table to answer Questions 20–22.

Mammal	Gestation Period	Time Spent Caring for Young After Birth
Deer mouse	0.75 month	1 month
Chimpanzee	8 months	24 months
Harp seal	11 months	0.75 month
Elephant	21 months	24 months
Bobcat	2 months	8 months

20. **Graphing** Decide which kind of graph would be best for showing the data in the table. Then construct two graphs—one for gestation period and the other for time spent caring for young.

21. **Interpreting Data** Which mammals in the table care for their young for the longest time? The shortest time?

22. **Drawing Conclusions** What seems to be the general relationship between the size of the mammal and the length of time for which it cares for its young? Which animal is the exception to this pattern?

Thinking Critically

23. **Predicting** If a rodent were fed a diet consisting only of soft food that it did not need to gnaw, what might its front teeth look like after several months?

24. **Making Generalizations** What is the general relationship between whether an animal is an endotherm and whether it has a four-chambered heart? Relate this to the animal's need for energy.

25. **Comparing and Contrasting** Why might monotremes be considered a link between reptiles and mammals?

Performance Assessment

CHAPTER PROJECT 4 Wrap Up

Presenting Your Project When you present your project to your classmates, display the graphs, charts, and pictures you constructed. Be sure to include a description of the ways in which birds eat and interesting examples of bird behavior that you observed.

Reflect and Record In your journal, analyze how successful the project was. Was the bird feeder located in a good place for attracting birds and observing them? Did many birds come to the feeder—if not, why might this have happened? What are the advantages and limitations of using field guides for identifying birds? What did you learn from completing the project?

Getting Involved

In Your Community Many communities have animal shelters that try to find homes for stray animals. Find a shelter in or near your community. Find out how the shelter finds homes for animals and how the animals at the shelter are cared for. What requirements must a family fulfill before adopting an animal? Make up an information sheet about the shelter. With your teacher's permission, post it or distribute it in your school.

Program Resources

◆ **Inquiry Skills Handbook** Provides teaching and review of all inquiry skills.

Performance Assessment

Wrap Up
Presenting Your Project
Students can present their projects in a number of ways. Students can turn in a written report with sketches and graphs, make posters that show the different birds that visited their feeders and their behaviors, or give an oral presentation that focuses on their observations or on the behavior of a single type of bird.

Encourage students to be creative in the way they report their data. On their graphs, students could add illustrations of the different types of birds rather than just the names.

Reflect and Record In assessing their work, students should explain why they think the bird feeder was or was not placed in a good location. They should say explicitly which parts of their work were most and least successful. Finally, they should summarize the new content and science procedures they learned during the project.

Getting Involved

In Your Community Consider asking someone who works or volunteers at an animal shelter to visit the class. The students may interview this person as a class to find the information they need for their information sheet. Encourage students to ask more questions about animal shelters. Organize students in small groups to make the information sheets.

Animal Behavior

Sections	Time	Student Edition Activities	Other Activities	
CHAPTER PROJECT 5 **Learning New Tricks** p. 151	Ongoing (2 weeks)	Check Your Progress, pp. 158, 172 Wrap Up, p. 175	TE	Chapter 5 Project Notes, pp. 150–151
1 Why Do Animals Behave as They Do? pp. 152–159 ◆ Describe the functions of animals' behaviors. ◆ Compare instinctive and learned behavior.	8 periods/ 4 blocks	**Discover** What Can You Observe About a Vertebrate's Behavior? p. 152 **Sharpen Your Skills** Predicting, p. 154 **Try This** Line Them Up, p. 157 **Skills Lab: Designing Experiments** Become a Learning Detective, p. 159	TE TE TE TE IES	Demonstration, p. 153 Inquiry Challenge, p. 155 Including All Students, p. 156 Integrating Technology, p. 156 "Sleuth's Supper," p. 37
2 Patterns of Behavior pp. 160–169 ◆ Describe some ways in which animals relate to one another and explain the functions of those behaviors. ◆ Describe animal behavior cycles and explain how they are important for an animal's survival.	5 periods/ 3 blocks	**Discover** What Can You Express Without Words? p. 160 **Try This** Worker Bees, p. 163 **Science at Home** p. 167 **Real-World Lab: You and Your Environment** One for All, pp. 168–169	TE TE TE ISLM	Demonstration, p. 161 Cultural Diversity, p. 164 Integrating Environmental Science, p. 167 B-5, "Family Life of Bettas"
3 **INTEGRATING CHEMISTRY** **The Chemistry of Communication** pp. 170–172 ◆ Describe how animals use pheromones to communicate.	$1\frac{1}{2}$ periods/ 1 block	**Discover** Can You Match the Scents? p. 170	TE TE	Activating Prior Knowledge, p. 170 Building Inquiry Skills: Inferring, pp. 171, 172
Study Guide/Chapter Review pp. 173–175	1 period/ $\frac{1}{2}$ block		ISAB	Provides teaching and review of all inquiry skills

For Standard or Block Schedule The Resource Pro® CD-ROM gives you maximum flexibility for planning your instruction for any type of schedule. Resource Pro® contains Planning Express®, an advanced scheduling program, as well as the entire contents of the Teaching Resources and the Computer Test Bank.

CHAPTER PLANNING GUIDE

Program Resources	Assessment Strategies	Media and Technology
TR Chapter 5 Project Teacher Notes, pp. 130–131 **TR** Chapter 5 Project Overview and Worksheets, pp. 132–135 **TR** Chapter 5 Project Scoring Rubric, p. 136	**SE** Performance Assessment: Wrap Up, p. 175 **TE** Check Your Progress, pp. 158, 172 **TR** Chapter 5 Project Scoring Rubric, p. 136	Science Explorer Internet Site
TR 5-1 Lesson Plan, p. 137 **TR** 5-1 Section Summary, p. 138 **TR** 5-1 Review and Reinforce, p. 139 **TR** 5-1 Enrich, p. 140 **TR** Chapter 5 Skills Lab, pp. 149–150	**SE** Section 1 Review, p. 158 **SE** Analyze and Conclude, p. 159 **TE** Ongoing Assessment, pp. 153, 155, 157 **TE** Performance Assessment, p. 158 **TR** 5-1 Review and Reinforce, p. 139	Audiotapes: English-Spanish Summary 5-3 Transparency 19, "Pavlov's Experiment" Interactive Student Tutorial CD-ROM, B-5
TR 5-2 Lesson Plan, p. 141 **TR** 5-2 Section Summary, p. 142 **TR** 5-2 Review and Reinforce, p. 143 **TR** 5-2 Enrich, p. 144 **TR** Chapter 5 Real-World Lab, pp. 151–153 **SES** Book E, *Environmental Science,* Chapter 1	**SE** Section 2 Review, p. 167 **SE** Analyze and Conclude, p. 169 **TE** Ongoing Assessment, pp. 161, 163, 165 **TE** Performance Assessment, p. 167 **TR** 5-2 Review and Reinforce, p. 143	Exploring Life Science Videodisc, Unit 3 Side 2, "Travelin' Along" Audiotapes: English-Spanish Summary 5-2 Transparency 20, "Exploring a Honeybee Society" Interactive Student Tutorial CD-ROM, B-5
TR 5-3 Lesson Plan, p. 145 **TR** 5-3 Section Summary, p. 146 **TR** 5-3 Review and Reinforce, p. 147 **TR** 5-3 Enrich, p. 148 **SES** Book E, *Environmental Science,* Chapter 2	**SE** Section 3 Review, p. 172 **TE** Ongoing Assessment, p. 171 **TE** Performance Assessment, p. 172 **TR** 5-3 Review and Reinforce, p. 147	Audiotapes: English-Spanish Summary 5-3 Interactive Student Tutorial CD-ROM, B-5
TR Chapter 5 Performance Assessment, pp. 194–196 **TR** Chapter 5 Test, pp. 197–200	**SE** Chapter Review, pp. 173–175 **TR** Chapter 5 Performance Assessment, pp. 194–196 **TR** Chapter 5 Test, pp. 197–200 **CTB** Test B-5	Computer Test Bank, Test B-5 Interactive Student Tutorial CD-ROM, B-5 Got It! Video Quizzes

Key: **SE** Student Edition
CTB Computer Test Bank
ISAB Inquiry Skills Activity Book

TE Teacher's Edition
SES Science Explorer Series Text
PTA Product Testing Activities by *Consumer Reports*

TR Teaching Resources
ISLM Integrated Science Laboratory Manual
IES Interdisciplinary Explorations Series

Meeting the National Science Education Standards and AAAS Benchmarks

National Science Education Standards	Benchmarks for Science Literacy	Unifying Themes
Science as Inquiry (Content Standard A) ◆ **Ask questions that can be answered by scientific investigations** Students pose questions about teaching an animal and design an procedure to investigate their questions. *(Chapter Project)* ◆ **Think critically and logically to make the relationships between evidence and explanations** Ant social and group behavior provides a starting point from which scientific investigation and discussion can proceed. Evidence may be contrary to students' previous opinions and will be the source of lively scientific inquiry. *(Real World Lab)* **Life Science** (Content Standard C) ◆ **Regulation and Behavior** Behavior is a response to a stimulus. Behavior has an adaptive function, and it enables animals to meet basic needs such as finding food. Animal behaviors, such as migration and hibernation, are regulated by seasonal and other environmental changes. *(Sections 1–3)* ◆ **Diversity and adaptations of organisms** Different animals behave in different ways, but most behaviors serve adaptive functions, such as reproduction or finding food. Different kinds of animals may exhibit similar behavior patterns, such as establishing a territory or living in groups. *(Sections 2 and 3)* ◆ **Populations and ecosystems** Behavior and environment are related. Interactions with the ecosystem affect animal behaviors, such as hibernation and migration, and animal behaviors can alter the ecosystem. *(Sections 1–3)*	**1B Scientific Inquiry** Students use both logic and imagination in devising a plan to train an animal. Students base analysis of ant behavior on observations. They also design an experiment to evaluate learning and control the variables in that experiment. *(Chapter Project, Skills Lab, Real World Lab)* **3A Technology and Science** Pheromone chemistry is the basis for the development of new technologies in controlling insect pests.	◆ **Patterns of Change** Behavior is a recognizable pattern of activity that benefits an animal in some way. Behavior patterns change in response to new stimuli, such as changing seasons. Behavior patterns of animals can be altered through a learning process. *(Sections 1–3; Chapter Project)* ◆ **Modeling** Students perform simple experiments about learning in order to model the concepts incorporated in a behavioral experiment. *(Skills Lab)* ◆ **Systems and Interactions** The environment and the resources within it constitute an ecological system. Interactions in the form of animal behaviors within this system can insure survival and reproduction. *(Sections 2 and 3)* ◆ **Unity and Diversity** While different animals behave in different ways, most animal behaviors help an animal survive and reproduce. Different kinds of animals may exhibit similar behavior patterns, such as establishing a territory or living in groups. *(Sections 2 and 3)*

Media and Technology

Exploring Life Science Videodisc

◆ **Section 2** "Travelin' Along" allows viewers to travel with sea turtles from birth to death.

Interactive Student Tutorial CD-ROM

◆ **Chapter Review** Interactive questions help students to self-assess their mastery of key chapter concepts.

Student Edition Connection Strategies

◆ **Section 1** Integrating Technology, p. 156
◆ **Section 2** Social Studies Connection, p. 166
◆ **Section 3** Integrating Chemistry, p. 170
   Integrating Environmental Science, p. 172

USING THE INTERNET

www.science-explorer.phschool.com

Visit the Science Explorer Internet site to find an up-to-date activity for Chapter 5 of *Animals*.

ACTIVITY	Time (minutes)	Materials Quantities for one work group	Skills
Section 1			
Discover, p. 152	15	**Nonconsumable** one or more small, active vertebrates such as gerbils, guppies, or anoles in an appropriate cage or aquarium **Consumable** Appropriate food for animal(s)	Predicting
Sharpen Your Skills, p. 154	10	**Consumable** No special materials are required.	Predicting
Try This, p. 157	15	**Consumable** paper and pencil	Inferring
Skills Lab, p. 159	20	**Consumable** paper and pencil	Designing Experiments
Section 2			
Discover, p. 160	15	**Consumable** No special materials are required.	Forming Operational Definitions
Try This, p. 163	15	**Consumable** sheets of paper, 22 × 28 cm **Nonconsumable** scissors; paste, glue, or stapler; timer	Calculating
Real-World Lab, pp. 168–169	20	**Consumable** water, bread crumbs, sugar, black paper, tape **Nonconsumable** large glass jar, sandy soil, shallow pan, wire screen, sponge, 20–30 ants, hand lens, glass-marking pencil, forceps, large thick rubber band	Observing, Inferring, Posing Questions
Section 3			
Discover, p. 170	20	**Nonconsumable** pairs of small, foil-covered containers holding a variety of nontoxic substances with distinctive scents	Observing

A list of all materials required for the Student Edition activities can be found on pages T15–T16. You can order Materials Kits by calling 1-800-828-7777 or by accessing the Science Explorer Internet site at **www.science-explorer.phschool.com.**

Learning New Tricks

Students learn about animal behavior and types of learning by attempting to teach a specific behavior to a pet or other animal.

Purpose To help students understand the difference between instinctive and learned behavior

Skills Focus Students will be able to
◆ observe natural behavior patterns in an animal;
◆ observe the animal's learning over a period of time;
◆ draw conclusions about the animal's ability to learn new behaviors;
◆ communicate their findings about the animals' ability to learn to their classmates.

Project Time Line Before beginning the project, see Chapter 5 Project Teacher Notes on pages 130–131 in Teaching Resources for more details on carrying out the project. Also distribute the students' Chapter 5 Project Overview and Worksheet and Scoring Rubric on pages 132–136 in Teaching Resources. During the first week, students should familiarize themselves with their animal's natural behaviors. They should also decide what behavior they plan to teach their animal and what method (trial and error or conditioning) they will use to train the animal. Plan on at least two weeks for training. You will probably need to schedule several different days to allow students to showcase their animals' new behaviors.

Possible Materials Students will need animals. In addition, they may need:
◆ materials to construct a maze
◆ food to use as a reward
◆ glue, tape, stopwatches, timers
◆ posterboard and markers for their presentation
◆ camera, sketchbook, or video camera to record behavior

Launching the Project When introducing the project, bring an animal into the classroom and show the students a behavior it has learned. Talk about who trained the animal, how it was trained, and any difficulties that were encountered during the training process.

CHAPTER 5 Animal Behavior

WHAT'S AHEAD

SECTION 1 Why Do Animals Behave as They Do?
Discover **What Can You Observe About a Vertebrate's Behavior?**
Sharpen Your Skills **Predicting**
Try This **Line Them Up**
Skills Lab **Become a Learning Detective**

SECTION 2 Patterns of Behavior
Discover **What Can You Express Without Words?**
Try This **Worker Bees**
Real-World Lab **One for All**

SECTION 3 Integrating Chemistry
The Chemistry of Communication
Discover **Can You Match the Scents?**

150 ◆ B

Allow time for students to read the Chapter Project Overview on pages 132–133 in Teaching Resources. Then encourage discussions on the types of behaviors that might be taught, materials that could be used, and any initial questions students may have. Pass out copies of the Chapter 5 Project Worksheets on pages 134–135 in Teaching Resources for students to review.

Safety

Be sure that students are not allergic to any animals with which they may be working. The animal's owner and, if the owner is a child, a grown-up should be present during training and handling the animal.

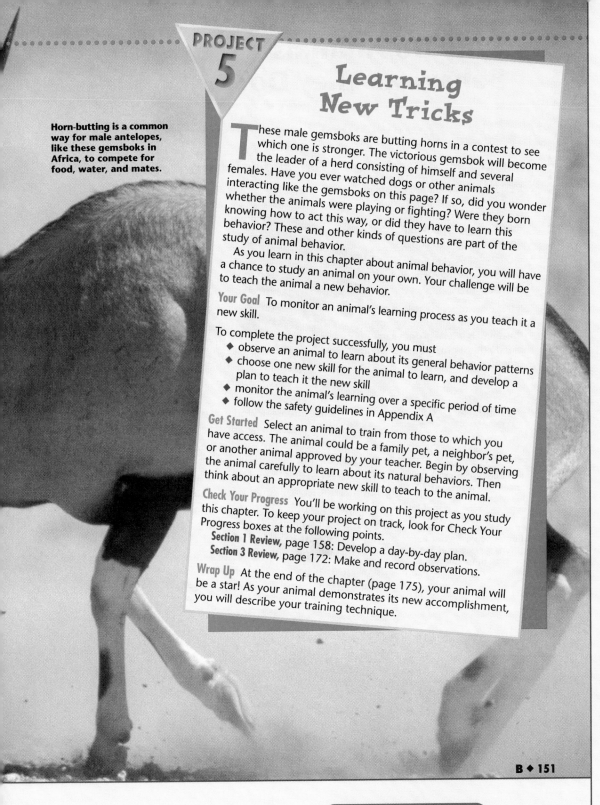

Horn-butting is a common way for male antelopes, like these gemsboks in Africa, to compete for food, water, and mates.

Learning New Tricks

These male gemsboks are butting horns in a contest to see which one is stronger. The victorious gemsbok will become the leader of a herd consisting of himself and several females. Have you ever watched dogs or other animals interacting like the gemsboks on this page? If so, did you wonder whether the animals were playing or fighting? Were they born knowing how to act this way, or did they have to learn this behavior? These and other kinds of questions are part of the study of animal behavior.

As you learn in this chapter about animal behavior, you will have a chance to study an animal on your own. Your challenge will be to teach the animal a new behavior.

Your Goal To monitor an animal's learning process as you teach it a new skill.

To complete the project successfully, you must
◆ observe an animal to learn about its general behavior patterns
◆ choose one new skill for the animal to learn, and develop a plan to teach it the new skill
◆ monitor the animal's learning over a specific period of time
◆ follow the safety guidelines in Appendix A

Get Started Select an animal to train from those to which you have access. The animal could be a family pet, a neighbor's pet, or another animal approved by your teacher. Begin by observing the animal carefully to learn about its natural behaviors. Then think about an appropriate new skill to teach to the animal.

Check Your Progress You'll be working on this project as you study this chapter. To keep your project on track, look for Check Your Progress boxes at the following points.
Section 1 Review, page 158: Develop a day-by-day plan.
Section 3 Review, page 172: Make and record observations.

Wrap Up At the end of the chapter (page 175), your animal will be a star! As your animal demonstrates its new accomplishment, you will describe your training technique.

Students must decide what behaviors they will teach their animals. Worksheet 1 may help them think of ideas. Worksheet 2 will then help students organize their schedules. If students have problems training their animals, they should confer with you. Help them determine whether they need to plan additional trials or develop new strategies for teaching the behaviors. At the conclusion of the project, students should demonstrate their animals' behaviors to the class. If possible, students can bring in the animals to present to the class; check your school's policy regarding live animals in the classroom. If not, students can sketch, photograph, or videotape their trained animals. During their presentations, students should discuss how they trained their animals, including any difficulties they encountered.

Program Resources

◆ **Teaching Resources** Chapter 5 Project Teacher's Notes, pp. 130-131; Chapter 5 Project Student Overview and Worksheets, pp. 132-135; Chapter 5 Project Scoring Rubric, p. 136

Performance Assessment

The Chapter 5 Project Scoring Rubric on page 136 of Teaching Resources will help you evaluate how well students complete the Chapter 5 Project. You may wish to share the scoring rubric with your students so they are clear about what will be expected of them. Students will be assessed on
◆ how well they choose appropriate animal, trick, stimulus, and reward; how thoroughly they plan a workable regimen;
◆ the completeness of their observation entries, including what their animals do during training and descriptions of external factors that may affect that process;
◆ the thoroughness and organization of their presentations.

Why Do Animals Behave as They Do?

Objectives

After completing the lesson, students will be able to
- identify the function of an animal's behaviors;
- compare instinctive and learned behavior.

Key Terms behavior, stimulus, response, instinct, learning, conditioning, trial-and-error learning, insight learning, artificial intelligence, imprinting

1 Engage/Explore

Activating Prior Knowledge

Make a two-column table on the board. Labeled "What Happens" and "Way Animal Behaves." List events in the first column that may produce a response in an animal. (*Sample: Dog hears doorbell, kitten sees ball of yarn, fish sees food*) Have students describe how the pet might respond in each case and list the responses in the second column.

DISCOVER ACTIVITY

Skills Focus predicting
Materials *small vertebrates, a cage or aquarium, food*
Time 15 minutes
Tips Students should not handle the animals. Advise students to wait patiently for animals to show some kind of behavior. Students must wash their hands afterward.
Expected Outcome Students should observe that food, other animals, or disturbing sounds cause behaviors such as feeding, social interaction, hiding, or escape attempts.
Think It Over Some possible answers include the addition of another animal, a loud noise, or addition of food.
learning modality: visual

Why Do Animals Behave as They Do?

DISCOVER ········· ACTIVITY

What Can You Observe About a Vertebrate's Behavior?

1. For a few minutes, carefully observe the behavior of a small vertebrate, such as a gerbil or a goldfish. Write down your observations.

2. Place some food near the animal and watch what the animal does.

3. If there are other animals in the cage or aquarium, observe how the animals interact—for example, do they fight, groom each other, or ignore each other?

4. Tap gently on the cage or aquarium and see how the animal reacts. Note any other events that seem to make the animal change its behavior (from resting to moving, for example).

Think It Over
Predicting What are some circumstances under which you might expect an animal's behavior to change suddenly?

GUIDE FOR READING

- What are the functions of most of an animal's behaviors?
- How does instinctive behavior compare with learned behavior?

Reading Tip Before you read, rewrite the headings in the section as *how, why,* or *what* questions. As you read, write answers to those questions.

Figure 1 These two anoles are displaying their dewlaps in a dispute over space.

A male anole—a kind of lizard—stands in a patch of sun. As another male approaches, the first anole begins to lower and raise its head and chest in a series of quick push-ups. From beneath its neck a dewlap, a bright red flap of skin, flares out and then collapses, over and over. The anoles stare at one another, looking like miniature dinosaurs about to do battle. The first anole seems to be saying, "This area belongs to me. You'll have to leave or fight!"

The push-ups, piercing stares, and dewlap displays are all behaviors that warn another male to go away.

READING STRATEGIES

Reading Tip Before students read the section, have partners discuss possible answers to the *how, why,* and *what* questions they wrote. Ask students to jot down proposed answers to the questions. Then direct students to read the section. Have students work with the same partners to check the accuracy of the answers they wrote in the prereading activity.

Vocabulary Have students write the key terms *instinct, insight,* and *imprinting* and underline the prefixes *in-* and *im-*. Point out that the prefixes are related and have more than one meaning. Provide student pairs with a dictionary, and have them look up the various meanings of the prefixes.

An animal's **behavior** consists of all the actions it performs—for example, the things that it does to obtain food, avoid predators, and find a mate. To understand animals, it is important to know not only what their body structures are like, but also how and why they behave as they do. Like their body structures, the behaviors of animals are adaptations that have evolved over long periods of time.

Most behavior is a complicated process in which different parts of an animal's body work together. The first anole saw the second anole with his eyes and interpreted the sight with his brain. His brain and nervous system then directed his muscles to perform the push-up movement and to display his bright red dewlap.

Why Behavior Is Important

When an animal looks for food or hides to avoid a predator, it is obviously doing something that helps it stay alive. When animals search for mates and build nests for young, they are behaving in ways that help them reproduce. **Most behaviors help an animal survive or reproduce.**

As an example of a survival behavior, consider what happens when a water current carries a small crustacean to a hydra's tentacles. After stinging cells on the tentacles paralyze the prey, the tentacles bend, pulling the captured crustacean toward the hydra's mouth. At the same time, the hydra's mouth opens to receive the food. If the tentacles didn't pull the food toward the hydra's mouth, or if the mouth didn't open, then the hydra couldn't take the food into its body. If the hydra couldn't feed, it would die.

The small crustacean acted as a stimulus to the hydra. A **stimulus** (plural *stimuli*) is a signal that causes an organism to react in some way. The organism's reaction to the stimulus is called a **response.** The hydra responded to the crustacean by stinging it and then eating it. All animal behavior is caused by stimuli. Some stimuli come from an animal's external environment, while other stimuli, such as hunger, come from inside the animal's body. An animal's response may include external actions, internal changes (such as a faster heartbeat), or both.

✓ *Checkpoint* **Give an example of a stimulus to which a hydra would respond.**

Figure 2 When a hungry sea star finds a clam, the clam acts as a stimulus. The sea star's response is to approach the clam, grab the clam's shell with its tube feet, and open it. The sea star can then force its stomach inside the shell and consume the clam. *Applying Concepts How is this behavior important to the sea star's survival?*

2 Facilitate

Why Behavior Is Important

Demonstration

The automatic "blink" response is common among most mammals. Divide students into pairs. Have one member of the pair hold a clear sheet of plastic in front of his or her face, while the other member gently tosses a soft foam ball at the sheet. Most students will involuntarily blink, even though they know the ball can't hit them. Students may exchange places and repeat the activity. Ask: **How does this automatic response aid a mammal's survival?** *(It helps to avoid injury to the eye.)*. **learning modality: kinesthetic**

Including All Students

For the benefit of students who lack proficiency in English, point out that *behavior* can have different meanings. It can refer to a person's conduct, as in the sentence, "Proper behavior requires people to cover their mouths when they cough." *Behavior* can also refer to the actions an animal performs. Invite students to name other words with multiple meanings. *(glass, cry, fork, nail, and so forth)* Ask students to identify multiple-meaning words in languages other than English. **limited English proficiency**

Program Resources

◆ **Teaching Resources** 5-1 Lesson Plan, p. 137; 5-1 Section Summary, p. 138

Media and Technology

🎧 **Audiotapes** English-Spanish Summary 5-1

Answers to Self-Assessment

✓ *Checkpoint*

Sample: Having its tentacles touched by a toothpick.

Caption Question

Figure 2 The behavior enables the sea star to get food.

Ongoing Assessment

Writing Have students name one animal behavior and suggest how the behavior is beneficial for the animal.

Instinctive Behavior

Addressing Naive Conceptions

Some students may think that only simple behaviors are instinctive. However, this is not the case. For example, seasonal migration is a complex behavior that is at least partly instinctive. Point out other examples of complex animal behaviors that are wholly or partly instinctive, such as cranes performing elaborate "dances" during courtship.
learning modality: verbal

Learning

Sharpen your Skills

Predicting

Time 10 minutes

Tips Prepare students to  predict the chicks' responses by asking them to compare the shadow shapes. Suggest they note similarities and differences that a chick might use as clues for distinguishing between the shadows.

Expected Outcome An older chick would learn not to crouch when it sees a shadow shaped like B, while shadows A and C would continue to elicit crouching behavior. This learning is a form of conditioning that modifies instinctive behavior.

Extend Have students propose a design for an experiment that tests whether hawks are more likely to capture chicks that are upright or chicks that are crouching. *(Sample: Set up decoys of upright and crouching chicks. Periodically check for evidence of hawk attacks.)*
learning modality: visual

Sharpen your Skills

Predicting

Hawks, which have short necks, prey on gull chicks. Geese, which have long necks, do not prey on the chicks. When newly hatched gull chicks see any bird's shadow, they instinctively crouch down. As the chicks become older, they continue to crouch when they see the shadow of a hawk, but they learn not to crouch when they see a goose's shadow. Predict how older gull chicks will behave when they see bird shadows shaped like A, B, and C. Which type of learning does this behavior show? Explain.

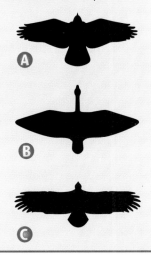

Ⓐ

Ⓑ

Ⓒ

Instinctive Behavior

Some animal behaviors must be learned, while others are inborn—the animal knows how to do them by **instinct**, without being taught. An instinct is a behavior pattern that is inborn and that an animal performs correctly the first time. For example, a newborn kangaroo instinctively crawls into its mother's pouch and attaches itself to a nipple. A dragonfly nymph will instinctively shoot out its lower jaw and catch any bite-sized animal that comes within range. The dragonfly nymph has not been taught how to capture food. Rather, it knows instinctively how to use its mouthparts to do that. Most behaviors of invertebrates, such as insects, echinoderms, and worms, are instinctive.

Like learned behaviors, instinctive behaviors are responses to stimuli. Earthworms, for example, instinctively crawl away from a bright light. The light is the stimulus, and the earthworms respond by moving away from it.

The behavior of earthworms in response to strong light is fairly simple. However, some instinctive behaviors are complex. Spiders instinctively spin complicated webs without making mistakes in the pattern. Most birds build their nests without ever being taught how.

☑ *Checkpoint* *What is instinctive behavior?*

Learning

Think back to the first time you rode a bicycle. It probably took a few tries before you could do it well—you had to learn how. **Learning** is the process that leads to changes in behavior based on practice or experience. In general, the larger an animal's brain is, the more the animal can learn.

Unlike instincts, learned behaviors result from an animal's experience and are not usually done perfectly the first time. Lion cubs must practice many times before they can successfully kill prey. Gradually, by participating in hunting and imitating their mother's behavior, cubs learn to creep up on a prey animal, pounce on it, and kill it.

All learned behaviors depend in part on inherited traits that have passed from parents to offspring. Even though lion cubs must learn specific methods of hunting, they are born with claws that help them capture prey. In addition, lion cubs will instinctively pounce on any object that attracts their attention. The cubs have inherited some physical features and skills that are necessary for hunting, in much the same way that a talented basketball player has inherited above-average height and good eye-hand

Background

Facts and Figures Most bird songs are vocalizations made by male birds during the mating season. If they do not learn the same songs as other birds of their species, male birds will not be able to defend their territories, warn others of danger, or find and secure a mate.

To learn whether bird songs are inherited or learned, eighteenth-century naturalists studied birds raised without others of their species. They found that some birds could sing their species song from birth, although they did not sing it very well. However, other bird species raised with foster parents of a different species learned the songs of their foster parents.

Recent research has determined that in some bird species, birds must learn their songs during an early critical period, or they will not learn the songs at all.

coordination. But both lions and athletes must practice in order to develop their abilities.

Animals learn new behaviors in different ways. These include conditioning, trial-and-error learning, and insight learning.

Conditioning When a dog sees its owner approaching with a leash, the dog may get excited, eager to go for a walk. The dog has learned to associate the sight of the leash with a walk. Learning to connect some kind of stimulus with a good or bad event is called **conditioning**. In the case of the dog and the leash, the stimulus of the leash is associated with a pleasant event—a brisk walk. Animals can also be conditioned to avoid bad outcomes. Think of what happens when a predator tries to attack a skunk. The skunk sprays the predator with a substance that stings and smells awful. In the future, the predator is likely to avoid skunks, because the predator associates the sight of a skunk with its terrible spray.

During the early 1900s, the Russian scientist Ivan Pavlov performed a series of experiments involving conditioning. In Figure 3, see how Pavlov conditioned a dog to respond to the stimulus of a bell.

Figure 3 Steps 1, 2, and 3 show the procedure that Pavlov used when he conditioned a dog to salivate at the sound of a bell. *Predicting* Predict what the dog would do if it heard a bell ringing in another part of the house.

1. When a hungry dog sees or smells food, it produces saliva. Food is the stimulus, and the dog's response is salivation. Dogs do not usually salivate in response to other stimuli, such as the sound of a ringing bell.

2. For many days, when Pavlov gave food to a dog, he also rang a bell at the same time. The sight and smell of food were associated with the ringing of a bell. Pavlov did this every time he fed the dog. The dog salivated each time the two stimuli were introduced.

3. Finally, Pavlov rang a bell but did not give the dog food. The dog still produced saliva. The stimulus of the bell by itself produced the same response—salivation—that only food would normally produce.

Program Resources

◆ **Interdisciplinary Exploration Series** "Sleuth's Supper," p. 37

Media and Technology

 Transparencies "Pavlov's Experiment," Transparency 19

Answers to Self-Assessment

Caption Question

Figure 3 The dog would salivate. The dog is conditioned to salivate when it hears a bell, no matter where the bell is located.

☑ *Checkpoint*

Instinctive behavior is an inborn behavior pattern that an animal can perform correctly the first time.

Using the Visuals: Figure 3

Ask students to cover the numbered descriptions in the figure with a sheet of paper. Then have them describe what is happening in the figure, using just the illustrations. Make sure students' descriptions include the dog's behavior and the stimulus for the behavior. Finally, ask students to identify the kind of learning being demonstrated by the sequence of drawings. *(conditioning)* **learning modality: visual**

Real-Life Learning

Divide the class into small groups. In the groups, have the students describe their response to the school's fire alarm. Have the groups problem-solve to decide whether the described response is an example of learning or conditioning. **learning modality: verbal**

Inquiry Challenge

Divide the class into cooperative groups. Instruct each group to design an experiment to investigate a particular animal's response to a stimulus, such as a dog's response to the ringing of a doorbell. Groups can assign the tasks of the designing process—posing a question, developing a hypothesis, controlling variables, and forming operational definitions—to specific students. Inform students that if they wish to perform the experiment, they must write a description of the procedure and obtain your approval for their procedure. Advise students to use safe and inexpensive materials, and to treat the animal safely and gently. Allow time for initial brainstorming. At the end of the activity, have groups discuss their experiments and explain why they chose the specific variables they did. **cooperative learning**

Ongoing Assessment

Oral Presentation Ask students to present an example of conditioning they have witnessed in either themselves, another person, or in animals. Have them present their example to the class, and explain how the example demonstrates conditioning.

Learning, continued

Including All Students

Materials *six pairs of charts, each pair showing (in different orders) a red star, a blue circle, a yellow triangle, and a green square; small rewards*
Time 20 minutes

Students whose hearing is impaired will benefit from this activity because the meanings of trial-and-error learning and insight learning will be communicated visually. Decide beforehand which shape on the charts will be associated with a reward. Divide the class into six groups of three or four students each. Select one student in each group as the test administrator. The administrator will select another student to select any shape from one chart. The student will continue selecting until the reward is given. Now the administrator will show the second chart to the test subject. The subject will probably choose the shape first associated with the reward. Next, the administrator will ask another student to choose shapes from the charts. The student will probably choose the shape associated with the reward given to the first student. Continue until all students in the group have received a reward. Ask students: **What kind of learning did the first test subject use to find the shape that led to the reward?** *(Trial and error)* **The second subject?** *(insight)* Instruct students to explain their answers.
learning modality: visual

Integrating Technology

Allow students to explore the abilities and limits of artificial intelligence by allowing them to play one of the many checkers-playing programs available on the Internet. You can download free trial versions or inexpensive checkers playing programs from **www.shareware.com** or help students find another appropriate site. After students play, ask them to describe how it was different to play checkers with a computer compared to playing with a friend. **learning modality: logical/mathematical**

Figure 4 Rescue dogs, like this English springer spaniel, are specially trained to find and rescue people trapped by accidents or natural disasters. Trainers use conditioning to teach rescue dogs these skills.

Conditioning is often used to train animals. Suppose, for example, that you want to train a dog to come to you when you call it. Every time the dog comes when you call, you reward it with a dog biscuit and a friendly pat. Your dog soon will learn to associate the pleasant experience of food and a pat with the behavior of coming when called. So the dog is likely to repeat that behavior.

Trial-and-Error Learning When a young chicken first hatches and begins to look for food, it will peck at almost any spot on the ground. Gradually the chick learns that only some of these spots are seeds or insects that are good to eat. The chicken has learned through trial and error which objects are food. **Trial-and-error learning** occurs when an animal, through repeated practice, learns to perform a behavior more and more skillfully. When you learned to ride a bicycle, you did it by trial and error. You may have wobbled or even fallen at first, especially when turning corners, but after a while you learned to ride smoothly. You got better because you learned that some movements were more likely to keep you upright than others.

Insight Learning The first time you try out a new video game, you may not need someone to explain how to play it. Instead, you may use what you already know about other video games to figure out how the new one works. When you solve a problem or learn how to do something new by applying what you already know, without a period of trial and error, you are using **insight learning**.

Insight learning is most common in primates, such as gorillas, chimpanzees, and humans. Figure 5 shows the results of an experiment done with chimpanzees. The animals used insight to come up with a way to reach a bunch of bananas—they stacked boxes on top of one another. In contrast, if a dog accidentally wraps its leash around a pole, the dog cannot figure out how to unwrap the leash.

INTEGRATING TECHNOLOGY People once thought that machines were incapable of learning. However, some computers can now learn and solve problems. **Artificial intelligence** is the capacity of a computer to perform complex tasks such as learning from experience and solving problems. Computers with artificial intelligence can play chess and beat human opponents. The computer, like a human chess player, can figure out

---

Background

Facts and Figures Recent studies suggest that many birds are capable of insight learning. Both pigeons and canaries can solve the *oddity problem*—picking out the "odd" object in a set of three objects. In addition, canaries can generalize this principle to other sets of odd objects. For example, they were able to pick out the odd objects in other sets the first time they saw them.

Scientists once believed that birds were capable only of mimicry or simple association. However, Dr. Irene Pepperberg at the University of Arizona has taught African gray parrots to say simple phrases that the birds apparently relate to actual situations. Alex, the most famous of the parrots, can make simple requests for food or at times use language creatively.

Figure 5 In this experiment, a hungry chimpanzee faced a problem—it couldn't reach the bananas. The chimpanzee figured out how to reach the bananas by stacking the boxes and climbing to the top of the stack. *Applying Concepts Explain how the chimpanzee's behavior shows insight learning.*

strategies and moves in advance. As scientists working in the field of artificial intelligence try to program computers to learn, they have a growing appreciation for the amazing abilities of the human brain.

☑ *Checkpoint* *In which animals is insight learning most common?*

Imprinting

A female Canada goose swims across a stream. One by one, her goslings paddle after her. The goslings follow their mother wherever she goes because they have undergone a process called imprinting. In **imprinting**, certain newly hatched birds and newborn mammals learn to recognize and follow the first moving object they see, which is usually their mother. Imprinting occurs very shortly after a young animal hatches or is born.

Imprinting involves a combination of instinctive behavior and learning. The young animal has an instinct to follow a moving object, but the youngster is not born knowing what its mother looks like. The young animal must learn from experience what object to follow.

Imprinting is valuable for two reasons. First, it keeps young animals close to their mothers, who know where to find food and how to avoid predators. Second, imprinting allows young

Line Them Up

Try to solve the following problem.
There are five girls: Maureen, Lupita, Jill, PoYee, and Tanya. They are standing in a row. Neither Maureen nor Lupita is next to PoYee. Neither Lupita nor Maureen is next to Tanya. Neither PoYee nor Lupita is next to Jill. Tanya is just to the right of Jill. Name the girls from left to right.

Inferring What kind or kinds of learning did you use to solve the problem? Explain.

Imprinting

TRY THIS

Skills Focus inferring
Materials *paper and pencil*
Time 15 minutes
Tips Have students work in pairs. Suggest they write the names of the girls on slips of paper, then arrange the slips in the correct order.
Expected Outcome The correct order is Lupita, Maureen, Jill, Tanya, and PoYee.
Inferring Students will probably solve the problem by trial-and-error—moving the slips of paper around until they find the correct arrangement.
Extend Ask volunteers to describe and characterize the methods they used.
learning modality: logical/mathematical

Real-Life Learning

Explain that one successful endangered animal-breeding program, the program to reintroduce the California condor, is raising these rare birds in captivity so they can be returned to the wild. Hand puppets that resemble condor parents are used to feed and nurture the babies. Ask students: **If these precautions were not taken, would humans be a danger to these condors when they are released? Why or why not?** (*Yes, because the condors would associate humans with food and be attracted to them. If this happened, the birds might be injured by people who were afraid of them.*) Explain that the only way to be sure that captive animals do not imprint on humans is to keep them away from humans until the animals are mature. **learning modality: verbal**

Answers to Self-Assessment

Caption Question

Figure 5 The chimpanzee used insight learning because it solved a problem by applying what it already knew, that stacking the boxes would enable it to get higher.

☑ *Checkpoint*

Insight learning is most common in primates such as gorillas and humans.

Ongoing Assessment

Skills Check Have students list three of their learned behaviors and classify them as trial and error or insight learning. (*Sample: learning subtraction based on knowledge of addition—insight; learning to skate with roller blades—trial and error*)

3 Assess

Section 1 Review Answers

1. Most behaviors help animals survive or reproduce.

2. Instinctive behaviors are inborn. The animal performs them correctly the first time. Learned behaviors result from an animal's experience and are not done perfectly the first time.

3. Trial-and-error learning occurs when an animal, through repetition, learns to perform a behavior more skillfully. In insight learning, an animal performs a behavior by applying previous knowledge, without a period of trial and error.

4. The duckling will probably try to follow the tricycle, because ducklings follow the first moving object they see after hatching. This behavior is called imprinting.

Check Your Progress
CHAPTER PROJECT 5

Review students' training plans. Check to make sure students have obtained permission from the owners of the animals. Also make sure that the skills students are planning to teach their animals are reasonable. Ensure that students have chosen appropriate rewards for the animals, and that the animals will not be harmed during the training process.

Figure 6 These ducks imprinted on scientist Konrad Lorenz when they were ducklings. Even as adults, they followed him when he went for a swim.

animals to learn what other animals of their own species look like. This ability protects the animals while they are young. In addition, it is important later in life when the animals are searching for mates.

Once imprinting takes place, it cannot be changed—even if the animal has imprinted on something other than its mother, such as a moving toy, or even a human. Konrad Lorenz, an Austrian scientist who first described imprinting in 1935, conducted experiments in which he, rather than the mother, was the first moving object that newly hatched birds saw. Figure 6 shows the result of one such experiment. Since the newly hatched birds imprinted on Lorenz, even as adults they followed him around.

Lorenz's experiments sometimes caused surprising results. One bird that had imprinted on Lorenz, a male jackdaw, apparently thought that Lorenz was a possible mate. Because jackdaws feed one another as part of their mating behavior, this bird often tried to feed worms to Lorenz—who politely refused to eat them!

Section 1 Review

1. Explain what roles behavior plays for animals.
2. Contrast instinctive behavior with learned behavior.
3. How is trial-and-error learning different from insight learning?
4. **Thinking Critically** **Predicting** Right after hatching, before seeing anything else, a duckling sees a child riding a tricycle. What will probably happen the next time the child rides the tricycle in front of the duckling? Explain, and identify the type of behavior that this shows.

158 ◆ B

Check Your Progress
CHAPTER PROJECT 5

By now, you should have written out a day-by-day plan for teaching your animal a new behavior. You may find ideas in books on training pets. Make sure that your plan will not harm the animal. Obtain your teacher's approval for your plan and begin training your animal. *(Hint:* Decide how you will monitor learning in your animal. What responses will show that the animal has mastered the skill?)

BECOME A LEARNING DETECTIVE

In this lab, you will design an experiment to investigate how people learn.

Problem

What are some factors that make it easier for people to learn new things?

Suggested Materials

paper and pencil

List A	List B
zop	bug
rud	rag
tig	den
wab	hot
hev	fur
paf	wax
mel	beg
kib	cut
col	sip
nug	job

Design a Plan

1. Look over the two lists of words in the table. Researchers use groups of words like these to investigate how people learn. Notice the way the two groups differ. The words in List A have no meanings in ordinary English. List B contains familiar, but unrelated, words.

2. What do you think will happen if people try to learn the words in each list? Write a hypothesis about which list will be easier to learn. How much easier will it be to learn that list?

3. With a partner, design an experiment to test your hypothesis. Brainstorm a list of the variables you will need to control in order to make your results reliable. Then write out your plan and present it to your teacher.

4. If necessary, revise your plan according to your teacher's instructions. Then perform your experiment using people your teacher has approved as test subjects. Keep careful records of your results.

Analyze and Conclude

1. Find the average (mean) number of words people learned from each list. How did these results compare with your hypothesis?

2. What factors may have made one list easier to learn than the other?

3. Share your results with the rest of the class. How do the results of the different experiments in your class compare? What might explain the similarities or differences?

4. **Think About It** Look back at your experimental plan. Think about how well you were able to carry it out in the actual experiment. What difficulties did you encounter? What improvements could you make, either in your plan or in the way you carried it out?

More to Explore

Plan an experiment to investigate how long people remember what they learn. Write a hypothesis, and design an experiment to test your hypothesis. Obtain your teacher's permission before carrying out your experiment.

Analyze and Conclude

1. Most test subjects should learn more from list B than list A.

2. It is easier to remember meaningful words than to recall nonsense words.

3. The actual number of words learned depends on the time allowed to learn.

4. Sample: Include more people to get a better sample.

Extending Inquiry

More to Explore Sample: Students might hypothesize that familiar words are remembered longer. Have several test subjects learn a list that includes familiar and unfamiliar words. Test the subjects' ability to write down the list after 1, 2 and 4 hours. Test again every day for the next few days.

Program Resources

◆ **Teaching Resources** Chapter 5 Skills Lab, pp. 149-150

Designing Experiments

Become a Learning Detective

Preparing for Inquiry

Key Concept Familiarity with a topic makes learning new material easier.

Skills Objective Students will be able to
◆ propose a hypothesis concerning human learning;
◆ design an experiment to test their hypothesis.

Time 40 minutes

Advanced Planning Decide who the test subjects will be. You may wish to use students in other classes.

Alternative Materials If students conduct this experiment on classmates, they must generate new lists that are unfamiliar to the test subjects.

Guiding Inquiry

Invitation To help students think about the various factors that affect how easy it is to learn, ask them if they learn better when they enjoy the subject, when they are motivated by rewards, when they are already familiar with the subject, or when there is much repetition.

Helping Design a Plan

Make sure that students come up with a measure of "easier to learn." For example, students may give a test subject five minutes to look at a list. The subject then has to write down as many words as she or he can remember. The test subject will remember more words from the list that was easier to learn.

Troubleshooting the Experiment

◆ Tell students to have test subjects write down words rather than speaking them so that individuals in other groups will not overhear.

Expected Outcome

◆ List B will be easier to learn than list A.
◆ Familiar words are easier to learn than unfamiliar ones.

Objectives

After completing the lesson, students will be able to

◆ describe some ways in which animals relate to one another and explain the functions of those behaviors;

◆ describe animal behavior cycles and explain how they are important for an animal's survival.

Key Terms aggression, territory, courtship behavior, society, circadian rhythms, hibernation, migration

1 Engage/Explore

Activating Prior Knowledge

Instruct students to immediately stop whatever they are doing. Choose students at random and ask them what they were doing when you asked them to stop. Explain that whatever each student was doing was a part of his or her behavior. Elicit students' comments about what they think was the purpose of their behaviors.

········ **DISCOVER** ········

Skills Focus forming operational definitions
Materials *none*
Time 15 minutes
Tips Have students write down the feeling or situation they are trying to convey. Then, after their partner guesses what is being communicated, students can refer to their notebooks to check. Students should use only natural facial expressions and simple body movements.
Expected Outcome Students should be able to interpret emotional communications. Abstract ideas are difficult to communicate without words.
Think It Over Most students will indicate that gestures and expressions should be included in our definition of communication.

DISCOVER ···················· **ACTIVITY**

What Can You Express Without Words?

1. Think of a feeling or situation that you can communicate without words, such as surprise or how to play a sport. Use facial expressions and body movements, but no words, to communicate it to your partner.

2. By observing your behavior, your partner should infer what you are communicating. Your partner should also note the behavior clues that led to this inference.

3. Now your partner should try to communicate a feeling or situation to you without words. Infer what your partner is trying to communicate, and note the behavior clues that led to your inference.

Think It Over
Forming Operational Definitions
Write your own definition of *communication*. How did this activity change your idea of communication?

GUIDE FOR READING

◆ What is the function of courtship behavior?

◆ How do animals benefit from living in groups?

◆ How is migration important for an animal's survival?

Reading Tip As you read, write an outline of this section. Use the headings as the main topics.

At this very moment, somewhere in Earth's oceans, blue whales are calling to one another. Whales communicate with a variety of sounds that scientists call songs. These songs consist of brassy trumpetings, long wails, clicks, and deep grunts. Whales locate one another using these sounds.

Icebergs dot the cold polar waters where these giant mammals spend their summers. After fattening up on small, shrimp-like animals called krill, blue whales migrate to warmer waters near the equator. It is in these tropical seas that the females give birth, usually to one calf.

Blue whales communicate with one another and migrate to breeding and resting places—behavior characteristics that they share with many other animals. In this section you will learn about some common behavior patterns of animals.

Blue whale ▼

READING STRATEGIES

Reading Tip Emphasize the usefulness of outlining as a study tool. Students can use headings as topic names. Remind students to write each main topic next to a Roman numeral. As a class, outline the first main topic, Competition and Aggression. Ask students questions such as: What information supports the main topic? What details support each subtopic?

Study and Comprehension After students read the section, have them use the outlines they created to generate questions about patterns of animal behavior. Direct students to write each question on a separate note card and to write answers to the questions on the backs of the cards. Then have students work with partners to answer one another's questions. After the activity, suggest that students use their question cards as study guides.

Figure 7 These Arctic hares are resolving their conflict by boxing. *Inferring What event might have led to this behavior?*

Competition and Aggression

Animals compete with one another for limited resources, such as food, water, space, shelter, and mates. Competition occurs among different species of animals, as when a pride of lions tries to steal a prey animal from a troop of hyenas that has just killed it. However, competition also occurs between members of the same species, as when a female aphid, a type of insect, kicks and shoves another female aphid while competing for the best leaf on which to lay eggs.

When they compete, animals may display **aggression**, which is a threatening behavior that one animal uses to gain control over another. Before a pride of lions settles down to eat its prey, individual lions show aggression by snapping, clawing, and snarling. First the most aggressive members of the pride eat their fill. Then the less aggressive and younger members of the pride get a chance to feed.

Aggression between members of the same species hardly ever results in the injury or death of any of the competitors. Usually the loser communicates "I give up" with its behavior. For example, to protect themselves from the aggressive attacks of older dogs, puppies roll over on their backs, showing their bellies. This signal calms the older dog, and the puppy can then creep away.

Establishing a Territory

On an early spring day, a male oriole fills the warm air with a flutelike song. You may think he is singing just because it is a beautiful day. But in fact, he is alerting other orioles that he is the "owner" of a particular territory. A **territory** is an area that is occupied and defended by an animal or group of animals.

Program Resources

◆ **Teaching Resources** 5-2 Lesson Plan, p. 141; 5-2 Section Summary, p. 142

Media and Technology

 Audiotapes English-Spanish Summary 5-2

Answers to Self-Assessment

Caption Question

Figure 7 The hares may be fighting over food or over a potential mate.

2 Facilitate

Competition and Aggression

Demonstration

To demonstrate competition or aggression in **ACTIVITY** animals, obtain two male bettas (also called Siamese fighting fish). Place each fish in its own glass jar filled with water. Place the jars next to each other on a table with an opaque card between them. Explain to students that the males of this species are very aggressive towards other males. To begin, allow students to observe the behavior of the two fish for a few minutes with the screen in place. Now remove the screen. Be sure each fish can clearly see the other. Have students observe and record behaviors they observe. After the demonstration, ask students to write short paragraphs to explain how they think these behaviors would benefit the bettas. *(The strongest and most aggressive males are those that survive and find mates.)* **learning modality: visual**

Establishing a Territory

Building Inquiry Skills: Predicting

Red-winged blackbirds display their red "epaulets" to defend a territory. Have students predict what would happen to a male blackbird whose red wing patches were dyed black. *(The male would lose its territory.)* **learning modality: logical/mathematical**

Ongoing Assessment

Oral Presentation Have students form small groups and list three competitive or aggressive human behaviors they have observed in the school cafeteria. Classify each behavior and describe its purpose. One member of each group can present the group's ideas.

Establishing a Territory, continued

Building Inquiry Skills: Inferring

Many students will have seen squirrels chasing each other in a park. Squirrels mark and aggressively defend their territories. Ask students to recall their observations of a park or other outdoor area in which squirrels live. Instruct students to use their observations to make an inference about whether a squirrel's territorial markings warn *all* animals away, or only other squirrels. *(Only other squirrels)* Ask students what knowledge they used to make this inference. *(Sample: A park may contain grackles and blackbirds as well as squirrels. The squirrels ignore the birds but chase other squirrels.)* Ask students to infer why squirrels do not defend their territory from birds. *(Birds don't compete for the same resources.)* **learning modality: logical/mathematical**

Mating and Raising Young

Addressing Naive Conceptions

What many people describe as "human nature" is not innate human behavior at all; it is the result of human culture. Tell students that culture is the way of life of people who share similar beliefs and customs. Ask students to list some behaviors that are aspects of culture *(Clothes, foods, ideas, sports, jobs, tools, and so on).* **learning modality: verbal**

If another animal of the same species enters the territory, the owner will attack the newcomer and try to drive it away. While birds use songs and aggressive behaviors to maintain their territories, other animals use calls, scratches, droppings, and scents. Cougars rake trees and earth with their claws and leave scent markings that advertise the boundaries of their territories.

By establishing a territory, an animal gains unlimited access to its resources, such as food and possible mates. A territory also provides a safe area in which animals can raise their young without competition from other members of their species. In most songbird species, and in many other animal species, a male cannot attract a mate unless he holds a territory.

☑ *Checkpoint* **How does a territory help an animal survive?**

Mating and Raising Young

A male and female salamander swim gracefully in the water, twining elegantly around one another. They are engaging in **courtship behavior**, which is behavior in which males and females of the same species prepare for mating. Males of some spider species court females by presenting them with prey before mating. Fireflies use light signals to indicate readiness for mating. **Courtship behavior ensures that the males and females of the same species recognize one another, so that mating and reproduction can take place.**

Birds have some of the most dramatic courtship behaviors. Figure 8 shows the elaborate bower that male bowerbirds prepare during courtship. Peregrine falcons have an acrobatic flight display as part of their courtship. As they soar through the air at

Figure 8 In the rain forest of Australia, a male satin bowerbird, left, creates a colorful welcome mat. He is decorating the entrance to the archlike bower he has built to attract a mate. By entering the bower, right, the green female bird lets the male know that she agrees to be his mate.

Background

Facts and Figures Scientists have long debated the adaptive advantage of birds' courtship behavior that seems to make no sense. According to one theory, complex courtship behaviors show that the male is in good physical and mental condition. Another theory holds that such behaviors advertise the singer's strength.

The males of one species of bower-bird decorate the bowers with the head plumes of birds of paradise. Because these plumes are difficult to come by, this behavior seems to support the first theory—the bird's superior physical and mental condition allowed him to find and retrieve these feathers. On the other hand, the fact that the bird of paradise has these feathers to begin with seems to support the second theory, since the bird of paradise must be strong to survive with large head plumes.

top speed, the male and female falcons dive and do figure eights and rolls.

Animal species differ in the amount of care they provide for their young. Most fishes, amphibians, and reptiles provide little or no parental care for their young. In contrast, most parent birds and mammals care for their young after hatching or birth. Not only do they feed and protect their young, but they also teach them survival skills, such as hunting.

Living in Groups

Although many animals are solitary and only rarely meet one of their own kind, other animals live in groups. Some fishes form schools, some insects live in large groups, and hoofed mammals, such as bison, often form herds. **Living in a group usually helps animals survive—group members protect each other and work together to find food.** Group members may help one another. If an elephant gets stuck in a mud hole, for example, other members of its herd will dig it out. When animals such as lions hunt in a group, they usually can kill larger prey than a single hunter can.

Safety in Groups Group living often protects animals against predators. Fishes that swim in schools are often safer than fishes that swim alone, because it is harder for predators to see and select an individual fish. In a herd, some animals may watch for danger while others feed. Furthermore, animals in a group sometimes cooperate in fighting off a predator. For example, North American musk oxen make a defensive circle against a predator, such as a wolf. Their young calves are sheltered in the middle of the circle while the adult musk oxen stand with their horns lowered, ready to charge. The predator often gives up rather than face a whole herd of angry musk oxen.

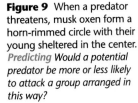

Figure 9 When a predator threatens, musk oxen form a horn-rimmed circle with their young sheltered in the center. *Predicting Would a potential predator be more or less likely to attack a group arranged in this way?*

TRY THIS

Worker Bees

In this activity, you will determine whether it is more productive to work alone or in a group, as honeybees do.

1. Make a paper chain by cutting paper strips for loops and gluing or taping the loops together. After 5 minutes, count the loops in the chain.
2. Now work in a small group to make a paper chain. Decide how to divide up the work before beginning. After 5 minutes, count the loops in the chain.

Calculating Find the difference between the number of loops in your individual and group chains. For Step 2, calculate the number of loops made per person by dividing the total number of loops by the number of people in your group. Was it more productive to work individually or as a group?

Living in Groups

TRY THIS

Skills Focus calculating
Materials 22 × 28 cm sheets of paper, scissors; paste, glue, or stapler; timer
Time 15 minutes
Tips Suggest students plan their work before beginning—both when they work as individuals and when they work in groups. When students work in groups, part of their planning should involve assigning tasks to each group member.
Expected Outcome Students should discover that by working cooperatively, they were able to make more paper-chain links per person.
Calculating The number of loops per individual and group will vary. Students should find it was more productive to work as a group, because group members can divide up the work so that no one person has to perform the whole task.
Extend Have students think about what kinds of tasks are probably performed more efficiently by one person than by a group. **cooperative learning**

Building Inquiry Skills: Applying Concepts

Have students describe other groups of animals not mentioned in the textbook and describe how living in a group benefits the individual. *(Flocks of birds—startle and confuse predators)* Prompt students to think about why humans live in groups. *(Mutual protection, sharing and division of labor)* **learning modality: visual**

Answers to Self-Assessment

☑ *Checkpoint*

A territory helps an animal survive because it provides unlimited access to its resources, which may include mates and food, as well as a safe place to raise young.

Caption Question

Figure 9 A predator would be less likely to attack a group arranged this way.

Ongoing Assessment

Writing Have students form groups to make a list of the advantages of aggression, establishing a territory, and living in groups. Be sure all individuals in the groups contribute.

Living in Groups, continued

Addressing Naive Conceptions

Students may confuse human societies with animal societies. Human societies may consist of associations of unrelated humans. Make sure students understand that all of the ants, termites, honeybees, naked mole rats, and pistol shrimp are close relatives, usually siblings. In addition, while roles in animal societies are usually rigid, roles in human societies are much more flexible. **learning modality: verbal**

Communication

Cultural Diversity

ACTIVITY

Explain that instinctive expressions such as smiling, screaming, and crying mean much the same thing in all human cultures. However, some expressions vary geographically. For example, in North America we shake our heads from side to side when we mean "no." In Greece, people nod their heads, and in Turkey they tilt their heads back and raise their eyebrows to convey the same idea. Cultures also differ in the way individuals greet each other. (Students have probably seen Russian political leaders kissing each other on the cheeks or Japanese political leaders bowing to each other.) Have pairs of students demonstrate examples of nonverbal communication, such as shaking hands, saluting, different forms of waving, and eye rolling, while the class describes the cultural meaning associated with the behavior. Have students from other cultures explain whether some of these gestures can convey different meanings in their culture. **learning modality: kinesthetic**

Animal Societies Some animals, including ants, termites, honeybees, naked mole rats, and pistol shrimp, live in groups called societies. A **society** is a group of closely related animals of the same species that work together for the benefit of the whole group. You can see an example in *Exploring a Honeybee Society.* Different members perform specific tasks, such as gathering food or caring for young. The behavior of the animals is instinctive and rigid—an animal in a society is "preprogrammed" to perform a specific job.

Communication

If you've ever seen one cat hissing at another, you've watched two animals communicating. Although animals don't use spoken or written language, they do communicate. Animals use sounds, body positions, movements, and scent to convey information to one another. Hissing cats, for example, are usually communicating aggression.

Animals communicate various kinds of information. Much animal communication is involved in courtship. Female crickets, for example, are attracted to the sound of a male's chirping. Other animal communication relates to defense and aggression. While attacking other animals or defending themselves, animals may growl, snarl, hiss, or assume positions that make them look larger—and thus more frightening—than they really are. Animals may also communicate warnings. When it sees a coyote or other predator approaching, a prairie dog makes a yipping sound that warns other prairie dogs to take cover in their burrows. This yipping sound is something like a dog barking—that's how prairie dogs got their name.

Animals also communicate information about food sources. One of the most complex systems of animal communication is used by honeybees to inform one another about the location of food—flower nectar and pollen. A worker bee that has found a new source of food will return to the hive and begin an excited "dance." The pattern of her movement communicates both the quality of the food and its distance and direction from the hive.

Figure 10 This lowland gorilla needs no words to say "Stay away!"

✓ *Checkpoint* What are four ways that animals communicate with one another?

EXPLORING a Honeybee Society

A honeybee hive usually consists of one queen bee, thousands of female worker bees, and a few hundred male drones.

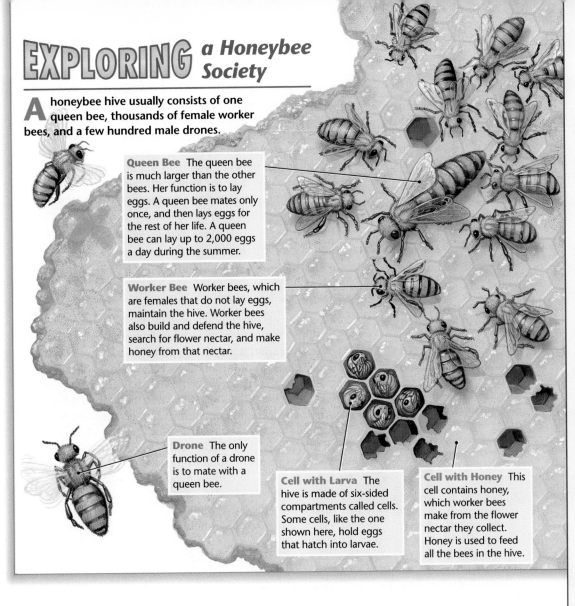

Queen Bee The queen bee is much larger than the other bees. Her function is to lay eggs. A queen bee mates only once, and then lays eggs for the rest of her life. A queen bee can lay up to 2,000 eggs a day during the summer.

Worker Bee Worker bees, which are females that do not lay eggs, maintain the hive. Worker bees also build and defend the hive, search for flower nectar, and make honey from that nectar.

Drone The only function of a drone is to mate with a queen bee.

Cell with Larva The hive is made of six-sided compartments called cells. Some cells, like the one shown here, hold eggs that hatch into larvae.

Cell with Honey This cell contains honey, which worker bees make from the flower nectar they collect. Honey is used to feed all the bees in the hive.

Behavior Cycles

Some animal behavior occurs in regular, predictable patterns. While blowflies, for example, search for food during the day, they are inactive at night. In contrast, field mice are active during the night and quiet by day. These daily behavior cycles of blowflies and mice are examples of **circadian rhythms** (sur KAY dee uhn rhythms), which are behavior cycles that occur over a period of approximately one day.

EXPLORING
a Honeybee Society

After students read the descriptions of the individuals in the honeybee society, ask: **Is any member of the honeybee society unimportant? Why?** *(None is unimportant. All members have their special tasks to perform.)* Invite a volunteer to list the three types of honeybees and their duties on the board. After reviewing the list, ask students why it is advantageous that there are more worker bees than other bees in the hive. *(Because worker bees have many different tasks to perform, such as caring for the hive, the queen, the larvae, and finding and making food. The queen and the drones each have only one task.)* **learning modality: logical/mathematical**

Behavior Cycles

Real-Life Learning

Explain to students that almost all animals, including humans, display obvious circadian rhythms. Ask students for examples of circadian rhythms in their own lives. *(Samples: Most people get sleepy after dark. People often get hungry at the same time each day.)* **learning modality: verbal**

Including All Students

To help students remember the definition of *circadian*, break the word into two parts: *circa/dian*. Explain that the prefix *circa-* means "approximately" and that *dian* comes from the Latin word for day, *dies*. **limited English proficiency**

Answers to Self-Assessment

☑ *Checkpoint*

Animals communicate using sound, body positions, movements, and scent.

Ongoing Assessment

Drawing Direct students to draw four pictures showing animals, including humans, communicating. *(Samples: A bear standing with its arms up in the air, a cat with the fur on its back standing straight up)*

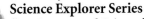 Students can save their drawings in their portfolios.

Behavior Cycles, continued

Including All Students

The shortened daylight hours of winter cause mild behavior problems for some people. Invite the students to discuss if they have more trouble waking up when it is still dark outside. Discuss ways of coping with the problem. **learning modality: verbal**

Migration

Social Studies
CONNECTION

Time 15 minutes

Students will use map skills to interpret a map. Review the functions of the map key and compass rose.

In Your Journal Students' journals should include the following answers:
1. Northern North America, central South America.
2. Approximately 10,000 km or 6,000 miles
3. Southward route over ocean, northward route over land.
4. The Mississippi River
Extend Ask students how one route south and another north might benefit the golden plovers. Stimulate discussion by pointing out that these migrations occur at different times of the year. *(Sample: Calmer weather conditions in the fall favor flying over the Atlantic. Spring conditions favor returning over land.)* **learning modality: visual**

Building Inquiry Skills: Comparing and Contrasting

Have students compare and contrast hibernation and migration as survival adaptations. *(Hibernation helps animals get through times of the year when there is insufficient food. Migration allows animals to move to areas with sufficient food.)* **learning modality: logical/ mathematical**

Social Studies
CONNECTION

Like geographers, biologists sometimes need to interpret maps. Examine the map below to see the migration pattern of the golden plover, a shorebird. The arrows on the map show the routes of the golden plover's migrations.

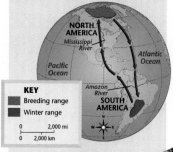

In Your Journal

Based on information on the map, write answers to the following questions.

1. On what continent does the golden plover spend its breeding season? Where does it spend the other seasons?

2. Use the scale to measure the approximate distance between the golden plover's two homes.

3. Compare the bird's southward route to its northward route. How do the routes differ?

4. What United States river does the golden plover follow when it heads northward?

Other behavior cycles are related to seasons. Some animals, such as woodchucks and chipmunks, are active during warm seasons, but hibernate during the winter. **Hibernation** is a state of greatly reduced body activity that occurs during the winter. During hibernation, all of an animal's body processes, such as breathing and heartbeat, slow down. Hibernating animals do not eat. Their bodies use stored fat to meet their reduced nutrition needs.

Behavior cycles usually help animals survive in some way. Hibernation not only helps animals live through severe cold, it also eliminates the need for feeding during a season when food is scarce. Animals that are active during the day can take advantage of sunlight, which makes food easy to see. On the other hand, animals that are active at night do not encounter predators that are active during the day.

☑ *Checkpoint* What happens to an animal during hibernation?

Migration

Another kind of behavior cycle involves movement from place to place. While many animals spend their lives in a single area, others migrate. **Migration** is the regular, periodic journey of an animal from one place to another and then back again. Some migrating animals travel thousands of kilometers. Arctic terns, for example, fly more than 17,000 kilometers between their summer homes in the Arctic Circle to their winter residence near the South Pole.

Animals usually migrate to an area that provides abundant food, or a favorable environment for reproduction, or both. Most migrations are related to the changing seasons and take place twice a year, in the spring and fall. American redstarts, insect-eating birds, spend the long days of summer in North America, where they mate and raise young. In the fall, however, days there grow shorter and cooler, and insects become scarce. The redstarts then migrate south to Central America, South America, and islands in the Caribbean Sea, where they can again find plentiful food.

Many other animals, such as salmon, migrate to the areas in which they reproduce. Adult salmon live in oceans. However, to mate and lay eggs, an adult salmon must migrate from the ocean to the same stream where it once hatched from an egg—sometimes more than 3,000 kilometers away. In her "home" stream, the female lays her eggs and the male fertilizes them. The young salmon that hatch from those eggs will eventually migrate back to the ocean, and the cycle will begin again.

While there is much yet to learn about how migrating animals find their way, scientists have discovered

---

Background

Facts and Figures There are several metabolic changes that resemble hibernation. These changes help animals survive periods of reduced food resources or environmental stress. Chickadees rely on fat stores they accumulate during the day to provide energy to keep their bodies at a constant temperature through the night. The chickadees go into torpor, which is a state in which body temperature becomes lower and metabolic activity decreases. If they did not do this, they would burn more fat during the night than they had when they went to roost in the evening.

Some amphibians survive heat and drought by becoming dormant during the summer. This behavior is called *estivation*.

that animals use sight, taste, and other senses, including some that humans do not have. Some birds and sea turtles, for example, have a magnetic sense that acts something like a compass needle. Migrating birds also seem to navigate by using the positions of the sun, moon, and stars, as human sailors have always done. Salmon use scent and taste to locate the streams where they were born.

 INTEGRATING ENVIRONMENTAL SCIENCE Human activities sometimes interfere with animal migration. For example, when fuel and water pipelines are built above ground, migrating animals cannot easily cross over them. Dams across streams and rivers can block the path of fish migration. Bright city lights can confuse birds that migrate at night. Each year, millions of birds strike skyscraper windows and die during migration. But humans are learning how to help migrating animals. During the spring migration of 1998, the lights in more than 80 skyscrapers in Toronto, Ontario, were turned off at night to make a safer path for the birds. The lights of the Empire State Building in New York City also darken at night during migration.

Figure 11 This caribou herd is migrating across Alaska on the same path its ancestors used for thousands of years. Recently, human construction and oil drilling have begun to threaten this migration path. Both native people, who rely on the caribou for food, and corporations are working to find a way to save the path.

Section 2 Review

1. Define courtship behavior and describe an example.
2. Identify two ways in which animals benefit from living in groups.
3. What are the two major advantages that animals gain by migrating?
4. **Thinking Critically** **Applying Concepts** A mockingbird sings from a tree on the left side of the schoolyard. Soon it flies to the pine tree on the right side of the schoolyard and sings again. When another mockingbird flies into the schoolyard, the first mockingbird flies at it and tries to peck it. Explain what is probably happening.

Science at Home

With a family member, spend some time making detailed observations of the behavior of an animal—a pet, an insect, a bird, or another animal. Watch the animal for signs of aggressive behavior or other communication. Try to figure out why the animal is behaving aggressively or what it is trying to communicate.

Chapter 5 **B ◆ 167**

 Integrating Environmental Science

Explain that migrating animals depend on different habitats at different times of the year. Protecting animals in one place may not prevent species decline. For example, the scarlet tanager and other North American songbirds winter in Central America. Ask the class to brainstorm steps that might help protect these birds. (*International agreements to preserve and restore habitat*) Ask students if they think a migratory animal can be protected if scientists do not know about its full life cycle. (*no*) **learning modality: verbal**

3 Assess

Section 2 Review Answers

1. Courtship behavior is behavior in which males and females of the same species prepare for mating. Example: peacocks displaying tail feathers.
2. Group members protect each other, work together, and divide labor.
3. Migrating animals can move to areas that provide food or favorable environments for reproduction.
4. The first mockingbird is establishing the boundaries of its territory. When it attacks the second mockingbird, it is defending this territory.

Science at Home

Materials *notebook or sketch pad*
Tips Encourage students to observe active animals in a location where they are likely to interact with other animals.

Answers to Self-Assessment

☑ *Checkpoint*
During hibernation, all body activities, including breathing and heart-beat, slow down. Animals use stored body fat for nutrition.

Performance Assessment

Organizing Information Have students list at least five different behaviors they have observed among zoo animals or pets, classify each according to the divisions in this section, and state the survival value of each behavior.

One For All

Preparing for Inquiry

Key Concept In ant colonies, individual members perform different tasks.

Skills Objective Students will be able to:

◆ observe ants perform several different tasks;

◆ infer the division of labor in an ant colony.

Time 45 minutes

Advanced Planning CAUTION: *Avoid fire ants as they are extremely aggressive. To check if a colony contains fire ants, tap on the mound with a small straw or twig. If the ants immediately swarm in large numbers, they are probably fire ants.*

Have students bring a glass jar to class a few days in advance. Large condiment jars would work well. Ants can be collected from a colony in nature. Collect sufficient soil from the area close to the colony for students to use in their jars. Try to collect ants of various sizes from the colony. Dig up only a small part of the colony. Place the container with the ants you have collected in the refrigerator to slow the ants down. Keep ants chilled before adding to students' jars. Place 20-30 ants directly into students' jars so that students do not handle the ants. When finished, return all the ants to the refrigerator and then return them to their original colony.

Alternative Materials Nylon screen can be substituted for the wire screen as it is easier to cut with scissors. You may prefer to purchase an "ant farm" from a scientific supply house.

Guiding Inquiry

Invitation Have students think about the society in which they live, especially how tasks are divided so that some grow food, some build houses, and so on. Have students predict how these tasks are accomplished in an ant society.

Introducing the Procedure

◆ Tell students that they may not observe some tasks. For example there may be no eggs, larvae, or pupae for adult ants to care for.

◆ Students should think about how they will describe various behaviors. For example, ants may carry dirt grains (from digging), carry food, or interact with each other. Students should observe the tasks that ants of different sizes perform.

◆ Students should look for tunnels, for food storage locations, and for a refuse pile in the jar.

ONE FOR ALL

Have you ever stopped to watch a group of busy ants? In this lab, you will find out what goes on in an ant colony.

Problem

How does an ant society show organization and cooperative behavior?

Skills Focus

observing, inferring, posing questions

Materials

large glass jar	sandy soil	shallow pan
water	wire screen	sponge
20–30 ants	hand lens	bread crumbs
sugar	black paper	tape
glass-marking pencil		forceps
large, thick rubber band		

Procedure

1. Read over the entire lab to preview the kinds of observations you will be making. Copy the data table into your notebook. You may also want to leave space for sketches.

2. Mark the outside of a large jar with four evenly spaced vertical lines, as shown in the photograph on the next page. Label the sections with the letters A, B, C, and D. You can use these labels to identify the sections of soil on and below the surface.

3. Fill the jar about three-fourths full with soil. Place the jar in a shallow pan of water to prevent any ants from escaping. Place a wet sponge on the surface of the soil as a water source for the ants.

4. Observe the condition of the soil, both on the surface and along the sides of the jar. Record your observations.

5. Add the ants to the jar. Immediately cover the jar with the wire screen, using the rubber band to hold the screen firmly in place.

6. Observe the ants for at least 10 minutes. Look for differences in the appearance of adult ants, and look for eggs, larvae, and pupae. Examine both individual behavior and interactions between the ants.

7. Remove the screen cover, and add small amounts of bread crumbs and sugar to the soil surface. Close the cover. Observe the ants for at least 10 more minutes.

8. Create dark conditions for the ants by covering the jar with black paper above the water line. Remove the paper only when you are making your observations.

9. Observe the ant colony every day for two weeks. Remove the dark paper, and make and record your observations. Look at the soil as well as the ants, and always examine the food. If any food has started to mold, use forceps to remove it. Place the moldy food in a plastic bag, seal the bag, and throw it away. Add more food as necessary, and keep the sponge moist. When you finish your observations, replace the dark paper.

10. At the end of the lab, follow your teacher's directions for returning the ants.

Safety

Do not use fire ants or other ants that aggressively bite or sting. Caution students not to touch ants. Tell them to be very careful when carrying glass jars around the room.

Program Resources

◆ **Teaching Resources** Real-World Lab blackline masters, pp. 151-153

DATA TABLE

Date	Section A	Section B	Section C	Section D

Analyze and Conclude

1. Describe the various types of ants you observed. What differences, if any, did you observe in their behavior? What evidence did you observe that different kinds of ants perform different tasks?
2. How do the different behaviors you observed contribute to the survival of the colony?
3. How did the soil change over the period of your observations? What caused those changes? How do you know?
4. **Apply** What kinds of environmental conditions do you think ant colonies need to thrive outdoors? Use the evidence obtained in this lab to support your answer.

Design an Experiment

Design an experiment to investigate how an ant colony responds when there is a change in the ants' environment, such as the introduction of a new type of food. Obtain your teacher's approval before carrying out your experiment.

Troubleshooting the Experiment
◆ Students should try not to touch the ants.

Expected Outcome
◆ Ants will excavate tunnels and perform various tasks. Some will carry refuse to a pile (midden). Other ants will place dead ants and dirt on this pile. Ants will retrieve food and place it in a storage tunnel. If eggs, larvae, and pupae are present, they will be stored in an underground location.
◆ The main task for students will be to observe and describe the behaviors. Make sure that students infer how the behavior contributes to the colony's survival.

Analyze and Conclude
1. Answers will vary. Sample: Some ants carried food to the food store, dug tunnels, and took items to the refuse pile.
2. Answers will vary depending on the behavior observed. The behaviors result in a home being built, food stored, trash removed, offspring cared for, and protection set up.
3. Tunnels were dug through the soil over the course of the experiment. Ants must have caused these changes since no other organisms were present.
4. Sample: Ants require soil in which they can dig and a source of food and water.

Extending Inquiry
Design an Experiment Sample: Students could decide to introduce a new kind of food or to present it in a different way.

Sample Data Table

Date	Section A	Section B	Section C	Section D
9/12 Start	20 ants on surface moving about	3 ants on surface moving about	4 ants on surface moving about rapidly	No ants visible
9/12 Food added	15 ants on surface, 3 move food	7 ants on surface moving about	3 ants on surface	2 ants on surface
9/13	5 ants move in tunnel. 8 surface ants collect food	3 ants in room in tunnel with food	No tunnel. 3 large ants sit at surface	Refuse pile on surface. 2 ants add dirt to pile

SECTION 3 The Chemistry of Communication

Objective

After completing the lesson, students will be able to

◆ describe how animals use pheromones to communicate.

Key Terms pheromone, bioluminescence

1 Engage/Explore

Activating Prior Knowledge

Place a strong-but pleasant-smelling object somewhere in the classroom. Tell students you have hidden an object in the room and they are to find it by some sense other than sight. After they have located the object, ask them what sense they used. Tell them that many animals use scent as a means of communication.

•••••• DISCOVER ••••••

Skills Focus observing
Materials *pairs of small, foil-covered containers holding a variety of nontoxic substances with distinctive scents*
Time 20 minutes
Tips Emphasize that students should not sniff the materials directly, and demonstrate the technique for wafting fumes under the nose. **CAUTION:** *Strong scents are known to trigger migraine headaches and asthma attacks.* Excuse students with known reactions to smells from this activity or ask them to act as observers. Kitchen spices are the safest and easiest to use.
Expected Outcome Students should eventually locate the matching scents.
Think It Over Depending on the materials, it should be fairly easy for students to find the matching scents. Identifying and detecting scents helps an animal to locate food, to find mates, and to identify other individuals or their territories.

SECTION 3 The Chemistry of Communication

⬭ DISCOVER ••••••••••••••••••••••••••••ACTIVITY••••

Can You Match the Scents?

1. From your teacher, obtain a container covered with aluminum foil with holes punched in it.

2. Carefully sniff the contents of the container. **CAUTION:** *Never sniff an unknown substance directly. When testing an odor, use a waving motion with your hand to direct the vapor toward your nose.*

3. One other person in your class has a container with the same substance. Use your sense of smell to find the container whose scent matches the one in your container.

Think It Over
Observing How easy was it for you and your classmates to match scents? What advantage might identifying or detecting scents have to an animal?

GUIDE FOR READING

◆ **How do animals use pheromones to communicate?**

Reading Tip As you read, make a list of main ideas and supporting details about pheromones and bioluminescence.

Figure 12 These ants are finding their way to the sugar by following a pheromone trail. The first ant to find the sugar began the trail, and each ant adds to its strength.

Oh no—ants have gotten into the sugar! As you watch in dismay, a stream of ants moves along the kitchen counter, heading right for the sugar bowl. Using their sense of smell, the ants follow a chemical trail that was first laid down by the ant that discovered the sugar. Each ant contributes to the trail by depositing a tiny droplet of scent onto the counter. If you watch carefully, you may see the ants doing this. The droplet quickly evaporates, making an invisible cloud of scent that hangs in the air above the path of the ants.

All the ants running to and from the sugar bowl are enveloped in an ant-sized tunnel of scent. It's like an invisible ant highway. The ants hold their antennae forward and use them to sniff their way to the sugar bowl. Then they turn around and follow the same chemical signal back to their nest.

Pheromones

The scent tunnel that leads ants to the sugar bowl is made of pheromones. A **pheromone** (FER uh mohn) is a chemical released by one animal that affects the behavior of another

---

READING STRATEGIES

Reading Tip Before students make their lists, have volunteers define *main ideas* and *supporting details.* *(Main ideas are important points the author wants to make about a topic; supporting details are facts that support each main idea.)* Provide an example from an earlier section, such as *Some animals behave by instinct.* (main idea) *Earthworms crawl away from bright light.* (supporting detail)

Program Resources

◆ **Teaching Resources** 5-3 Lesson Plan, p. 145; 5-3 Section Summary, p. 146

Media and Technology

 Audiotapes English-Spanish Summary 5-3

animal of the same species. **Animals communicate with pheromones to establish territories, locate food, attract mates, and distinguish members of their own group from members of other groups.** Animals release these very powerful chemicals only in tiny quantities.

Why Pheromones Are Specific

Most pheromones are chemical compounds that are made up of long chains of atoms. Each pheromone has a unique combination of atoms in it. Because the atoms join together in specific ways, each pheromone has a different chemical shape. The different shapes of pheromones make them highly specific—when an animal releases a pheromone, it usually only causes a response in other animals of the same species. Just as the key to your front door will not work in the lock of your neighbor's door, the pheromones released by a luna moth will not trigger a response in a gypsy moth.

Pheromones and Behavior

Pheromones enable many animals to recognize group members and establish territories. Every ant colony, for example, has its own pheromones that identify colony members. If an ant wanders into a colony other than its own, the intruder ant's pheromones will be recognized as foreign. The intruder will be attacked and killed. Many mammals mark their territories with pheromones in urine or sprays. Male house cats often spray the trees in their yards with a musky scent containing pheromones. The pheromones advertise the presence of that male cat to other cats in the neighborhood.

Pheromones play an important role in mating and reproduction. A female silkworm moth, for example, releases a pheromone when she is ready to mate. When the sense organs on a male's antennae pick up the scent of the pheromone, the male flies toward the scent to mate with the female.

☑ *Checkpoint* *How do pheromones enable ants to identify members of another ant colony?*

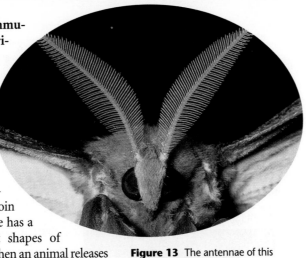

Figure 13 The antennae of this male Atlas silkworm moth allow him to find females that are ready to mate. Sense organs on the antennae pick up the female pheromone scent. The male moth then follows the scent to the female. *Predicting How might injured antennae affect a male moth's ability to find a mate?*

Answers to Self-Assessment

Caption Question

Figure 13 Injured antennae might be less sensitive to pheromones and make it difficult for the male to find a mate.

☑ *Checkpoint*

The ants in each colony have a unique pheromone. When ants sense another ant's unfamiliar pheromone, they know the ant is foreign.

---

2 Facilitate

Pheromones

Including All Students

The key terms in this section are *pheromone* and *bioluminescence*. Explain to students that the term *bioluminescence* comes from the Greek root *bios*, meaning "life," and the Latin root *lumen*, meaning "light." Challenge students to think of other words using those roots. (*Samples: biology, illuminate*) Allow students to use a dictionary to determine how the word pheromone was formed. (*From combining the Greek word* pherein, *"to bear" combined with* hormone) **limited English proficiency**

Building Inquiry Skills: Inferring

Obtain a number of index cards equal to half the number of students in class. Cut each card in two parts following a random, zigzag line. Place all the pieces in a paper sack and shuffle them. Have students draw one piece. After all pieces are drawn, have the students find the matching pieces. Ask: **How does this model the behavior of pheromones?** (*Pheromones are chemical compounds that have unique shapes that only match the proper receptors.*) **learning modality: kinesthetic**

Ongoing Assessment

Oral Presentation Have students describe two situations in which animals use pheromones. (*Samples: A male cat may mark his territory by spraying a scent containing pheromones. An ant colony can detect an intruder ant because the intruder has different pheromones.*)

Pheromones, continued

Integrating Environmental Science

Discuss with students the advantage of pheromone-based pest traps. *(They do not poison beneficial animals)* **learning modality: verbal**

Communicating with Light

Building Inquiry Skills: Inferring

Have groups devise a code using flashlights. Allow the groups to attempt to communicate with each other across the room. Have a spokesperson report to the class on their success. **cooperative learning**

ACTIVITY

3 Assess

Section 3 Review Answers

1. Establish territories (male cat), attract mates (silkworm moths), distinguish their own group (ants), locate food (ants following trail)
2. Pheromones are used to bait traps.
3. Their readiness to mate
4. The ants will be unable to follow the scent trail.

Check Your Progress

CHAPTER PROJECT 5

Review students' progress. Help students modify their training plans if they are having problems. If students cannot bring their animals into the classroom, discuss alternative presentations.

Performance Assessment

Writing Have students write fictional accounts of a day in the life of an animal. Accounts should include at least one of the four ways animals communicate with pheromones. Students can save their accounts in their portfolios.

Pheromones and Pest Control Some pheromones can be

INTEGRATING ENVIRONMENTAL SCIENCE

made in laboratories and then used to attract and eliminate pest insects. Manufactured pheromones lure insects into traps. In some cases, the insects are killed in the traps. In some other cases, male insects that collect in these traps can be exposed to X-rays that kill their sperm cells. Even though these altered males will mate with females after they are released, no offspring will result. The population of the insects will eventually decrease. A common pheromone trap lures Japanese beetles, which damage rosebushes. They are lured into a bag from which they can't escape. Then they can be killed or relocated.

Figure 14 This flashlight fish uses a bioluminescent organ beneath its eye to see. The organ is also used to attract prey, to confuse predators, and to communicate with other flashlight fish.

Communicating with Light

Pheromones are only one form of chemical communication used by animals. Some animals, such as fireflies and some species of fish, use light to communicate. **Bioluminescence** (by oh loo muh NEHS uhns) is the production of light by a living organism. That light is generated by chemical reactions that take place in the organism's cells.

On a warm summer night, when you see a meadow lit up with fireflies, you are actually watching fireflies using bioluminescence in courtship. A male firefly sends a blinking signal to female fireflies in the grass below. Each species of firefly has a distinctive signal. When an interested female sees the signal of a male of her species, she flashes a reply. If the male sees her signal, he will land near her and they may mate.

Section 3 Review

1. List three things that animals communicate with pheromones. Using a specific animal, give an example of each type of communication.
2. How are pheromones used to control insect pests?
3. What do fireflies communicate with their bioluminescence?
4. **Thinking Critically** **Predicting** While a stream of ants is traveling to and from the sugar bowl, you take a sponge and wash away a six-inch section of their path. Predict how the ants will respond.

Check Your Progress

CHAPTER PROJECT 5

At this point, you should be continuing with your training plan and monitoring your animal's progress. Be sure to keep good records of your animal's daily progress. Make modifications to your plan now if they are needed. Also begin to think about how you will present your results to the class. *(Hint:* You may want to make drawings or take photos of your animal in action to use in your presentation.)

Program Resources

◆ **Teaching Resources** 5-3 Review and Reinforce, p. 147; 5-3 Enrich, p. 148
  Science Explorer Series *"Environmental Science,"* Chapter 2

Media and Technology

Interactive Student Tutorial CD-ROM B-5

SECTION 1 — Why Do Animals Behave as They Do?

Key Ideas
◆ Most behaviors help an animal survive and reproduce. Examples include behaviors involved in obtaining food, avoiding predators, and finding a mate.
◆ An instinct is an inborn behavior pattern that the animal performs correctly the first time. Most behaviors of invertebrates are instinctive.
◆ Learning changes an animal's behavior as a result of experience. Some ways in which animals learn include conditioning, trial-and-error learning, and insight learning.
◆ Imprinting, in which very young animals learn to follow the first moving object they see, involves both instinct and learning.

Key Terms
behavior
response
learning
trial-and-error learning
artificial intelligence

stimulus
instinct
conditioning
insight learning
imprinting

SECTION 2 — Patterns of Behavior

Key Ideas
◆ Animals use aggression to compete for limited resources, such as food or shelter.
◆ Many animals establish territories from which they exclude other members of their species.
◆ Courtship behavior ensures that males and females of the same species recognize one another so that they can reproduce.
◆ There is usually some survival advantage to living in a group, such as cooperation in getting food and protection from danger.
◆ Animals use sounds, scents, body positions, and movements to communicate.
◆ Some animal behaviors occur in regular patterns. Circadian rhythms are one-day behavior cycles. Hibernation is a period of inactivity during winter.
◆ Some animals migrate to places where they can more easily find food, reproduce, or both.

Key Terms
aggression
courtship behavior
circadian rhythm
migration

territory
society
hibernation

SECTION 3 — The Chemistry of Communication

INTEGRATING **CHEMISTRY**

Key Ideas
◆ Pheromones are chemicals that animals use to establish a territory, locate food, attract a mate, and identify group members.
◆ Male fireflies use bioluminescence, or the production of light by a living organism, to attract mates.

Key Terms
pheromone

bioluminescence

USING THE INTERNET
www.science-explorer.phschool.com

Chapter 5 **B ◆ 173**

C H A P T E R **5** R E V I E W

Reviewing Content:
Multiple Choice

1. b 2. a 3. d 4. c 5. c

True or False

6. instinctive 7. conditioning 8. true
9. migration 10. true

Checking Concepts

11. Imprinting involves a combination of instinct and learning because the young animal has an instinct to follow a moving object, but it must learn from experience what object to follow.
12. You are exhibiting aggression; the dog is showing submission.
13. Courtship often occurs within an animal's territory. In some species, a male cannot mate unless he has established a territory.
14. No, because this movement is a one-time event, rather than a cyclical, back-and-forth movement.
15. The pheromones of each species have a unique chemical structure, so they usually only cause a response in animals of the same species.
16. Students' interviews should include details of the structure of the society and roles of the different members. These details should parallel the structure and roles of the honeybee society.

Thinking Visually

17. **a.** trial and error **b.** insight
c. teaching a dog to sit

Applying Skills

18. The bee stung the toad, and the toad spat it out in an effort to get rid of it.
19. The toad will probably not try to catch the insect, because the toad will associate the bee with the sting.
20. Conditioning, because the toad has learned to connect a stimulus, the bee, with a bad event, being stung.

Thinking Critically

21. Students' answers should involve genuine insight learning. Sample: I learned how to operate a friend's VCR because it was similar to the one my family has.
22. The fireflies probably would not be able to reproduce, because they depend

Reviewing Content

 For more review of key concepts, see the Interactive Student Tutorial CD-ROM.

Multiple Choice
Choose the letter of the best answer.

1. The scent of a female moth causes a male to fly toward her. The scent is an example of
   a. a response. **b.** a stimulus.
   c. aggression. **d.** insight learning.
2. If you could play the saxophone by instinct, you would
   a. play well the first time you tried.
   b. need someone to teach you.
   c. have to practice frequently.
   d. know how to play other instruments.
3. When a male and female falcon perform an acrobatic flight display with each other, they are exhibiting
   a. learning. **b.** imprinting.
   c. migration. **d.** courtship behavior.
4. When an American redstart travels from its winter home in South America to its nesting area in New York, this is called
   a. learning. **b.** conditioning.
   c. migration. **d.** bioluminescence.
5. A trap contains strong-smelling chemicals. Insects fly into the trap because of
   a. conditioning. **b.** insight learning.
   c. pheromones. **d.** bioluminescence.

True or False
If the statement is true, write true. If it is false, change the underlined word or words to make the statement true.

6. A spider building a web exhibits <u>learned</u> behavior.
7. Every day after school, you take your dog for a walk. Lately, he greets your arrival with his leash in his mouth. Your dog's behavior is an example of <u>instinct</u>.
8. A <u>territory</u> is an area that an animal will fight to defend.
9. When salmon return to freshwater streams to reproduce, their behavior is an example of <u>circadian rhythm</u>.
10. The production of light by an organism is called <u>bioluminescence</u>.

Checking Concepts

11. Explain how both instinct and learning are involved in imprinting.
12. Your German shepherd puppy has just shredded your favorite pair of sneakers. When you loudly scold him, he rolls over on his back. What kind of behavior are you exhibiting to the dog? What is the meaning of his response?
13. Explain how courtship and territorial behavior are related.
14. Because a highway has been constructed through a forest, many of the animals that once lived there have had to move to a different wooded area. Is their move an example of migration? Explain.
15. How does a pheromone's structure account for the fact that it usually affects the behavior of only one species?
16. **Writing to Learn** After landing on a distant planet, you discover creatures who look something like humans but whose society is organized like that of honey-bees. Write an interview with one creature, who explains the structure of the society and the roles of different members.

Thinking Visually

17. **Concept Map** Copy the concept map below onto a separate sheet of paper. Then complete the map. (For more on concept maps, see the Skills Handbook.)

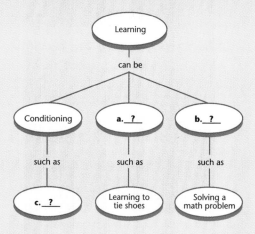

on visual cues—light flashes—to indicate their readiness and whereabouts for mating.
23. A racehorse's ability to win races is based on a combination of the traits it inherits, such as strong limbs and lungs, and the training it receives. It may learn through conditioning to associate the pleasant event of the race with a stimulus such as a special treat. It may learn the stages of a successful race through trial and error.

24. Answers may vary. Sample: Every time the dog jumps on the sofa, the owner could move it off the sofa and say "No" in a firm voice. That way, the dog would learn by conditioning to associate the stimulus of jumping on the sofa with the negative outcome of its owner's disapproval.

Applying Skills

The toad in the pictures below caught a bee and then spit it out. Use the pictures to answer Questions 18–20.

18. Inferring Explain why the toad probably behaved as it did in picture B.

19. Predicting If another bee flies by, how will the toad probably behave? Give a reason to support your prediction.

20. Classifying What type of learning will probably result from the toad's experience? Explain.

Thinking Critically

21. Applying Concepts Give an example of something you have learned by insight learning. Explain how you used past knowledge and experience in learning it.

22. Predicting Suppose a disease blinded a population of fireflies. How might the reproduction rate be affected? Explain.

23. Applying Concepts Explain how a racehorse's ability to win races is a combination of inherited and learned characteristics.

24. Problem Solving A dog keeps jumping onto a sofa. Describe a procedure that the owner might use to train the dog not to do this. The procedure must not involve any pain or harm to the dog.

Performance Assessment

CHAPTER PROJECT 5 — Wrap Up

Presenting Your Project Now is your chance to explain—or demonstrate—what your trained animal can do and to describe your training plan. Obtain your teacher's permission before bringing an animal to class. If you cannot bring in the animal, you can show photographs or illustrations of the animal's training. Be sure to discuss any surprises or setbacks you experienced.

Reflect and Record In your journal, describe your success in training your animal. What did you discover about the animal's learning process? How could you have improved your training plan? What questions do you still have about your animal's behavior?

Getting Involved

In Your Community Contact someone in your community who has experience training dogs, such as a trainer who runs a dog-obedience school or an experienced dog owner. Make an appointment to interview the person about dog-training methods. Before you go to the interview, write down a few of your questions. During the interview, discuss which training methods work well and which do not. Use what you have learned to prepare an illustrated dog-training manual.

Program Resources

- ◆ **Teaching Resources** Chapter 5 Project Teacher's Notes, pp. 130–131; Chapter 5 Project Overview and Worksheets, pp. 132–134; Chapter 5 Project Scoring Rubric, p. 135
- ◆ **Inquiry Skills Handbook** Provides teaching and review of all inquiry skills

Performance Assessment

CHAPTER PROJECT 5 — Wrap Up

Presenting Your Project Encourage each student to demonstrate how well his or her animal learned its trick. Students should explain how they trained their animals. Encourage students to use vocabulary from the text.

Reflect and Record It is likely that some, perhaps many, students will have been unable to train their animals. It is important that every student who made an honest attempt feels successful. Whether the animal was trained or not, students can still write about their experiences and think about ways of improving training.

Getting Involved

In Your Community You may wish to develop a list of willing dog trainers or owners for students to contact for interviews. You could also invite an expert to come to the classroom, so that students can ask their questions there. Sample questions students might have: I could not train my dog to roll over. How do you train dogs to do that? or, I used dog treats to train my dog to fetch. Now he won't fetch unless I give him a dog treat first. How can I train him to fetch without a dog treat?

The Secret of Silk

This interdisciplinary feature presents the central theme of silk by connecting four different disciplines: science, social studies, mathematics, and language arts. The four explorations are designed to capture students' interest and help them see how the content they are studying in science relates to other school subjects and to real-world events. The unit is particularly suitable for team teaching.

1 Engage/Explore

Activating Prior Knowledge

Help students recall what they learned in Chapter 2, Section 3, Insects, by asking questions such as: **What is the name of the process by which an insect changes in form during its life cycle?** *(metamorphosis)* and **In which stage of metamorphosis does an insect look most like a worm?** *(larval stage)* Then ask: **What do you know about silkworms?** *(Accept all responses without comment at this time.)*

Introducing the Unit

If possible, bring an item made of silk to show the class. You may not want students to touch the item as silk is easy to damage. If an item is not available, ask students who have seen items made of silk to describe how they look and feel. Point out that insects make silk thread that is woven into silk cloth. Ask: **What is a product we eat that insects make?** *(honey)*

Have students name some products that they think are made of silk *(Record students' responses on the board.)*

The Secret of Silk

What animal—

was a secret for thousands of years?

was smuggled across mountains in a hollow cane?

is good to eat, especially stir-fried with garlic and ginger?

is not really what its name says it is?

I f you guessed that this amazing animal is the silkworm, you are right. The silk thread that this caterpillar spins is woven into silk cloth. For at least 4,000 years people have treasured silk.

Chinese legends say that in 2640 B.C., a Chinese empress accidentally dropped a silkworm cocoon in warm water and watched the thread unravel. She had discovered silk. But for thousands of years, the Chinese people kept the work of silkworms a secret. Death was the penalty for telling the secret.

Then, it is said, in A.D. 552, two travelers from Persia visited China and returned to the West carrying silkworm eggs hidden in their hollow canes. Ever since then, the world has enjoyed the beauty of silk—its warmth, strength, softness, and shimmer.

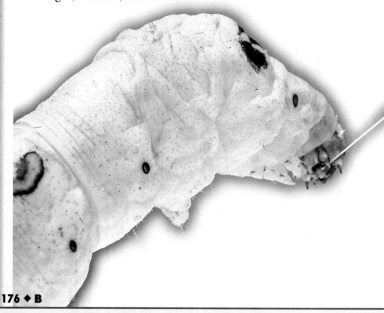

176 ◆ B

Program Resources

◆ **Teaching Resources** Interdisciplinary Explorations, Science, pp. 154–155; Social Studies, pp. 159–162; Mathematics, pp. 156–158; Language Arts, pp. 163–165

Metamorphosis of the Silkworm

The silkworm is not really a worm; it's the larva of an insect—a moth named *Bombyx mori*. In its entire feeding period, this larva consumes about 20 times its own weight in mulberry leaves. The silkworm undergoes complete metamorphosis during its life.

① The adult female moth lays 300 to 500 eggs, each the size of a pinhead. After about ten days at 27°C, the larvae—which people call silkworms—hatch from the eggs and begin to eat. Mulberry leaves are the insects' source of food.

② For the next 40 to 45 days, the larvae consume great quantities of mulberry leaves. The silkworms molt each time their exoskeletons become too tight. After the last molting and feeding stage, the silkworms begin to build their cocoons.

③ To spin its cocoon, each silkworm produces two single strands from its two silk glands. Another pair of glands produces a sticky substance that binds the two strands together. The silkworm pushes this single strand out through a small tube in its head. Once in the air, the strand hardens and the silkworm winds the strand around itself in many layers to make a thick cocoon. The single silk strand may be as long as 900 meters—more than two laps around an Olympic track.

④ After 14 to 18 days, the adult moths emerge from the cocoons. The new moth does not eat or fly. It mates, the female lays eggs, and 2 to 3 days later both the male and female die.

Science Activity

Examine a silkworm cocoon. After softening the cocoon in water, find the end of the strand of silk. Pull this strand, wind it onto an index card, and measure its length.

With a partner, design an experiment to compare the strength of the silk thread you just collected to that of cotton and/or nylon thread of the same weight or thickness.

◆ Develop a hypothesis about the strength of the threads.

◆ Decide on the setup you will use to test the threads.

◆ Check your safety plan with your teacher. ⚠

B ◆ 177

◆ Silkworm cocoons can be obtained from biological supply companies.
◆ Have students review what they recall about the larval stage of insects. Summarize students' responses on the board.
◆ Ask students: **What is complete metamorphosis?** *(a type of metamorphosis with four stages: egg, larva, pupa, and adult)* **What is the other pattern of metamorphosis? How is it different from complete metamorphosis?** *(Gradual metamorphosis; an egg hatches into a nymph, which can look like an adult insect.)*
◆ Ask a volunteer to review what an exoskeleton is and how larvae molt.
◆ To extend this exploration, invite an entomologist to tell the class more about silkworms. If possible, ask the entomologist to bring some silkworms to show the class.

Science Activity

Ask: **How will you measure the length?** *(Measure the width of the card and multiply by 2. Multiply the answer by the number of times you wind the strand around the card.)*

3 Assess

Activity Assessment

Evaluate students' experiment setups. Students should recognize that they will need a very accurate scale to measure the weight of the threads correctly. For students who are choosing to compare threads by width instead of weight, check that they describe a scientific method for measuring the width of the threads. Make sure students start with small weights so their planned experiments will not immediately fail by accidentally breaking all the threads they test.

Program Resources

◆ **Teaching Resources** The following worksheets correlate with this page: Ways the Chinese Use Insects, page 154; and Spider Silk, page 155.

2 Facilitate

- Show students a map of the United States and Canada. Challenge students to find two cities that are about 6,400 kilometers apart. Ask: **Start in Miami, Florida, and travel northwest. What city is about 6,400 kilometers from Miami?** (*Answers may vary; sample: Prince Rupert, British Columbia, Canada*) Help students appreciate how formidable a journey this would be traveling with pack animals such as camels, horses, or yaks.

- Have students brainstorm a list of reasons why traveling the Silk Road might be treacherous. Remind students that the travelers were carrying valuable wares. Prompt students by asking: **What dangers would merchants face from other people?**

- Ask: **Why did the Chinese "of course" keep the secret of the silkworm?** (*They were making a lot of money selling silk to Rome.*) Ask: **Do we keep similar secrets today?** (*Answers may vary. Lead students to recognize that patented formulas such as the formulas for soft drinks are similar to the secret of the silkworm.*)

- Invite some students to read the descriptions corresponding to the numbers on the map while other students trace the route with their fingers.

- Students will need help pronouncing many of the place names.

The Silk Road

Long before the rest of the world learned how silk was made, the Chinese were trading this treasured fabric with people west of China. Merchants who bought and sold silk traveled along a system of hazardous routes that came to be known as the Silk Road. The Silk Road stretched 6,400 kilometers from Ch'ang-an in China to the Mediterranean Sea. Silk, furs, and spices traveled west toward Rome along the road. Gold, wool, glass, grapes, garlic, and walnuts moved east toward China.

Travel along the Silk Road was treacherous and difficult. For safety, traders traveled in caravans of many people and animals. Some kinds of pack animals were better equipped to handle certain parts of the journey than others. Camels, for instance, were well suited to the desert; they could store large amounts of water and withstand most sandstorms. Yaks were often used in the high mountains.

The entire journey along the Silk Road could take years. Many people and animals died along the way. Very few individuals or caravans traveled the length of the Silk Road.

Silk fabric became highly prized in Rome. In fact, it was said that the first silk products to reach Rome after 50 B.C. were worth their weight in gold. The Chinese, of course, kept the secret of the silkworm and controlled silk production. They were pleased that the Romans thought that silk grew on trees. It was not until about A.D. 550 that the Roman Empire learned the secret of silk.

In time, silk production spread around the world. The Silk Road, though, opened forever the exchange of goods and ideas between China and the West.

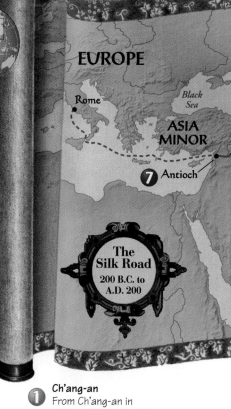

EUROPE

Rome

Black Sea

ASIA MINOR

7 Antioch

The Silk Road 200 B.C. to A.D. 200

1 Ch'ang-an
From Ch'ang-an in northern China, the Silk Road headed west along a corridor between the Nan Shan Mountains and the Gobi Desert.

2 Dunhuang
At Dunhuang, in an oasis, or fertile green area, of the Gobi Desert, caravans took on rested pack animals. Beyond Dunhuang, the silk route split.

3 Takla Makan Desert
The desert is well named— Takla Makan means "Go in and you won't come out!" Most travelers avoided the scorching heat of the desert and journeyed along the edges of this great wasteland of sand.

Social Studies Activity

Suppose you are a merchant traveling from Dunhuang to Kashgar. You will be carrying silk, furs, and cinnamon to Kashgar where you'll trade for gold, garlic, and glass, which you will carry back to Dunhuang. Plan your route and hire a guide.

- Look at the map to find the distances and the physical features you will see on your journey.
- Explain why you chose the route you did.
- List the animals and supplies that you will take.
- Write a help-wanted ad for a guide to lead your caravan.

Background

Facts and Figures Yaks are huge animals similar in appearance to American buffalo. They have thick hair and are native to the cold mountains of central Asia. Yaks are valuable as pack animals and because of their milk, meat, hair, and hide.

Camels are native to the deserts of Asia and northern Africa. There are two kinds of camels: Arabian and Bactrian. Both have humps that store fat, enabling them to go without food or water for several days.

The Arabian camel is better adapted to desert conditions. Its feet can tolerate the heat of the sand, and its nostrils and eyes are protected from sandstorms.

The two-humped Bactrian camel is better suited for cooler mountain conditions. It has a furry coat that it sheds every year, allowing it to withstand a huge range of temperatures.

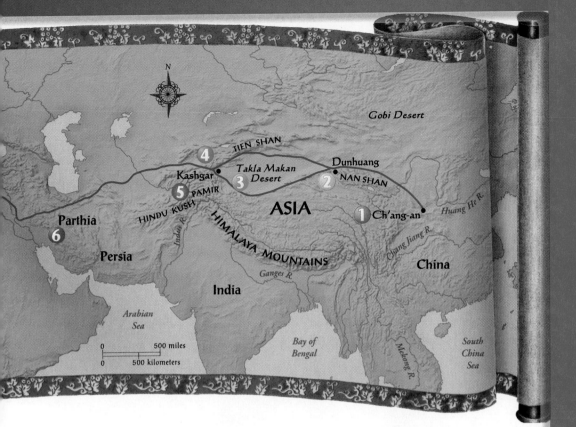

♦ Invite interested students to research the typical weather conditions travelers could expect along their routes. Students may wish to sketch a map and add notations about the average maximum and minimum temperatures along the route.

♦ Ask students to define the word *dazzle*. Then ask: **Why do you think the Roman soldiers surrendered when they were dazzled by the gold cloth?** *(They may have been blinded or confused by the display or overwhelmed by the beauty of the cloth.)*

♦ To extend this exploration, challenge interested students to research about the merchants who traveled the Silk Road. Have students find out the kinds of hardships the travelers encountered. Invite students to share their findings. Alternatively, find students who have experienced mountain hiking trips and primitive camping. Ask the students to share with the class what they learned about the kinds of clothes, equipment, and tools hikers take along. Ask them to describe the kinds of hardships and extreme conditions that hikers might have to deal with.

Social Studies Activity

Make sure students understand how to read and use the scale correctly.

3 Assess

Activity Assessment

Students should have a reasonable estimate of how long the journey will take. Their list of animals and supplies for the journey should take into consideration the length of the trip, the types of terrain, and the types of weather and temperature conditions. Their guide should be experienced.

4 Kashgar

The silk routes along the northern and southern edges of the Takla Makan Desert came together at Kashgar. The perilous part of the Silk Road was still ahead.

5 Pamir Mountains

Traveling west from Kashgar, caravans faced some of the highest mountains in the world. The towering Pamir Mountains are more than 6,000 meters high. Once traders crossed the mountains, though, travel on the Silk Road was less difficult. Traders journeyed west through Persia to cities on the Mediterranean Sea.

6 Parthia

For a while, Parthian traders controlled part of the Silk Road. In 53 B.C., Rome was a mighty power around the Mediterranean Sea. That year when the Roman and Parthian armies were at battle, the Parthians suddenly turned to face their enemy and attacked with deadly arrows. Then, in the bright light of noon, the Parthians unrolled huge banners of gold-embroidered silk. The Romans were so dazzled by the brilliance that they surrendered.

7 Antioch

Trade flourished in Antioch, where silk was traded for gold. Ships carried silk and spices on the Mediterranean Sea from Antioch to Rome, Egypt, and Greece.

B ♦ 179

Program Resources

♦ **Teaching Resources** The following worksheets correlate with this page: World Populations, page 159; Interpreting a Map, page 160; and Finding Cities Along the Silk Road, page 161.

2 Facilitate

- Before students read the story, draw their attention to the creature on page 180. Ask: **What do you think this is?** (Answers may vary; samples: a dragon, a silkworm goddess)
- To extend this exploration, have students describe other myths they have read that explain natural phenomena.
- Make sure students are familiar with the usage of *appears* that means "to come into sight."
- Ask: **Why do you think the girl lied to her father about what she had said to the horse?** (Accept all reasonable answers.)
- Ask: **Why do you think the horse was acting strangely and would not eat?** (Answers may vary; samples: the horse was confused or angry.)
- Draw students' attention to the second sentence in the paragraph on page 181 that begins "But before she could finish . . ." Point out the semicolon. Explain that you use a semicolon between two sentences that are very closely related. You could use a period instead of a semicolon, but a semicolon is more appropriate in this example. The semicolon tells the reader that the second sentence is closely connected to the first sentence.
- Ask: **What did the other children see happen to the girl?** Challenge students to write a news story for a newspaper or for the evening news on television describing what happened. Students may wish to present a follow-up story covering what the neighbors found some days later.
- Ask a volunteer to explain what the phrase "in vain" means.

The Gift of Silk

A myth is a story handed down from past cultures—often to explain an event or natural phenomenon. Myths may be about gods and goddesses or about heroes.

The Yellow Emperor, Huang Di, who is mentioned in this Chinese myth, was a real person. Some stories say that he was the founder of the Chinese nation. He was thought to be a god who came to rule on Earth. Here the silkworm goddess appears to him at a victory celebration.

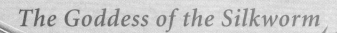

The Goddess of the Silkworm

A GODDESS descended from the heavens with a gift for the Yellow Emperor. Her body was covered with a horse's hide, and she presented two shining rolls of silk to the god. She was the "goddess of the silkworm", sometimes called the "lady with a horse's head". Long, long ago she had been a beautiful girl, but now a horse's skin grew over her body. If she pulled the two sides of the skin close to her body she became a silkworm with a horse's head, spinning a long, glittering thread of silk from her mouth. It is said she lived in a mulberry tree, producing silk day and night in the wild northern plain. This is her story.

Once in ancient times there lived a man, his daughter and their horse. Often the man had to travel, leaving his daughter alone at home to take care of the beast. And often the girl was lonely. One day, because she missed her father she teased the horse: "Dear long-nosed one, if you could bring my father home right how, I'd marry you and be your wife." At that the horse broke out of his harness. He galloped away and came quickly to the place where the master was doing business. The master, surprised to see his beast, grasped his

mane and jumped up on his back. The horse stood mournfully staring in the direction he had come from, so the man decided there must be something amiss at home and hurried back.

When they arrived home, the daughter explained that she had only remarked that she missed her father and the horse had dashed off wildly. The man said nothing but was secretly pleased to own such a remarkable animal and fed him special sweet hay. But the horse would not touch it and whinnied and reared each time he saw the girl.

The man began to worry about the horse's strange behavior, and one day he said to the girl,

180 ◆ B

History Chinese tradition claims that the wife of the Yellow Emperor discovered silk around the 27th century B.C. The silkworm moth was originally native to China. The Chinese succeeded in guarding the secret of silk for about 3,000 years.

In A.D. 552, a Roman emperor sent two Persian monks to China. They risked their lives stealing mulberry seeds and silkworm eggs. They hid the seeds and eggs inside their walking staffs and smuggled them out of China.

Silk production spread gradually to many countries in Europe. However, the climate in England and the United States was not right for silkworms and they did not flourish in either country.

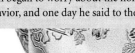

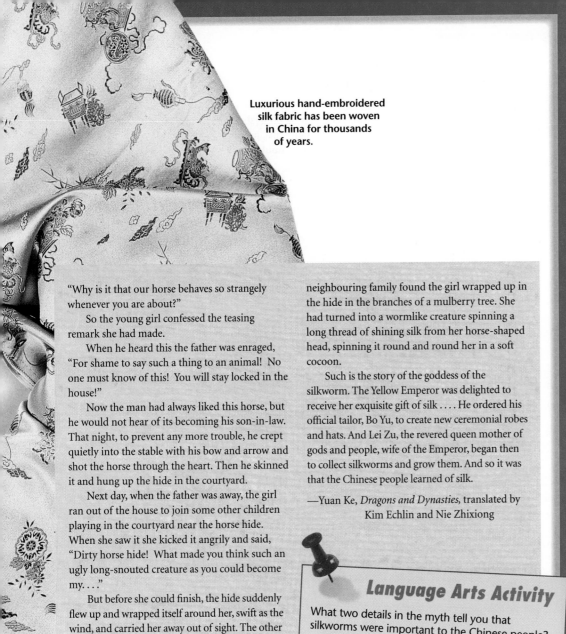

Luxurious hand-embroidered silk fabric has been woven in China for thousands of years.

"Why is it that our horse behaves so strangely whenever you are about?"

So the young girl confessed the teasing remark she had made.

When he heard this the father was enraged, "For shame to say such a thing to an animal! No one must know of this! You will stay locked in the house!"

Now the man had always liked this horse, but he would not hear of its becoming his son-in-law. That night, to prevent any more trouble, he crept quietly into the stable with his bow and arrow and shot the horse through the heart. Then he skinned it and hung up the hide in the courtyard.

Next day, when the father was away, the girl ran out of the house to join some other children playing in the courtyard near the horse hide. When she saw it she kicked it angrily and said, "Dirty horse hide! What made you think such an ugly long-snouted creature as you could become my. . . ."

But before she could finish, the hide suddenly flew up and wrapped itself around her, swift as the wind, and carried her away out of sight. The other children watched dumbfounded; there was nothing they could do but wait to tell the old man when he arrived home.

Her father set out immediately in search of his daughter, but in vain. Some days later a neighbouring family found the girl wrapped up in the hide in the branches of a mulberry tree. She had turned into a wormlike creature spinning a long thread of shining silk from her horse-shaped head, spinning it round and round her in a soft cocoon.

Such is the story of the goddess of the silkworm. The Yellow Emperor was delighted to receive her exquisite gift of silk . . . . He ordered his official tailor, Bo Yu, to create new ceremonial robes and hats. And Lei Zu, the revered queen mother of gods and people, wife of the Emperor, began then to collect silkworms and grow them. And so it was that the Chinese people learned of silk.

—Yuan Ke, *Dragons and Dynasties*, translated by Kim Echlin and Nie Zhixiong

Language Arts Activity

What two details in the myth tell you that silkworms were important to the Chinese people?

The girl in the myth gets into trouble because she breaks her promise. Write a story of your own using the idea of a broken promise.
- Decide on the place, time, and main characters.
- Think about the events that will happen and how your story will conclude.

◆ Ask: **How would you describe the personality of the girl?** *(Answers may vary; samples: teasing, selfish)*
◆ Challenge students to create an explanation of how the girl, who was a wormlike creature at the end of the story, ended up becoming a goddess. Interested students may wish to research Chinese mythology to find out how people became gods and goddesses.

Language Arts Activity

Challenge students to write a myth to explain some natural phenomenon. For example, students could write a story that explains where fog or moss or mushrooms came from.

3 Assess

Activity Assessment

Make sure students' stories include a broken promise. Remind students that, like many myths, their stories do not have to be factual.

Program Resources

◆ **Teaching Resources** The following worksheets correlate with this page: Silk Vocabulary, page 163; Writing Your Own Myth, page 164; A Broken Promise, page 165.

2 Facilitate

- Before you work the problem, estimate aloud to demonstrate how to estimate to students. Write on the board "125 trees feed 6,000 silkworms." Write "100 trees" below 125 trees. Point out that 100 trees is about a fifth less than 125 trees. Explain that 1,000 is a bit more than one fifth of 6,000. So you estimate that the answer will be a little less than 5,000 silkworms.

- Review proportions. Make sure students understand that the two ratios must be in the same form each time; for example $\frac{trees}{silkworm}$.

- If students are not familiar with cross multiplication, or cannot recall why it works, show them with a simpler example, such as $\frac{1}{2} = \frac{2}{4}$.

- Once you have calculated the answer, compare it to your original estimate. Stress to students how estimating first can help them avoid mistakes.

- To extend this exploration, have pairs of students write problems for each other that can be solved using a proportion. Have students compare answers and work together to resolve any discrepancies.

Math Activity

Group students in pairs. Remind students to estimate each answer before they calculate. Then they can compare the answer to the estimate to check their work. Remind students to keep the form the same in both ratios.

3 Assess

Activity Assessment

1. 16 sacks
2. 120 trays
3. (a) 1,824 centimeters per hour, (b) 109,440 centimeters
4. (a) 9 blouses; (b) 54 ties

Counting on Caterpillars

Lai opened the door to the silkworm room. She was greeted by the loud sound of thousands of silkworms crunching on fresh leaves from mulberry trees. Lai enjoyed raising silkworms, but it was hard work. Over its lifetime, each silkworm eats about twenty times its own weight.

Lai had a chance to care for more silkworms. But first she had to figure out how many more she could raise. She now had 6,000 silkworms that ate the leaves from 125 mulberry trees. Should she have her parents buy another piece of land with another 100 mulberry trees? If she had 100 more trees, how many more silkworms could she feed?

Analyze. 125 trees can feed 6,000 silkworms. You want to know the number of silkworms 100 trees will feed. Write a proportion, using n to represent the number of silkworms.

Write the proportion.

$$\frac{trees}{silkworms} \text{ Æ } \frac{125}{6,000} = \frac{100}{n} \cdot \frac{trees}{silkworms}$$

Cross multiply. $\qquad 125 \times n = 6,000 \times 100$

Simplify. $\qquad 125n = 600,000$

Solve. $\qquad n = \dfrac{600,000}{125} \qquad n = 4,800$

Think about it. "Yes," she decided. She could raise 4,800 more silkworms!

▲ Silkworms are fed fresh mulberry leaves every four hours, around the clock.

Math Activity

Solve the following problems.

1. Lai's friend Cheng also raises silkworms. He buys mulberry leaves. If 20 sacks of leaves feed 12,000 silkworms a day, how many sacks of leaves will 9,600 silkworms eat per day?

2. When Lai's silkworms are ready to spin, she places them in trays. If 3 trays can hold 150 silkworms, how many trays does Lai use for her 6,000 silkworms?

3. A silkworm spins silk at a rate of about 30.4 centimeters per minute. (a) How many centimeters can it spin in an hour? (b) It takes a silkworm 60 hours to spin the entire cocoon. How many centimeters is that?

4. Lai's silk thread contributes to the creation of beautiful silk clothes. It takes the thread of 630 cocoons to make a blouse and the thread of 110 cocoons to make a tie. (a) If each of Lai's 6,000 silkworms produces a cocoon, how many blouses can be made from the thread? (b) How many ties can be made?

Program Resources

- **Teaching Resources** The following worksheets correlate with this page: Graphing Mountain Heights, page 156; Your Weight in Food, page 157; and A Trip on the Silk Road, page 158.

Plan a Silk Festival

People use silk in many ways other than just to make fine clothing. Did you know that silk was used for parachutes during World War II? Or that some bicycle racers choose tires containing silk because they provide good traction? Today, silk is used for a variety of purposes, including:

◆ recreation: fishing lines and nets, bicycle tires;

◆ business: electrical insulations, typewriter and computer ribbons, surgical sutures;

◆ decoration: some silkscreen printing, artificial flowers

Work in small groups to learn about one of the ways that people have used silk in the past or are using it today. Devise an interesting way to share your project with the class, such as

◆ a booth to display or advertise a silk product;

◆ a skit in which you wear silk;

◆ a historical presentation on the uses of silk in other countries;

◆ a presentation about a process, such as silkscreen painting or silk flowers.

Ask volunteers to bring pictures or silk products to class. After rehearsing or reviewing your presentation, work with other groups to decide how to organize your Silk Festival.

▼ **Racers at the Tour de France often use tires containing silk on their bicycles.**

B ◆ 183

Time 1 week (2 days for research, 2 days for preparing the displays, 1 day for the Silk Festival)

Tips Have students work in groups of four or five. If possible, group students so that each group contains at least one student who knows how to research on the Internet or in science journals. Have groups each choose one bulleted item from the list on page 183 that they are most interested in. You may need to rearrange groups so that most students are working on the aspect of the project that most interests them.

◆ Most of the students' research should be readily available from encyclopedias. Groups who are researching innovative uses for silk may need to search in science journals or, with supervision, on the Internet.

◆ If students wish to bring a sample of silk to show the class, suggest that they bring it in a clear plastic bag so that it is less likely to be damaged.

◆ Encourage students to bring photocopies of interesting silk products or draw their own illustrations.

Other Resources Some suggested books that students may want to consult include: *The Empress and the Silkworm*, Lily Toy Hong, School & Library Binding, Albert Whitman & Co., 1995; *Between the Dragon and the Eagle*, Mical Schneider, Carolrhoda Books, 1997; *The Silk Route: 7,000 Miles of History*, John S. Major, HarperTrophy, 1996; *Exploration by Land (The Silk and Spice Routes)*, Paul Strathern, Library Binding, New Discovery, 1994.

Extend Challenge students to find out how to raise silkworms. (Silkworm eggs and food can be obtained from biological supply companies.) Ask questions such as: **What kind of container do you need to keep silkworms in? What do they need beside mulberry leaves? Where do you get mulberry leaves? Do silkworms need water? What kind of temperature and humidity do they need? How much do silkworms eat? How do you get the moths to lay eggs? What conditions do the eggs need to hatch?**

Developing scientific thinking in students is important for a solid science education. To learn how to think scientifically, students need frequent opportunities to practice science process skills, critical thinking skills, as well as other skills that support scientific inquiry. The *Science Explorer* Skills Handbook introduces the following key science skills:

- Science Process Skills
- SI Measuring Skills
- Skills for Conducting a Scientific Investigation
- Critical Thinking Skills
- Information Organizing Skills
- Data Table and Graphing Skills

The Skills Handbook is designed as a reference for students to use whenever they need to review a science skill. You can use the activities provided in the Skills Handbook to teach or reinforce the skills.

Think Like a Scientist

Observing

ACTIVITY

Before students look at the photograph, remind them that an observation is only what they can see, hear, smell, taste, or feel. Ask: **Which senses will you use to make observations from this photograph?** *(Sight is the only sense that can be used to make observations from the photograph.)* **What are some observations you can make from the photograph?** *(Answers may vary. Sample answers: The boy is wearing sneakers, sport socks, shorts, and a tee shirt; the boy is sitting in the grass holding something blue against his knee; the boy is looking at his knee; there is a soccer ball laying beside the boy.)* List the observations on the chalkboard. If students make any inferences or predictions about the boy at this point, ask: **Can you be sure your statement is factual and accurate from just observing the photograph?** Help students understand how observations differ from inferences and predictions.

Inferring

ACTIVITY

Review students' observations from the photograph. Then ask: **What inferences can you

make from your observations?** *(Students may say that the boy hurt his knee playing soccer and is holding a coldpack against his injured knee.)* **What experience or knowledge helped you make this inference?** *(Students may have experienced knee injuries from playing soccer, and they may be familiar with coldpacks like the one the boy is using.)* **Can anyone suggest another possible explanation for these observations?** *(Answers may vary. Sample answer: The boy hurt his knee jogging, and he just happened to sit beside a soccer ball his sister

---

Think Like a Scientist

Although you may not know it, you think like a scientist every day. Whenever you ask a question and explore possible answers, you use many of the same skills that scientists do. Some of these skills are described on this page.

Observing

When you use one or more of your five senses to gather information about the world, you are **observing.** Hearing a dog bark, counting twelve green seeds, and smelling smoke are all observations. To increase the power of their senses, scientists sometimes use microscopes, telescopes, or other instruments that help them make more detailed observations.

An observation must be factual and accurate—an exact report of what your senses detect. It is important to keep careful records of your observations in science class by writing or drawing in a notebook. The information collected through observations is called evidence, or data.

Inferring

When you explain or interpret an observation, you are **inferring,** or making an inference. For example, if you hear your dog barking, you may infer that someone is at your front door. To make this inference, you combine the evidence—the barking dog—and your experience or knowledge—you know that your dog barks when strangers approach—to reach a logical conclusion.

Notice that an inference is not a fact; it is only one of many possible explanations for an observation. For example, your dog may be barking because it wants to go for a walk. An inference may turn out to be incorrect even if it is based on accurate observations and logical reasoning. The only way to find out if an inference is correct is to investigate further.

Predicting

When you listen to the weather forecast, you hear many predictions about the next day's weather—what the temperature will be, whether it will rain, and how windy it will be. Weather forecasters use observations and knowledge of weather patterns to predict the weather. The skill of **predicting** involves making an inference about a future event based on current evidence or past experience.

Because a prediction is an inference, it may prove to be false. In science class, you can test some of your predictions by doing experiments. For example, suppose you predict that larger paper airplanes can fly farther than smaller airplanes. How could you test your prediction?

 Use the photograph to answer the questions below.

Observing Look closely at the photograph. List at least three observations.

Inferring Use your observations to make an inference about what has happened. What experience or knowledge did you use to make the inference?

Predicting Predict what will happen next. On what evidence or experience do you base your prediction?

---

left in the yard.) **How can you find out whether an inference is correct?** *(by further investigation)*

Predicting

ACTIVITY

After coming to some consensus about the inference that the boy hurt his knee, encourage students to make predictions about what will happen next. *(Students' predictions may vary. Sample answers: The boy will go to the doctor. A friend will help the boy home. The boy will get up and continue playing soccer.)*

Classifying

Could you imagine searching for a book in the library if the books were shelved in no particular order? Your trip to the library would be an all-day event! Luckily, librarians group together books on similar topics or by the same author. Grouping together items that are alike in some way is called **classifying.** You can classify items in many ways: by size, by shape, by use, and by other important characteristics.

Like librarians, scientists use the skill of classifying to organize information and objects. When things are sorted into groups, the relationships among them become easier to understand.

ACTIVITY

Classify the objects in the photograph into two groups based on any characteristic you choose. Then use another characteristic to classify the objects into three groups.

Making Models

Have you ever drawn a picture to help someone understand what you were saying? Such a drawing is one type of model. A model is a picture, diagram, computer image, or other representation of a complex object or process. **Making models** helps people understand things that they cannot observe directly.

Scientists often use models to represent things that are either very large or very small, such as the planets in the solar system, or the parts of a cell. Such models are physical models—drawings or three-dimensional structures that look like the real thing. Other models are mental models—mathematical equations or words that describe how something works.

ACTIVITY

This student is using a model to demonstrate what causes day and night on Earth. What do the flashlight and the tennis ball in the model represent?

Communicating

Whenever you talk on the phone, write a letter, or listen to your teacher at school, you are communicating. **Communicating** is the process of sharing ideas and information with other people. Communicating effectively requires many skills, including writing, reading, speaking, listening, and making models.

Scientists communicate to share results, information, and opinions. Scientists often communicate about their work in journals, over the telephone, in letters, and on the Internet. They also attend scientific meetings where they share their ideas with one another in person.

ACTIVITY

On a sheet of paper, write out clear, detailed directions for tying your shoe. Then exchange directions with a partner. Follow your partner's directions exactly. How successful were you at tying your shoe? How could your partner have communicated more clearly?

Classifying

ACTIVITY

Encourage students to think of other common things that are classified. Then ask: **What things at home are classified?** *(Clothing might be classified by placing it in different dresser drawers; glasses, plates, and silverware are grouped in different parts of the kitchen; screws, nuts, bolts, washers, and nails might be separated into small containers.)* **What are some things that scientists classify?** *(Scientists classify many things they study, including organisms, geological features and processes, and kinds of machines.)* After students have classified the different fruits in the photograph, have them share their criteria for classifying them. *(Some characteristics students might use include shape, color, size, and where they are grown.)*

Making Models

ACTIVITY

Ask students: **What are some models you have used to study science?** *(Students may have used human anatomical models, solar system models, maps, stream tables.)* **How did these models help you?** *(Models can help you learn about things that are difficult to study, either because they are too big, too small, or complex.)* Be sure students understand that a model does not have to be three-dimensional. For example, a map in a textbook is a model. Ask: **What do the flashlight and tennis ball represent?** *(The flashlight represents the sun, and the ball represents Earth.)* **What quality of each item makes this a good model?** *(The flashlight gives off light, and the ball is round and can be rotated by the student.)*

Communicating

ACTIVITY

Challenge students to identify the methods of communication they've used today. Then ask: **How is the way you communicate with a friend similar to and different from the way scientists communicate about their work to other scientists?** *(Both may communicate using various methods, but scientists must be very detailed and precise, whereas communication between friends may be less detailed and precise.)* Encourage students to communicate like a scientist as they carry out the activity. *(Students' directions should be detailed and precise enough for another person to successfully follow.)*

On what did you base your prediction? *(Scientific predictions are based on knowledge and experience.)* Point out that in science, predictions can often be tested with experiments.

Making Measurements

Measuring in SI

Review SI units in class with students. Begin by providing metric rulers, graduated cylinders, balances, and Celsius thermometers. Use these tools to reinforce that the meter is the unit of length, the liter is the unit of volume, the gram is the unit of mass, and the degree Celsius is the unit for temperature. Ask: **If you want to measure the length and width of the floor in this classroom, which SI unit would you use?** *(meter)* **Which unit would you use to measure the amount of matter in your textbook?** *(gram)* **Which would you use to measure how much water a drinking glass holds?** *(liter)* **When would you use the Celsius scale?** *(To measure the temperature of something)* Then use the measuring equipment to review SI prefixes. For example, ask: **What are the smallest units on the metric ruler?** *(millimeters)* **How many millimeters are there in 1 cm?** *(10 mm)* **How many in 10 cm?** *(100 mm)* **How many centimeters are there in 1 m?** *(100 cm)* **What does 1,000 m equal?** *(1 km)*

Length *(Students should state that the shell is 4.6 centimeters, or 46 millimeters, long.)* If students need more practice measuring length, have them use meter sticks and metric rulers to measure various objects in the classroom.

Liquid Volume *(Students should state that the volume of water in the graduated cylinder is 62 milliliters.)* If students need more practice measuring liquid volume, have them use a graduated cylinder to measure different volumes of water.

Making Measurements

When scientists make observations, it is not sufficient to say that something is "big" or "heavy." Instead, scientists use instruments to measure just how big or heavy an object is. By measuring, scientists can express their observations more precisely and communicate more information about what they observe.

Measuring in SI

The standard system of measurement used by scientists around the world is known as the International System of Units, which is abbreviated as SI (in French, *Système International d'Unités*). SI units are easy to use because they are based on multiples of 10. Each unit is ten times larger than the next smallest unit and one tenth the size of the next largest unit. The table lists the prefixes used to name the most common SI units.

Common SI Prefixes		
Prefix	**Symbol**	**Meaning**
kilo-	k	1,000
hecto-	h	100
deka-	da	10
deci-	d	0.1 (one tenth)
centi-	c	0.01 (one hundredth)
milli-	m	0.001 (one thousandth)

Length To measure length, or the distance between two points, the unit of measure is the **meter (m).** One meter is the approximate distance from the floor to a doorknob. Long distances, such as the distance between two cities, are measured in kilometers (km). Small lengths are measured in centimeters (cm) or millimeters (mm). Scientists use metric rulers and meter sticks to measure length.

Common Conversions
1 km = 1,000 m
1 m = 100 cm
1 m = 1,000 mm
1 cm = 10 mm

The larger lines on the metric ruler in the picture show centimeter divisions, while the smaller, unnumbered lines show millimeter divisions. How many centimeters long is the shell? How many millimeters long is it? **ACTIVITY**

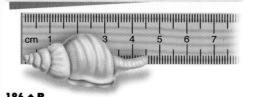

Liquid Volume To measure the volume of a liquid, or the amount of space it takes up, you will use a unit of measure known as the **liter (L).** One liter is the approximate volume of a medium-sized carton of milk. Smaller volumes are measured in milliliters (mL). Scientists use graduated cylinders to measure liquid volume.

Common Conversion
1 L = 1,000 mL

The graduated cylinder in the picture is marked in milliliter divisions. Notice that the water in the cylinder has a curved surface. This curved surface is called the *meniscus.* To measure the volume, you must read the level at the lowest point of the meniscus. What is the volume of water in this graduated cylinder? **ACTIVITY**

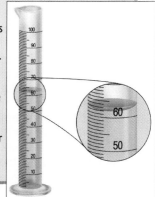

Mass To measure mass, or the amount of matter in an object, you will use a unit of measure known as the **gram** (**g**). One gram is approximately the mass of a paper clip. Larger masses are measured in kilograms (kg). Scientists use a balance to find the mass of an object.

Common Conversion

1 kg = 1,000 g

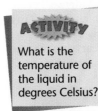

The electronic balance displays the mass of an apple in kilograms. What is the mass of the apple? Suppose a recipe for applesauce called for one kilogram of apples. About how many apples would you need?

Temperature
To measure the temperature of a substance, you will use the **Celsius scale**. Temperature is measured in degrees Celsius (°C) using a Celsius thermometer. Water freezes at 0°C and boils at 100°C.

ACTIVITY

What is the temperature of the liquid in degrees Celsius?

Converting SI Units

To use the SI system, you must know how to convert between units. Converting from one unit to another involves the skill of **calculating**, or using mathematical operations. Converting between SI units is similar to converting between dollars and dimes because both systems are based on multiples of ten.

Suppose you want to convert a length of 80 centimeters to meters. Follow these steps to convert between units.

1. Begin by writing down the measurement you want to convert—in this example, 80 centimeters.

2. Write a conversion factor that represents the relationship between the two units you are converting. In this example, the relationship is *1 meter = 100 centimeters*. Write this conversion factor as a fraction, making sure to place the units you are converting from (centimeters, in this example) in the denominator.

3. Multiply the measurement you want to convert by the fraction. When you do this, the units in the first measurement will cancel out with the units in the denominator. Your answer will be in the units you are converting to (meters, in this example).

Example

80 centimeters = ___?___ meters

$$80 \text{ centimeters} \times \frac{1 \text{ meter}}{100 \text{ centimeters}} = \frac{80 \text{ meters}}{100}$$

$$= 0.8 \text{ meters}$$

Convert between the following units.

ACTIVITY

1. 600 millimeters = _?_ meters
2. 0.35 liters = _?_ milliliters
3. 1,050 grams = _?_ kilograms

B ◆ 187

Mass *(Students should state that the mass of the* **ACTIVITY** *apple is 0.1 kilograms. They would need 10 apples to make 1 kilogram.)* If students need practice determining mass, have them use a balance to determine the mass of various common objects, such as coins, paper clips, and books.

Temperature *(Students* **ACTIVITY** *should state that the temperature of the liquid is 35°C.)* If students need practice measuring temperature, have them use a Celsius thermometer to measure the temperature of various water samples.

Converting SI Units

ACTIVITY

Review the steps for converting SI units and work through the example with students. Then ask: **How many millimeters are in 80 centimeters?** *(Students should follow the steps to calculate that 80 centimeters is equal to 800 millimeters.)*

Have students do the conversion problems in the activity. *(***1.** *600 millimeters = 0.6 meters;* **2.** *0.35 liters = 350 milliliters;* **3.** *1,050 grams = 1.05 kilograms)* If students need more practice converting SI units, have students make up conversion problems and trade with a partner.

Conducting a Scientific Investigation

Posing Questions

Before students do the activity on the next page, walk them through the steps of a typical scientific investigation. Begin by asking: **Why is a scientific question important to a scientific investigation?** *(It is the reason for conducting a scientific investigation and how every investigation begins.)* **What is the scientific question in the activity at the bottom of the next page?** *(Is a ball's bounce affected by the height from which it is dropped?)*

Developing a Hypothesis

Emphasize that a hypothesis is a prediction about the outcome of a scientific investigation, but it is *not* a guess. Ask: **On what information do scientists base their hypotheses?** *(Their observations and previous knowledge or experience)* Point out that a hypothesis does not always turn out to be correct. Ask: **In that case, do you think the scientist wasted his or her time? Explain your answer.** *(No, because the scientist probably learned from the investigation and maybe could develop another hypothesis that could be supported.)*

Designing an Experiment

Have a volunteer read the Experimental Procedure in the box. Then call on students to identify the manipulated variable *(amount of salt added to water)*, the variables that are kept constant *(amount and starting temperature of water, placing containers in freezer)*, the responding variable *(time it takes water to freeze)*, and the control *(Container 3)*.

Ask: **How might the experiment be affected if Container 1 had only 100 mL of water?** *(It wouldn't be a fair comparison with the containers that have more water.)* **What if Container 3 was not included in the experiment?** *(You wouldn't have anything to compare the other two containers to know if their freezing times were faster or slower than normal.)* Help students understand the importance of

Conducting a Scientific Investigation

In some ways, scientists are like detectives, piecing together clues to learn about a process or event. One way that scientists gather clues is by carrying out experiments. An experiment tests an idea in a careful, orderly manner. Although all experiments do not follow the same steps in the same order, many follow a pattern similar to the one described here.

Posing Questions

Experiments begin by asking a scientific question. A scientific question is one that can be answered by gathering evidence. For example, the question "Which freezes faster— fresh water or salt water?" is a scientific question because you can carry out an investigation and gather information to answer the question.

Developing a Hypothesis

The next step is to form a hypothesis. A **hypothesis** is a prediction about the outcome of the experiment. Like all predictions, hypotheses are based on your observations and previous knowledge or experience. But, unlike many predictions, a hypothesis must be something that can be tested. A properly worded hypothesis should take the form of an *If...then...* statement. For example, a hypothesis might be *"If I add salt to fresh water, then the water will take longer to freeze."* A hypothesis worded this way serves as a rough outline of the experiment you should perform.

188 ◆ B

keeping all variables constant except the manipulated variable. Also be sure they understand the role of the control. Then ask: **What operational definition is used in this experiment?** *("Frozen" means the time at which a wooden stick can no longer move in a container.)*

Designing an Experiment

Next you need to plan a way to test your hypothesis. Your plan should be written out as a step-by-step procedure and should describe the observations or measurements you will make.

Two important steps involved in designing an experiment are controlling variables and forming operational definitions.

Controlling Variables In a well-designed experiment, you need to keep all variables the same except for one. A **variable** is any factor that can change in an experiment. The factor that you change is called the **manipulated variable.** In this experiment, the manipulated variable is the amount of salt added to the water. Other factors, such as the amount of water or the starting temperature, are kept constant.

The factor that changes as a result of the manipulated variable is called the responding variable. The **responding variable** is what you measure or observe to obtain your results. In this experiment, the responding variable is how long the water takes to freeze.

An experiment in which all factors except one are kept constant is a **controlled experiment.** Most controlled experiments include a test called the control. In this experiment, Container 3 is the control. Because no salt is added to Container 3, you can compare the results from the other containers to it. Any difference in results must be due to the addition of salt alone.

Forming Operational Definitions

Another important aspect of a well-designed experiment is having clear operational definitions. An **operational definition** is a statement that describes how a particular variable is to be measured or how a term is to be defined. For example, in this experiment, how will you determine if the water has frozen? You might decide to insert a stick in each container at the start of the experiment. Your operational definition of "frozen" would be the time at which the stick can no longer move.

EXPERIMENTAL PROCEDURE

1. Fill 3 containers with 300 milliliters of cold tap water.

2. Add 10 grams of salt to Container 1; stir. Add 20 grams of salt to Container 2; stir. Add no salt to Container 3.

3. Place the 3 containers in a freezer.

4. Check the containers every 15 minutes. Record your observations.

Interpreting Data

The observations and measurements you make in an experiment are called data. At the end of an experiment, you need to analyze the data to look for any patterns or trends. Patterns often become clear if you organize your data in a data table or graph. Then think through what the data reveal. Do they support your hypothesis? Do they point out a flaw in your experiment? Do you need to collect more data?

Drawing Conclusions

A conclusion is a statement that sums up what you have learned from an experiment. When you draw a conclusion, you need to decide whether the data you collected support your hypothesis or not. You may need to repeat an experiment several times before you can draw any conclusions from it. Conclusions often lead you to pose new questions and plan new experiments to answer them.

Is a ball's bounce affected by the height from which it is dropped? Using the steps just described, plan a controlled experiment to investigate this problem. **ACTIVITY**

B ◆ 189

Interpreting Data

Emphasize the importance of collecting accurate and detailed data in a scientific investigation. Ask: **What if the students forgot to record the times that they made their observations in the experiment?** *(They wouldn't be able to completely analyze their data to draw valid conclusions.)* Then ask: **Why are data tables and graphs a good way to organize data?** *(They often make it easier to compare and analyze data.)* You may wish to have students review the Skills Handbook pages on Creating Data Tables and Graphs at this point.

Drawing Conclusions

Help students understand that a conclusion is not necessarily the end of a scientific investigation. A conclusion about one experiment may lead right into another experiment. Point out that in scientific investigations, a conclusion is a summary and explanation of the results of an experiment.

Tell students to suppose that for the Experimental Procedure described on this page, they obtained the following results: Container 1 froze in 45 minutes, Container 2 in 80 minutes, and Container 3 in 25 minutes. Ask: **What conclusions can you draw about this experiment?** *(Students might conclude that the more salt that is added to fresh water, the longer it takes the water to freeze. The hypothesis is supported, and the question of which freezes faster is answered—fresh water.)*

You might wish to have students work in pairs to plan the controlled experiment. **ACTIVITY** *(Students should develop a hypothesis, such as "If I increase the height from which a ball is dropped, then the height of its bounce will increase." They can test the hypothesis by dropping balls from varying heights (the manipulated variable). All trials should be done with the same kind of ball and on the same surface (constant variables). For each trial, they should measure the height of the bounce (responding variable).)* After students have designed the experiment, provide rubber balls and invite them to carry out the experiment so they can collect and interpret data and draw conclusions.

B ◆ 189

Thinking Critically

Comparing and Contrasting

ACTIVITY

Emphasize that the skill of comparing and contrasting often relies on good observation skills, as in this activity. (*Students' answers may vary. Sample answer: Similarities—both are dogs and have four legs, two eyes, two ears, brown and white fur, black noses, pink tongues; Differences—smooth coat vs. rough coat, more white fur vs. more brown fur, shorter vs. taller, long ears vs. short ears.*)

Applying Concepts

ACTIVITY

Point out to students that they apply concepts that they learn in school in their daily lives. For example, they learn to add, subtract, multiply, and divide in school. If they get a paper route or some other part-time job, they can apply those concepts. Challenge students to practice applying concepts by doing the activity. (*Antifreeze lowers the temperature at which the solution will freeze, and thus keeps the water in the radiator from freezing.*)

Interpreting Illustrations

ACTIVITY

Again, point out the need for good observation skills. Ask: **What is the difference between "interpreting illustrations" and "looking at the pictures"?** (*"Interpreting illustrations" requires thorough examination of the illustration, caption, and labels, while "looking at the pictures" implies less thorough examination.*) Encourage students to thoroughly examine the diagram as they do the activity. (*Students' paragraphs may vary, but should describe the internal anatomy of an earthworm, including some of the organs in the earthworm.*)

Thinking Critically

Has a friend ever asked for your advice about a problem? If so, you may have helped your friend think through the problem in a logical way. Without knowing it, you used critical-thinking skills to help your friend. Critical thinking involves the use of reasoning and logic to solve problems or make decisions. Some critical-thinking skills are described below.

Comparing and Contrasting

When you examine two objects for similarities and differences, you are using the skill of **comparing and contrasting.** Comparing involves identifying similarities, or common characteristics. Contrasting involves identifying differences. Analyzing objects in this way can help you discover details that you might otherwise overlook.

Compare and contrast **ACTIVITY** the two animals in the photo. First list all the similarities that you see. Then list all the differences.

Applying Concepts

When you use your knowledge about one situation to make sense of a similar situation, you are using the skill of **applying concepts.** Being able to transfer your knowledge from one situation to another shows that you truly understand a concept. You may use this skill in answering test questions that present different problems from the ones you've reviewed in class.

You have just learned **ACTIVITY** that water takes longer to freeze when other substances are mixed into it. Use this knowledge to explain why people need a substance called antifreeze in their car's radiator in the winter.

Interpreting Illustrations

Diagrams, photographs, and maps are included in textbooks to help clarify what you read. These illustrations show processes, places, and ideas in a visual manner. The skill called **interpreting illustrations** can help you learn from these visual elements. To understand an illustration, take the time to study the illustration along with all the written information that accompanies it. Captions identify the key concepts shown in the illustration. Labels point out the important parts of a diagram or map, while keys identify the symbols used in a map.

Blood vessels
Reproductive organs
Hearts
Brain
Mouth
Bristles
Digestive tract
Waste-removal organs
Nerve cord
Intestine

▲ Internal anatomy of an earthworm

Study the diagram above. Then write a short paragraph explaining what you have learned. **ACTIVITY**

Relating Cause and Effect

If one event causes another event to occur, the two events are said to have a cause-and-effect relationship. When you determine that such a relationship exists between two events, you use a skill called **relating cause and effect.** For example, if you notice an itchy, red bump on your skin, you might infer that a mosquito bit you. The mosquito bite is the cause, and the bump is the effect.

It is important to note that two events do not necessarily have a cause-and-effect relationship just because they occur together. Scientists carry out experiments or use past experience to determine whether a cause-and-effect relationship exists.

You are on a camping trip and your flashlight has stopped working. List some possible causes for the flashlight malfunction. How could you determine which cause-and-effect relationship has left you in the dark?

Making Generalizations

When you draw a conclusion about an entire group based on information about only some of the group's members, you are using a skill called **making generalizations.** For a generalization to be valid, the sample you choose must be large enough and representative of the entire group. You might, for example, put this skill to work at a farm stand if you see a sign that says, "Sample some grapes before you buy." If you sample a few sweet grapes, you may conclude that all the grapes are sweet—and purchase a large bunch.

A team of scientists needs to determine whether the water in a large reservoir is safe to drink. How could they use the skill of making generalizations to help them? What should they do?

Making Judgments

When you evaluate something to decide whether it is good or bad, or right or wrong, you are using a skill called **making judgments.** For example, you make judgments when you decide to eat healthful foods or to pick up litter in a park. Before you make a judgment, you need to think through the pros and cons of a situation, and identify the values or standards that you hold.

Should children and teens be required to wear helmets when bicycling? Explain why you feel the way you do.

Problem Solving

When you use critical-thinking skills to resolve an issue or decide on a course of action, you are using a skill called **problem solving.** Some problems, such as how to convert a fraction into a decimal, are straightforward. Other problems, such as figuring out why your computer has stopped working, are complex. Some complex problems can be solved using the trial and error method—try out one solution first, and if that doesn't work, try another. Other useful problem-solving strategies include making models and brainstorming possible solutions with a partner.

B ◆ 191

Relating Cause and Effect

Emphasize that not all events that occur together have a cause-and-effect relationship. For example, tell students that you went to the grocery and your car stalled. Ask: **Is there a cause-and-effect relationship in this situation? Explain your answer.** *(No, because going to the grocery could not cause a car to stall. There must be another cause to make the car stall.)* Have students do the activity to practice relating cause and effect. *(Students should identify that the flashlight not working is the effect. Some possible causes include dead batteries, a burned-out light bulb, or a loose part.)*

Making Generalizations

Point out the importance of having a large, representative sample before making a generalization. Ask: **If you went fishing at a lake and caught three catfish, could you make the generalization that all fish in the lake are catfish? Why or why not?** *(No, because there might be other kinds of fish you didn't catch because they didn't like the bait or they may be in other parts of the lake.)* **How could you make a generalization about the kinds of fish in the lake?** *(By having a larger sample)* Have students do the activity to practice making generalizations. *(The scientists should collect and test water samples from a number of different parts of the reservoir.)*

Making Judgments

Remind students that they make a judgment almost every time they make a decision. Ask: **What steps should you follow to make a judgment?** *(Gather information, list pros and cons, analyze values, make judgment)* Invite students to do the activity, and then to share and discuss the judgments they made. *(Students' judgments will vary, but should be supported by valid reasoning. Sample answer: Children and teens should be required to wear helmets when bicycling because helmets have been proven to save lives and reduce head injuries.)*

Problem Solving

Challenge student pairs to solve a problem about a soapbox derby. Explain that their younger brother is building a car to enter in the race. The brother wants to know how to make his soapbox car go faster. After student pairs have considered the problem, have them share their ideas about solutions with the class. *(Most will probably suggest using trial and error by making small changes to the car and testing the car after each change. Some students may suggest making and manipulating a model.)*

Organizing Information

Concept Maps

Challenge students to make a concept map with at least three levels of concepts to organize information about types of transportation. All students should start with the phrase *types of transportation* at the top of the concept map. After that point, their concept maps may vary. *(For example, some students might place* private transportation *and* public transportation *at the next level, while other students might have* human-powered *and* gas-powered. *Make sure students connect the concepts with linking words. Challenge students to include cross-linkages as well.)*

Compare/ Contrast Tables

Have students make their own compare/contrast tables using two or more different sports or other activities, such as playing musical instruments. Emphasize that students should select characteristics that highlight the similarities and differences between the activities. *(Students' compare/contrast tables should include several appropriate characteristics and list information about each activity for every characteristic.)*

Organizing Information

As you read this textbook, how can you make sense of all the information it contains? Some useful tools to help you organize information are shown on this page. These tools are called *graphic organizers* because they give you a visual picture of a topic, showing at a glance how key concepts are related.

Concept Maps

Concept maps are useful tools for organizing information on broad topics. A concept map begins with a general concept and shows how it can be broken down into more specific concepts. In that way, relationships between concepts become easier to understand.

A concept map is constructed by placing concept words (usually nouns) in ovals and connecting them with linking words. Often, the most general concept word is placed at the top, and the words become more specific as you move downward. Often the linking words, which are written on a line extending between two ovals, describe the relationship between the two concepts they connect. If you follow any string of concepts and linking words down the map, it should read like a sentence.

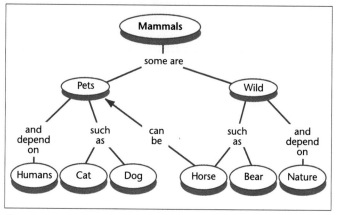

Some concept maps include linking words that connect a concept on one branch of the map to a concept on another branch. These linking words, called cross-linkages, show more complex interrelationships among concepts.

Compare/Contrast Tables

Compare/contrast tables are useful tools for sorting out the similarities and differences between two or more items. A table provides an organized framework in which to compare items based on specific characteristics that you identify.

To create a compare/contrast table, list the items to be compared across the top of a table. Then list the characteristics that will form the basis of your comparison in the left-hand column. Complete the table by filling in information about each characteristic, first for one item and then for the other.

Characteristic	Baseball	Basketball
Number of Players	9	5
Playing Field	Baseball diamond	Basketball court
Equipment	Bat, baseball, mitts	Basket, basketball

Venn Diagrams

Another way to show similarities and differences between items is with a Venn diagram. A Venn diagram consists of two or more circles that partially overlap. Each circle represents a particular concept or idea. Common characteristics, or similarities, are written within the area of overlap between the two circles. Unique characteristics, or differences, are written in the parts of the circles outside the area of overlap.

To create a Venn diagram, draw two overlapping circles. Label the circles with the names of the items being compared. Write the

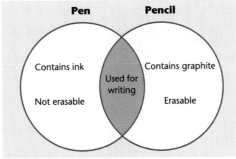

unique characteristics in each circle outside the area of overlap. Then write the shared characteristics within the area of overlap.

Flowcharts

A flowchart can help you understand the order in which certain events have occurred or should occur. Flowcharts are useful for outlining the stages in a process or the steps in a procedure.

To make a flowchart, write a brief description of each event in a box. Place the first event at the top of the page, followed by the second event, the third event, and so on. Then draw an arrow to connect each event to the one that occurs next.

Preparing Pasta

Boil water → Cook pasta → Drain water → Add sauce

Cycle Diagrams

A cycle diagram can be used to show a sequence of events that is continuous, or cyclical. A continuous sequence does not have an end because, when the final event is over, the first event begins again. Like a flowchart, a cycle diagram can help you understand the order of events.

To create a cycle diagram, write a brief description of each event in a box. Place one event at the top of the page in the center. Then, moving in a clockwise direction around an imaginary circle, write each event in its proper sequence. Draw arrows that connect each event to the one that occurs next, forming a continuous circle.

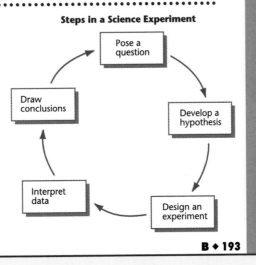

Steps in a Science Experiment

Pose a question → Develop a hypothesis → Design an experiment → Interpret data → Draw conclusions → (back to Pose a question)

B ◆ 193

Creating Data Tables and Graphs

Data Tables

Have students create a data table to show how much time they spend on different activities during one week. Suggest that students first list the main activities they do every week. Then they should determine the amount of time they spend on each activity each day. Remind students to give this data table a title. *(Students' data tables will vary. A sample data table is shown below.)*

Bar Graphs

Students can use the data from their data table above to make a bar graph showing how much time they spend on different activities during a week. The vertical axis should be divided into units of time, such as hours. Remind students to label both axes and give their graph a title. *(Students' bar graphs will vary. A sample bar graph is shown below.)*

Creating Data Tables and Graphs

How can you make sense of the data in a science experiment? The first step is to organize the data to help you understand them. Data tables and graphs are helpful tools for organizing data.

Data Tables

You have gathered your materials and set up your experiment. But before you start, you need to plan a way to record what happens during the experiment. By creating a data table, you can record your observations and measurements in an orderly way.

Suppose, for example, that a scientist conducted an experiment to find out how many Calories people of different body masses burn while doing various activities. The data table shows the results.

Notice in this data table that the manipulated variable (body mass) is the heading of one column. The responding variable (for Experiment 1, the number of Calories burned while bicycling) is the heading of the next column. Additional columns were added for related experiments.

CALORIES BURNED IN 30 MINUTES OF ACTIVITY			
Body Mass	Experiment 1 Bicycling	Experiment 2 Playing Basketball	Experiment 3 Watching Television
30 kg	60 Calories	120 Calories	21 Calories
40 kg	77 Calories	164 Calories	27 Calories
50 kg	95 Calories	206 Calories	33 Calories
60 kg	114 Calories	248 Calories	38 Calories

Bar Graphs

To compare how many Calories a person burns doing various activities, you could create a bar graph. A bar graph is used to display data in a number of separate, or distinct, categories. In this example, bicycling, playing basketball, and watching television are three separate categories.

To create a bar graph, follow these steps.

1. On graph paper, draw a horizontal, or *x*-, axis and a vertical, or *y*-, axis.
2. Write the names of the categories to be graphed along the horizontal axis. Include an overall label for the axis as well.
3. Label the vertical axis with the name of the responding variable. Include units of measurement. Then create a scale along the axis by marking off equally spaced numbers that cover the range of the data collected.
4. For each category, draw a solid bar using the scale on the vertical axis to determine the appropriate height. For example, for bicycling, draw the bar as high as the 60 mark on the vertical axis. Make all the bars the same width and leave equal spaces between them.
5. Add a title that describes the graph.

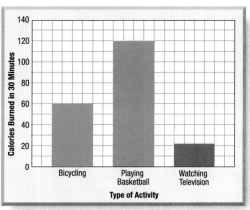

Calories Burned by a 30-kilogram Person in Various Activities

Time Spent on Different Activities in a Week				
	Going to Classes	Eating Meals	Playing Soccer	Watching Television
Monday	6	2	2	0.5
Tuesday	6	1.5	1.5	1.5
Wednesday	6	2	1	2
Thursday	6	2	2	1.5
Friday	6	2	2	0.5
Saturday	0	2.5	2.5	1
Sunday	0	3	1	2

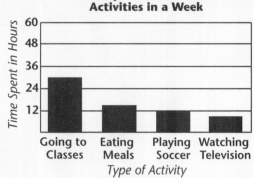

Time Spent on Different Activities in a Week

Line Graphs

To see whether a relationship exists between body mass and the number of Calories burned while bicycling, you could create a line graph. A line graph is used to display data that show how one variable (the responding variable) changes in response to another variable (the manipulated variable). You can use a line graph when your manipulated variable is *continuous*, that is, when there are other points between the ones that you tested. In this example, body mass is a continuous variable because there are other body masses between 30 and 40 kilograms (for example, 31 kilograms). Time is another example of a continuous variable.

Line graphs are powerful tools because they allow you to estimate values for conditions that you did not test in the experiment. For example, you can use the line graph to estimate that a 35-kilogram person would burn 68 Calories while bicycling.

To create a line graph, follow these steps.

1. On graph paper, draw a horizontal, or *x*-, axis and a vertical, or *y*-, axis.
2. Label the horizontal axis with the name of the manipulated variable. Label the vertical axis with the name of the responding variable. Include units of measurement.
3. Create a scale on each axis by marking off equally spaced numbers that cover the range of the data collected.
4. Plot a point on the graph for each piece of data. In the line graph above, the dotted lines show how to plot the first data point (30 kilograms and 60 Calories). Draw an imaginary vertical line extending up from the horizontal axis at the 30-kilogram mark. Then draw an imaginary horizontal line extending across from the vertical axis at the 60-Calorie mark. Plot the point where the two lines intersect.

Effect of Body Mass on Calories Burned While Bicycling

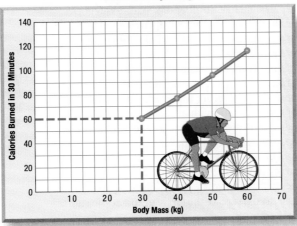

5. Connect the plotted points with a solid line. (In some cases, it may be more appropriate to draw a line that shows the general trend of the plotted points. In those cases, some of the points may fall above or below the line.)
6. Add a title that identifies the variables or relationship in the graph.

> **ACTIVITY**
> Create line graphs to display the data from Experiment 2 and Experiment 3 in the data table.

> **ACTIVITY**
> You read in the newspaper that a total of 4 centimeters of rain fell in your area in June, 2.5 centimeters fell in July, and 1.5 centimeters fell in August. What type of graph would you use to display these data? Use graph paper to create the graph.

B ◆ 195

Line Graphs

Walk students through the steps involved in creating a line graph using the example illustrated on the page. For example, ask: **What is the label on the horizontal axis? On the vertical axis?** *(Body Mass (kg); Calories Burned in 30 Minutes)* **What scales are used on each axis?** *(3 squares per 10 kg on the x-axis and 2 squares per 20 Calories on the y-axis)* **What does the second data point represent?** *(77 Calories burned for a body mass of 40 kg)* **What trend or pattern does the graph show?** *(The number of Calories burned in 30 minutes of cycling increases with body mass.)*

Have students follow the steps to carry out the first activity. *(Students should make a different graph for each experiment with different y-axis scales to practice making scales appropriate for data. See sample graphs below.)*

Have students carry out the second activity. *(Students should conclude that a bar graph would be best to display the data. A sample bar graph for these data is shown below.)*

Rainfall in June, July, and August

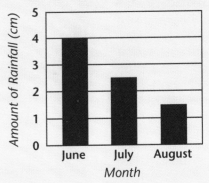

Effect of Body Mass on Calories Burned While Playing Basketball

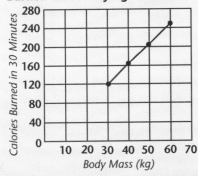

Effect of Body Mass on Calories Burned While Watching Television

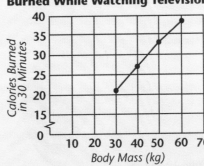

Circle Graphs

Emphasize that a circle graph has to include 100 percent of the categories for the topic being graphed. For example, ask: **Could the data in the bar graph titled "Calories Burned by a 30-kilogram Person in Various Activities" (on the previous page) be shown in a circle graph? Why or why not?** (*No, because it does not include all the possible ways a 30-kilogram person can burn Calories.*) Then walk students through the steps for making a circle graph. Help students to use a compass and a protractor. Use the protractor to illustrate that a circle has 360 degrees. Make sure students understand the mathematical calculations involved in making a circle graph.

You might wish to have students work in pairs to complete the activity. (*Students' circle graphs should look like the graph below.*)

Circle Graphs

Like bar graphs, circle graphs can be used to display data in a number of separate categories. Unlike bar graphs, however, circle graphs can only be used when you have data for *all* the categories that make up a given topic. A circle graph is sometimes called a pie chart because it resembles a pie cut into slices. The pie represents the entire topic, while the slices represent the individual categories. The size of a slice indicates what percentage of the whole a particular category makes up.

The data table below shows the results of a survey in which 24 teenagers were asked to identify their favorite sport. The data were then used to create the circle graph at the right.

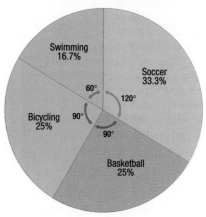

Sports That Teens Prefer

FAVORITE SPORTS	
Sport	Number of Students
Soccer	8
Basketball	6
Bicycling	6
Swimming	4

To create a circle graph, follow these steps.

1. Use a compass to draw a circle. Mark the center of the circle with a point. Then draw a line from the center point to the top of the circle.
2. Determine the size of each "slice" by setting up a proportion where *x* equals the number of degrees in a slice. (NOTE: A circle contains 360 degrees.) For example, to find the number of degrees in the "soccer" slice, set up the following proportion:

$$\frac{\text{students who prefer soccer}}{\text{total number of students}} = \frac{x}{\text{total number of degrees in a circle}}$$

$$\frac{8}{24} = \frac{x}{360}$$

Cross-multiply and solve for *x*.

$$24x = 8 \times 360$$
$$x = 120$$

The "soccer" slice should contain 120 degrees.

3. Use a protractor to measure the angle of the first slice, using the line you drew to the top of the circle as the 0° line. Draw a line from the center of the circle to the edge for the angle you measured.
4. Continue around the circle by measuring the size of each slice with the protractor. Start measuring from the edge of the previous slice so the wedges do not overlap. When you are done, the entire circle should be filled in.
5. Determine the percentage of the whole circle that each slice represents. To do this, divide the number of degrees in a slice by the total number of degrees in a circle (360), and multiply by 100%. For the "soccer" slice, you can find the percentage as follows:

$$\frac{120}{360} \times 100\% = 33.3\%$$

6. Use a different color to shade in each slice. Label each slice with the name of the category and with the percentage of the whole it represents.
7. Add a title to the circle graph.

ACTIVITY

In a class of 28 students, 12 students take the bus to school, 10 students walk, and 6 students ride their bicycles. Create a circle graph to display these data.

Ways Students Get to School

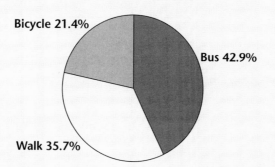

Bicycle 21.4%

Bus 42.9%

Walk 35.7%

Laboratory Safety

Safety Symbols

These symbols alert you to possible dangers in the laboratory and remind you to work carefully.

Safety Goggles Always wear safety goggles to protect your eyes in any activity involving chemicals, flames or heating, or the possibility of broken glassware.

Lab Apron Wear a laboratory apron to protect your skin and clothing from damage.

Breakage You are working with materials that may be breakable, such as glass containers, glass tubing, thermometers, or funnels. Handle breakable materials with care. Do not touch broken glassware.

Heat-resistant Gloves Use an oven mitt or other hand protection when handling hot materials. Hot plates, hot glassware, or hot water can cause burns. Do not touch hot objects with your bare hands.

Heating Use a clamp or tongs to pick up hot glassware. Do not touch hot objects with your bare hands.

Sharp Object Pointed-tip scissors, scalpels, knives, needles, pins, or tacks are sharp. They can cut or puncture your skin. Always direct a sharp edge or point away from yourself and others. Use sharp instruments only as instructed.

Electric Shock Avoid the possibility of electric shock. Never use electrical equipment around water, or when the equipment is wet or your hands are wet. Be sure cords are untangled and cannot trip anyone. Disconnect the equipment when it is not in use.

Corrosive Chemical You are working with an acid or another corrosive chemical. Avoid getting it on your skin or clothing, or in your eyes. Do not inhale the vapors. Wash your hands when you are finished with the activity.

Poison Do not let any poisonous chemical come in contact with your skin, and do not inhale its vapors. Wash your hands when you are finished with the activity.

Physical Safety When an experiment involves physical activity, take precautions to avoid injuring yourself or others. Follow instructions from your teacher. Alert your teacher if there is any reason you should not participate in the activity.

Animal Safety Treat live animals with care to avoid harming the animals or yourself. Working with animal parts or preserved animals also may require caution. Wash your hands when you are finished with the activity.

Plant Safety Handle plants in the laboratory or during field work only as directed by your teacher. If you are allergic to certain plants, tell your teacher before doing an activity in which those plants are used. Avoid touching harmful plants such as poison ivy, poison oak, or poison sumac, or plants with thorns. Wash your hands when you are finished with the activity.

Flames You may be working with flames from a lab burner, candle, or matches. Tie back loose hair and clothing. Follow instructions from your teacher about lighting and extinguishing flames.

No Flames Flammable materials may be present. Make sure there are no flames, sparks, or other exposed heat sources present.

Fumes When poisonous or unpleasant vapors may be involved, work in a ventilated area. Avoid inhaling vapors directly. Only test an odor when directed to do so by your teacher, and use a wafting motion to direct the vapor toward your nose.

Disposal Chemicals and other laboratory materials used in the activity must be disposed of safely. Follow the instructions from your teacher.

Hand Washing Wash your hands thoroughly when finished with the activity. Use antibacterial soap and warm water. Lather both sides of your hands and between your fingers. Rinse well.

General Safety Awareness You may see this symbol when none of the symbols described earlier appears. In this case, follow the specific instructions provided. You may also see this symbol when you are asked to develop your own procedure in a lab. Have your teacher approve your plan before you go further.

Laboratory Safety

Laboratory safety is an essential element of a successful science class. It is important for you to emphasize laboratory safety to students. Students need to understand exactly what is safe and unsafe behavior, and what the rationale is behind each safety rule.

Review with students the Safety Symbols and Science Safety Rules listed on this and the next two pages. Then follow the safety guidelines below to ensure that your classroom will be a safe place for students to learn science.

◆ Post safety rules in the classroom and review them regularly with students.

◆ Familiarize yourself with the safety procedures for each activity before introducing it to your students.

◆ Review specific safety precautions with students before beginning every science activity.

◆ Always act as an exemplary role model by displaying safe behavior.

◆ Know how to use safety equipment, such as fire extinguishers and fire blankets, and always have it accessible.

◆ Have students practice leaving the classroom quickly and orderly to prepare them for emergencies.

◆ Explain to students how to use the intercom or other available means of communication to get help during an emergency.

◆ Never leave students unattended while they are engaged in science activities.

◆ Provide enough space for students to safely carry out science activities.

◆ Keep your classroom and all science materials in proper condition. Replace worn or broken items.

◆ Instruct students to report all accidents and injuries to you immediately.

Laboratory Safety

Additional tips are listed below for the Science Safety Rules discussed on these two pages. Please keep these tips in mind when you carry out science activities in your classroom.

General Precautions

◆ For open-ended activities like Chapter Projects, go over general safety guidelines with students. Have students submit their procedures or design plans in writing and check them for safety considerations.

◆ In an activity where students are directed to taste something, be sure to store the material in clean, *nonscience* containers. Distribute the material to students in *new* plastic or paper dispensables, which should be discarded after the tasting. Tasting or eating should never be done in a lab classroom.

◆ During physical activity, make sure students do not overexert themselves.

◆ Remind students to handle microscopes and telescopes with care to avoid breakage.

Heating and Fire Safety

◆ No flammable substances should be in use around hot plates, light bulbs, or open flames.

◆ Test tubes should be heated only in water baths.

◆ Students should be permitted to strike matches to light candles or burners *only* with strict supervision. When possible, you should light the flames, especially when working with sixth graders.

◆ Be sure to have proper ventilation when fumes are produced during a procedure.

◆ All electrical equipment used in the lab should have GFI switches.

Using Chemicals Safely

◆ When students use both chemicals and microscopes in one activity, microscopes should be in a separate part of the room from the chemicals so that when students remove their goggles to use the microscopes, their eyes are not at risk.

Science Safety Rules

To prepare yourself to work safely in the laboratory, read over the following safety rules. Then read them a second time. Make sure you understand and follow each rule. Ask your teacher to explain any rules you do not understand.

Dress Code

1. To protect yourself from injuring your eyes, wear safety goggles whenever you work with chemicals, burners, glassware, or any substance that might get into your eyes. If you wear contact lenses, notify your teacher.
2. Wear a lab apron or coat whenever you work with corrosive chemicals or substances that can stain.
3. Tie back long hair to keep it away from any chemicals, flames, or equipment.
4. Remove or tie back any article of clothing or jewelry that can hang down and touch chemicals, flames, or equipment. Roll up or secure long sleeves.
5. Never wear open shoes or sandals.

General Precautions

6. Read all directions for an experiment several times before beginning the activity. Carefully follow all written and oral instructions. If you are in doubt about any part of the experiment, ask your teacher for assistance.
7. Never perform activities that are not assigned or authorized by your teacher. Obtain permission before "experimenting" on your own. Never handle any equipment unless you have specific permission.
8. Never perform lab activities without direct supervision.
9. Never eat or drink in the laboratory.
10. Keep work areas clean and tidy at all times. Bring only notebooks and lab manuals or written lab procedures to the work area. All other items, such as purses and backpacks, should be left in a designated area.
11. Do not engage in horseplay.

First Aid

12. Always report all accidents or injuries to your teacher, no matter how minor. Notify your teacher immediately about any fires.
13. Learn what to do in case of specific accidents, such as getting acid in your eyes or on your skin. (Rinse acids from your body with lots of water.)
14. Be aware of the location of the first-aid kit, but do not use it unless instructed by your teacher. In case of injury, your teacher should administer first aid. Your teacher may also send you to the school nurse or call a physician.
15. Know the location of emergency equipment, such as the fire extinguisher and fire blanket, and know how to use it.
16. Know the location of the nearest telephone and whom to contact in an emergency.

Heating and Fire Safety

17. Never use a heat source, such as a candle, burner, or hot plate, without wearing safety goggles.
18. Never heat anything unless instructed to do so. A chemical that is harmless when cool may be dangerous when heated.
19. Keep all combustible materials away from flames. Never use a flame or spark near a combustible chemical.
20. Never reach across a flame.
21. Before using a laboratory burner, make sure you know proper procedures for lighting and adjusting the burner, as demonstrated by your teacher. Do not touch the burner. It may be hot. And never leave a lighted burner unattended!
22. Chemicals can splash or boil out of a heated test tube. When heating a substance in a test tube, make sure that the mouth of the tube is not pointed at you or anyone else.
23. Never heat a liquid in a closed container. The expanding gases produced may blow the container apart.
24. Before picking up a container that has been heated, hold the back of your hand near it. If you can feel heat on the back of your hand, the container is too hot to handle. Use an oven mitt to pick up a container that has been heated.

Using Glassware Safely

◆ Use plastic containers, graduated cylinders, and beakers whenever possible. If using glass, students should wear safety goggles.

◆ Use only nonmercury thermometers with anti-roll protectors.

◆ Check all glassware periodically for chips and scratches, which can cause cuts and breakage.

Using Chemicals Safely

25. Never mix chemicals "for the fun of it." You might produce a dangerous, possibly explosive substance.
26. Never put your face near the mouth of a container that holds chemicals. Never touch, taste, or smell a chemical unless you are instructed by your teacher to do so. Many chemicals are poisonous.
27. Use only those chemicals needed in the activity. Read and double-check labels on supply bottles before removing any chemicals. Take only as much as you need. Keep all containers closed when chemicals are not being used.
28. Dispose of all chemicals as instructed by your teacher. To avoid contamination, never return chemicals to their original containers. Never simply pour chemicals or other substances into the sink or trash containers.
29. Be extra careful when working with acids or bases. Pour all chemicals over the sink or a container, not over your work surface.
30. If you are instructed to test for odors, use a wafting motion to direct the odors to your nose. Do not inhale the fumes directly from the container.
31. When mixing an acid and water, always pour the water into the container first and then add the acid to the water. Never pour water into an acid.
32. Take extreme care not to spill any material in the laboratory. Wash chemical spills and splashes immediately with plenty of water. Immediately begin rinsing with water any acids that get on your skin or clothing, and notify your teacher of any acid spill at the same time.

Using Glassware Safely

33. Never force glass tubing or thermometers into a rubber stopper or rubber tubing. Have your teacher insert the glass tubing or thermometer if required for an activity.
34. If you are using a laboratory burner, use a wire screen to protect glassware from any flame. Never heat glassware that is not thoroughly dry on the outside.
35. Keep in mind that hot glassware looks cool. Never pick up glassware without first checking to see if it is hot. Use an oven mitt. See rule 24.
36. Never use broken or chipped glassware. If glassware breaks, notify your teacher and dispose of the glassware in the proper broken-glassware container. Never handle broken glass with your bare hands.
37. Never eat or drink from lab glassware.
38. Thoroughly clean glassware before putting it away.

Using Sharp Instruments

39. Handle scalpels or other sharp instruments with extreme care. Never cut material toward you; cut away from you.
40. Immediately notify your teacher if you cut your skin when working in the laboratory.

Animal and Plant Safety

41. Never perform experiments that cause pain, discomfort, or harm to mammals, birds, reptiles, fishes, or amphibians. This rule applies at home as well as in the classroom.
42. Animals should be handled only if absolutely necessary. Your teacher will instruct you as to how to handle each animal species brought into the classroom.
43. If you know that you are allergic to certain plants, molds, or animals, tell your teacher before doing an activity in which these are used.
44. During field work, protect your skin by wearing long pants, long sleeves, socks, and closed shoes. Know how to recognize the poisonous plants and fungi in your area, as well as plants with thorns, and avoid contact with them.
45. Never eat any part of an unidentified plant or fungus.
46. Wash your hands thoroughly after handling animals or the cage containing animals. Wash your hands when you are finished with any activity involving animal parts, plants, or soil.

End-of-Experiment Rules

47. After an experiment has been completed, clean up your work area and return all equipment to its proper place.
48. Dispose of waste materials as instructed by your teacher.
49. Wash your hands after every experiment.
50. Always turn off all burners or hot plates when they are not in use. Unplug hot plates and other electrical equipment. If you used a burner, check that the gas-line valve to the burner is off as well.

Using Sharp Instruments

◆ Always use blunt-tip safety scissors, except when pointed-tip scissors are required.

Animal and Plant Safety

◆ When working with live animals or plants, check ahead of time for students who may have allergies to the specimens.
◆ When growing bacteria cultures, use only disposable petri dishes. After streaking, the dishes should be sealed and not opened again by students. After the lab, students should return the unopened dishes to you. Students should wash their hands with antibacterial soap.
◆ Two methods are recommended for the safe disposal of bacteria cultures. *First method:* Autoclave the petri dishes and discard without opening. *Second method:* If no autoclave is available, carefully open the dishes (never have a student do this) and pour full-strength bleach into the dishes and let stand for a day. Then pour the bleach from the petri dishes down a drain and flush the drain with lots of water. Tape the petri dishes back together and place in a sealed plastic bag. Wrap the plastic bag with a brown paper bag or newspaper and tape securely. Throw the sealed package in the trash. Thoroughly disinfect the work area with bleach.
◆ To grow mold, use a new, sealable plastic bag that is two to three times larger than the material to be placed inside. Seal the bag and tape it shut. After the bag is sealed, students should not open it. To dispose of the bag and mold culture, make a small cut near an edge of the bag and cook in a microwave oven on high setting for at least 1 minute. Discard the bag according to local ordinance, usually in the trash.
◆ Students should wear disposable nitrile, latex, or food-handling gloves when handling live animals or nonliving specimens.

End-of Experiment Rules

◆ Always have students use antibacterial soap for washing their hands.

A

abdomen The hind section of an arachnid's body that contains its reproductive organs and part of its digestive tract; the hind section of an insect's body. (p. 58)

adaptation A characteristic that helps an organism survive in its environment or reproduce. (p. 19)

aggression A threatening behavior that one animal uses to gain control over another. (p. 161)

amphibian An ectothermic vertebrate that spends its early life in water and its adulthood on land, returning to water to reproduce. (p. 96)

antenna An appendage on the head of an animal that contains sense organs. (p. 57)

anus The opening at the end of an organism's digestive system through which wastes exit. (p. 39)

arachnid An arthropod with only two body sections. (p. 58)

arthropod An invertebrate that has an external skeleton, a segmented body, and jointed attachments called appendages. (p. 55)

artificial intelligence The capacity of a computer to perform complex tasks such as learning from experience and solving problems. (p. 156)

asexual reproduction The process by which a single organism produces a new organism identical to itself. (p. 18)

atrium An upper chamber of the heart. (p. 96)

autotroph An organism that makes its own food. (p. 17)

B

behavior All the actions an animal performs. (p. 153)

bilateral symmetry Line symmetry; the quality of being divisible into two halves that are mirror images. (p. 24)

bioluminescence The production of light by a living organism by means of chemical reactions within the organism's cells. (p. 172)

bird An endothermic vertebrate that has feathers and a four-chambered heart, and lays eggs. (p. 121)

bivalve A mollusk that has two shells held together by hinges and strong muscles. (p. 50)

buoyant force The force that water exerts upward on any underwater object. (p. 92)

C

camouflage Protective coloration; a common animal defense. (p. 66)

canine teeth Sharply pointed teeth that stab food and tear into it. (p. 136)

carnivore An animal that eats only other animals. (p. 19)

cartilage A flexible, strong tissue that is softer than bone. (p. 83)

cephalopod A mollusk with feet adapted to form tentacles around its mouth. (p. 52)

chitin The tough, flexible material from which arthropod exoskeletons are made. (p. 55)

chordate The phylum whose members have a notochord, a nerve cord, and slits in their throat area at some point in their lives. (p. 82)

circadian rhythms Behavior cycles that occur over a period of approximately one day. (p. 165)

cnidarians Animals whose stinging cells are used to capture their prey and defend themselves, and who take their food into a hollow central cavity. (p. 31)

complete metamorphosis A type of metamorphosis characterized by four dramatically different stages: egg, larva, pupa, and adult. (p. 64)

conditioning The process of learning to connect a stimulus with a good or bad event. (p. 155)

contour feather A large feather that helps give shape to a bird's body. (p. 121)

courtship behavior The behavior that animals of the same species engage in to prepare for mating. (p. 162)

crop A bird's internal storage tank that allows it to store food inside its body after swallowing it. (p. 122)

crustacean An arthropod that has two or three body sections, five or more pairs of legs, two pairs of antennae, and usually three pairs of appendages for chewing. (p. 57)

D

diaphragm A large muscle in a mammal's chest that functions in breathing. (p. 136)

down feathers Short fluffy feathers that trap heat and keep a bird warm. (p. 122)

E

echinoderm A radially symmetrical invertebrate that lives on the ocean floor and has a spiny internal skeleton . (p. 73)

ectotherm An animal whose body does not produce much internal heat. (p. 84)

endoskeleton An internal skeleton. (p. 73)

endotherm An animal whose body controls and regulates its temperature by controlling the internal heat it produces. (p. 85)

exoskeleton A waxy, waterproof outer shell. (p. 55)

F

fertilization The joining of egg and sperm. (p. 18)

fish An ectothermic vertebrate that lives in the water and has fins. (p. 87)

fossil The hardened remains or other evidence of a living thing that existed a long time in the past. (p. 112)

gastropod A mollusk with a single shell or no shell. (p. 50)

gestation period The length of time between fertilization and birth of a mammal. (p. 143)

gill An organism's breathing organ that removes oxygen from water. (p. 49)

gizzard A thick-walled, muscular part of a bird's stomach that squeezes and grinds partially digested food. (p. 123)

gradual metamorphosis A type of metamorphosis in which an egg hatches into a nymph that resembles an adult, and which has no distinctly different larval stage. (p. 64)

habitat The specific environment in which an animal lives. (p. 100)

herbivore An animal that eats only plants. (p. 19)

heterotroph An organism that cannot make food for itself, and must obtain food by eating other organisms. (p. 17)

hibernation A state of greatly reduced body activity that occurs during the winter. (p. 166)

host An organism that provides food to a parasite that lives on or inside it. (p. 36)

hypothesis A prediction about the outcome of an experiment. (p. 188)

imprinting A process in which newly hatched birds or newborn mammals learn to follow the first object they see. (p. 157)

incisors Flat-edged teeth used to bite off and cut parts of food. (p. 136)

insect An arthropod with three body sections, six legs, one pair of antennae, and usually one or two pairs of wings. (p. 63)

insight learning The process of learning how to solve a problem or do something new by applying what is already known. (p. 156)

instinct An inborn behavior pattern that an animal performs correctly the first time. (p. 154)

insulator A material that does not conduct heat well and which therefore helps prevent it from escaping. (p. 122)

invertebrate An animal that does not have a backbone. (p. 22)

kidney An organ that removes the wastes produced by an animal's cells. (p. 49)

larva The immature form of an animal that looks very different from the adult. (p. 30)

learning The process that leads to changes in behavior based on practice or experience. (p. 154)

lift The difference in pressure between the upper and lower surfaces of a bird's wing that produces an upward force that causes the wing to rise. (p. 131)

mammal An endothermic vertebrate with a four-chambered heart, skin covered with fur or hair, and which has young fed with milk from the mother's body. (p. 133)

mammary glands The organs that produce the milk with which mammals feed their young. (p. 138)

manipulated variable The one factor that a scientist changes during an experiment. (p. 189)

marsupial A mammal whose young are born alive at an early stage of development, and which usually continue to develop in a pouch on their mother's body. (p. 142)

medusa The cnidarian body plan characterized by a bowl shape and which is adapted for a free-swimming life. (p. 32)

metamorphosis A process in which an animal's body undergoes dramatic changes in form during its life cycle. (p. 58)

migration The regular, periodic journey of an animal from one place to another and back again for the purpose of feeding or reproduction. (p. 166)

molars Teeth that, along with premolars, grind and shred food into tiny bits. (p. 136)

mollusk An invertebrate with a soft, unsegmented body; most are protected by hard outer shells. (p. 48)

molting The process of shedding an outgrown exoskeleton. (p. 56)

monotreme A mammal that lays eggs. (p. 142)

notochord A flexible rod that supports a chordate's back. (p. 82)

nymph A stage of gradual metamorphosis that usually resembles the adult insect. (p. 64)

omnivore An animal that eats both plants and animals. (p. 20)

operational definition A statement that describes how a particular variable is to be measured or how a term is to be defined. (p. 189)

paleontologist A scientist who studies extinct organisms, examines fossil structure, and makes comparisons to present-day organisms. (p. 114)

parasite An organism that lives inside or on another organism and takes food from the organism in or on which it lives. (p. 36)

pheromone A chemical released by one animal that affects the behavior of another animal of the same species. (p. 170)

phylum One of about 35 major groups into which biologists classify members of the animal kingdom. (p. 20)

placenta An organ in pregnant female placental mammals that passes materials between the mother and the developing embryo. (p. 146)

placental mammal A mammal that develops inside its mother's body until its body systems can function independently. (p. 143)

polyp The cnidarian body plan characterized by a vaselike shape and which is usually adapted for life attached to an underwater surface. (p. 31)

predator A carnivore that hunts and kills other animals and has adaptations that help it capture the animals it preys upon. (p. 19)

premolars Teeth that, along with molars, grind and shred food into tiny bits. (p. 136)

prey An animal that a predator feeds upon. (p. 20)

pupa The second stage of complete metamorphosis, in which an insect is enclosed in a protective covering and gradually changes from a larva to an adult. (p. 64)

radial symmetry The quality of having many lines of symmetry that all pass through a central point. (p. 24)

radula A flexible ribbon of tiny teeth in mollusks. (p. 49)

regeneration The ability of an organism to regrow body parts. (p. 36)

reptile An exothermic vertebrate that has lungs and scaly skin. (p. 101)

responding variable The factor that changes as a result of changes to the manipulated variable in an experiment. (p. 189)

response An organism's reaction to a stimulus. (p. 153)

sedimentary rock Rock formed from hardened layers of sediments—particles of clay, sand, mud, or silt. (p. 112)

sexual reproduction The process by which a new organism forms from the joining of two sex cells. (p. 17)

society A group of closely related animals of the same species that work together for the benefit of the whole group. (p. 164)

species A group of organisms that can mate with each other and produce offspring which can also mate and reproduce. (p. 17)

stimulus A signal that causes an organism to react in some way. (p. 153)

swim bladder An internal gas-filled organ that helps a bony fish stabilize its body at different water depths. (p. 92)

territory An area that is occupied and defended by an animal or group of animals. (p. 161)

thorax An insect's mid-section, to which its wings and legs are attached. (p. 63)

trial-and-error learning The learning that occurs when an animal learns to perform a behavior more and more skillfully. (p. 156)

urine The watery fluid in which the wastes produced by an animal's cells are excreted. (p. 103)

variable Any factor that can change in an experiment. (p. 189)

ventricle The lower chamber of the heart, which pumps blood out to the lungs and body. (p. 96)

vertebrae The bones that make up the backbone of an animal. (p. 83)

vertebrate An animal that has a backbone. (p. 22)

water vascular system A system of fluid-filled tubes in an echinoderm's body. (p. 74)

Acknowledgments

Illustration

Sally Bensusen: 51, 65
Warren Budd Associated Ltd.: 125
Patrice Rossi Calkin: 20, 22, 37, 83, 102, 136, 137, 155
Warren Cutler: 97, 123
John Edwards & Associates: 125
Andrea Golden: 27, 42, 58
Biruta Hansen: 104, 170–171, 173
Martucci Design: 71, 117
Fran Milner: 17, 59, 91, 99
Paul Mirocha: 157
Morgan Cain & Associates: 94, 139
Matt Myerchak: 44, 78, 174
Ortelius Design Inc.: 166
Matthew Pippin: 114
Walter Stuart: 29, 53, 75, 110, 165
J/B Woolsey Associates (Mark Desman): 21, 40, 56, 82, 86, 106–107, 175
J/B Woolsey Associates: 23, 24, 96, 126, 131, 154

Photography

Photo Research Sue McDermott
Cover image Davis/W. Bilenduke/TSI

Nature of Science
Page 10t,10b,12, Heinz Kluetmeier/Sports Illustrated; **13l,13r,** Russell A. Mittermeier, Ph.D./Conservation International

Chapter 1
Pages 14–15, Hal Beral/Visuals Unlimited; **16t,** Richard Haynes; **16–17b,** Gary Bell/Masterfile; **18,** Robert Maier/Animals Animals; **19t,** Oliver Strewe/TSI; **19b,** Frans Lanting/Minden Pictures; **20,** David & Tess Young/Tom Stack & Associates; **23,** Corel Corp.; **24,** William C Jorgensen/Visuals Unlimited; **25l,** Daniel W. Gotshall/Visuals Unlimited; **25r,** Tim Davis/TSI; **26,** Ted Kerasote/Photo Researchers; **28t,** Russ Lappa; **31t,** Biophoto Associates/Photo Researchers; **31bl,** Stuart Westmorland/Natural Selection; **31br,** David B. Fleetham/Tom Stack & Associates; **33t,** Nancy Sefton/Photo Researchers; **33b,** Linda Pitkin/Masterfile; **34,** James Watt/Animals Animals; **35t,** Richard Haynes; **35bl,** Ed Robinson/Tom Stack & Associates; **35br,** Mary Beth Angelo/Photo Researchers; **36,** Kiell B. Sandved/Visuals Unlimited; **38t,** David M. Dennis/Tom Stack & Associates; **38b,** Sinclair Stammers/Science Photo Library/Photo Researchers; **39l, 39r,** Kjell B. Sandved/Visuals Unlimited; **43l,** Corel Corp.; **43r,** Linda Pitkin/Masterfile.

Chapter 2
Pages 46–47, Michael Fogden/DRK Photo; **48b,** Richard Nowitz; **48t,** Corel Corp.; **49l,** Douglas Faulkner/Photo Researchers; **49r,** Bruce Watkins/Animals Animals; **50,** Pete Atkinson/Masterfile; **52,** Kevin & Cat Sweeney/TSI; **54t,** Richard Haynes; **52–53,** Gary Retherford/Photo Researchers; **53r,** Richard Haynes; **54b,** Ron Broda/Masterfile; **55l,** John Gerlach/Tom Stack & Associates; **55r,** Donald Specker/Animals Animals; **56,** Robert A. Lubeck/Animals Animals; **57,** Andrew Syred/Science Photo Library/Photo Researchers; **60t,** Robert Calentine/Visuals Unlimited; **60b,** Tom MuHugh/Photo Researchers; **60m,** Tim Flach/TSI; **61l,** Marty Cordano/DRK Photo; **61r,** Simon D. Pollard/Photo Researchers; **62t,** R Calentine/Visuals Unlimited; **62b,** Patti Murray/Animals Animals; **63,** CNRI/Science Photo Library/Photo Researchers; **64,** Belinda Wright/DRK Photo; **66l,** Valorie Hodgson/Visuals Unlimited; **66r,** Art Wolfe/Tony Stone Images; **67,** John Trager/Visuals Unlimited; **68,** Robert A. Lubeck/Animals Animals; **69, 70,** Richard Haynes; **71t,** Paul Silverman/Fundamental Photographs; **71b,** Richard Magna/Fundamental Photographs; **72,** Russ Lappa; **73t,** Richard Haynes; **73b,** Kjell B. Sandred/Visuals Unlimited; **74,** Ed Robinson/Tom Stack & Associates; **76tl,** Brian Parker/Tom Stack & Associates; **76tr,** Tammy Peluso/Tom Stack & Associates; **76b,** Fred Whitehead/Animals Animals; **77t,** Bruce Watkins/Animals Animals; **77b,** Andrew Syred/Science Photo Library/Photo Researchers.

Chapter 3
Pages 80–81, Norbert Wu/DRK Photo; **82,** Russ Lappa; **83,** G.J. Bernard/ Animals Animals; **84,** Michael Fodgen/DRK Photo; **85,** Corel Corp.; **87t,** Gerard Lacz/Animals Animals; **87b,** Flip Micklin/Minden Pictures; **89tl,** Larry Lipsky/DRK Photo; **89tr,** John d. Cummingham/Visuals Unlimited **89b,** Herve Berthoule Jacana/Photo Researchers; **90t,** Frank Burek/Animals Animals; **90b,** Jeff Rotman; **92l,** Norbert Wu; **92r,** Stuart Westmorland/ Photo Researchers; **93r,** Stuart Westmorland/TSI; **93l,** Norbert Wu/TSI; **95t,** Russ Lappa; **95b,** John M. Burnley/Photo Researchers; **96,** Michael Fogden/Photo Researchers; **98,** Richard Haynes; **100,** Justin W. Verforker/Visuals Unlimited; **101t,** Richard Haynes; **101b,** Joe McDonald/Tom Stack & Associates; **102,** Zig Leszczynski/Animals Animals; **103,** Brian Kenney/Natural Selection; **105l,** Joe McDonald/Tom Stack & Associates; **105r,** A.B. Sheldon/Animals Animals; **108t,** Dave B. Fleetham/Visuals Unlimited; **108m,** T.A. Wiewandt/DRK Photo; **108b,** M.C. Chamberlain/DRK Photo; **109,** Gerald & Buff Corsi/ Tom Stack & Associates; **111t,** Richard Haynes; **111b,** Tom Bean/DRK Photo; **112t,** Ernst Mayr Library of the Museum of Comparative Zoology,Harvard University. ©President and Fellows of Harvard; **112b,** By permission of the Houghton Library, Harvard University; **113t,** Louis Psihoyos Matrix; **113b,** James L. Amos/Photo Researchers; **115l,** Stuart Westmorland/TSI; **115r,** Joe McDonald/Tom Stack & Associates.

Chapter 4
Pages 118–119, Robert A. Tyrrell; **120,** Richard Haynes; **121,** Collection of The New York Historical Society; **122t,** Art Wolfe/TSI; **122m,** Jerome Wexler/Photo Researchers; **122b,** Darrell Gulin/DRK Photo; **124,** Richard Haynes; **127,** David Hosking/TSI; **128tl,** Dave Watts/Tom Stack & Associates; **128tm,** Stephen Krasemann/DRK Photo; **128tr,** S. Nielsen/DRK Photo; **128bl,** D. Allen/Animals Animals; **128br,** Joe McDonald/Visuals Unlimited; **129l,** Manfred Danegger/TSI; **129r,** Wayne Lankinen/DRK Photo; **130t,** Richard Haynes; **130b,** Stephen Dalton/Photo Researchers; **132,** David Tipling/TSI; **133t,** Richard Haynes; **133b,** Eric Valli/Minden Pictures; **134,** Daryl Balfour/ TSI; **135,** Art Wolfe/TSI; **136t,** Hilary Pooley/Animals Animals; **136–137b,** Michael Fogden/DRK Photo; **138,** Joe McDonald/Visuals Unlimited; **140,** Colin Milkins/Animals Animals; **141t,** Richard Haynes; **141bl,** Keren Su/TSI; **141br,** Penny Tweedie/TSI; **142l,142r,** Tom McHugh/Photo Researchers; **143t,** Dave Watts/Tom Stack & Associates; **143b,** Jack Dermid; **144tl,** Michael Habicht/Animals Animals; **144tm,** Art Wolfe/TSI; **144tr,** Roger Aitkenhead/Animals Animals; **144ml,** Stephen Krasemann/TSI; **144mr,** Jeanne Drake/TSI; **144bl,** Renee Lynn/TSI; **145tl,** Corel Corp.;**145tr,** M.P. Kahl/DRK Photo; **145ml,** Stephen Krasemann/TSI; **145bl,** Chuck Davis/TSI; **145br,** Johnny Johnson/DRK Photo; **146,** Johnny Johnson; **147l,** Joe McDonald/Visuals Unlimited; **147r,** Penny Tweedie/TSI.

Chapter 5
Pages 150–151, Tim Davis/TSI; **152t,** Jerome Wexler/Photo Researchers; **152b,** Michael Fogden/DRK Photo; **153,** Fred Winner/Jacana/Photo Researchers; **156,** Robert & Eunice Pearcy/Animals Animals; **158,** Nina Leen/Time-Warner, Life Magazine; **160t,** Richard Haynes; **160b,** Mark Jones/Minden Pictures; **161,** Art Wolfe/TSI; **162l,163,** Michael Fogden/DRK Photo; **163,** Jeff Lepore/Natural Selection; **164,** John Cancalosi/DRK Photo; **166,** M. A. Chappell/Animals Animals; **167,** Michio Hoshino/Minden Pictures; **168,** Doug Wechsler; **169,** Richard Haynes; **171,** Michael Fogden/Animals Animals; **173l,** John Cancalosi/DRK Photo.

Interdisciplinary Exploration
Page 176, Cary Wolinsky/Stock Boston; **177t,** E.R. Degginger/Animals Animals; **177m,177b,** Cary Wolinsky/Stock Boston; **177r,** Harry Rogers/Photo Researchers; **180,** Russ Lappa; **182t,** Xinhua/Gamma-Liaison International; **183t,** Russ Lappa; **183b,** Jean Marc Barey/Angence Vandystadt/Photo Researchers.

Skills Handbook
Page 184, Mike Moreland/Photo Network; **185t,** Foodpix; **185m,** Richard Haynes; **185b,** Russ Lappa; **188,** Richard Haynes; **190,** Ron Kimball; **191,** Renee Lynn/Photo Researchers.